The
ECONOMICS
of Nursing

The
ECONOMICS
of Nursing

Virginia S. Cleland, Ph.D., R.N., FAAN
Professor and Coordinator, Nursing Administration Program
School of Nursing
University of California, San Francisco

Consultant and Contributor
Richard C. McKibbin, Ph.D.
Senior Fellow, Health Policy and Economics
American Nurses' Association

APPLETON & LANGE
Norwalk, Connecticut

0-8385-2036-7

Copyright © 1990 by Appleton & Lange
A Publishing Division of Prentice Hall

90 91 92 93 94 / 10 9 8 7 6 5 4 3 2 1

Prentice Hall International (UK) Limited, *London*
Prentice Hall of Australia Pty. Limited, *Sydney*
Prentice Hall Canada, Inc., *Toronto*
Prentice Hall Hispanoamericana, S.A., *Mexico*
Prentice Hall of India Private Limited, *New Delhi*
Prentice Hall of Japan, Inc., *Tokyo*
Simon & Schuster Asia Pte. Ltd., *Singapore*
Editora Prentice Hall do Brasil Ltda., *Rio de Janeiro*
Prentice Hall, *Englewood Cliffs, New Jersey*

Library of Congress Cataloging-in-Publication Data

Cleland, Virginia S.
   The economics of nursing/Virginia S. Cleland; consultant and contributor, Richard C. McKibbin.
     p. cm.
   Includes index.
   ISBN 0-8385-2036-7
   1. Nursing—Economic aspects. I. McKibbin, Richard C. II. Title.
   [DNLM: 1. Economics, Nursing. WY 77 C624e]
   RT86.7.C54   1989
   362.1'73'068—dc20
   DNLM/DLC
   for Library of Congress   89-15076
                                                   CIP

Acquisitions Editor: Janet Foltin
Production Editor: Eileen Lagoss Burns
Designer: Ben Kahn
Cover: Michael J. Kelly

PRINTED IN THE UNITED STATES OF AMERICA

Contents

Preface

Nursing faces many challenges. As individuals, registered nurses confront a variety of choices regarding their careers. These include differing work patterns, alternative employment opportunities, specialization, and additional education. As a profession, nursing continues to struggle with attainment of equitable compensation, advancement of professional recognition and status, resolution of the educational base for nursing practice, and extension of nursing's influence in health care organization, delivery, and policy.

These challenges, and many others faced by nurses and the profession of nursing, involve economic considerations. Both the development of an individual's career and the progress of a profession are profoundly influenced by economic issues. These range from obvious factors—salary levels and scheduling patterns, for example—to more subtle ones, such as the effects of changes in reimbursement levels for various health services on their utilization rates, and thereby on nursing employment. Whether they are obvious or subtle, the economic issues that affect nurses and nursing are often inadequately understood.

An understanding of the role of economics is essential to nursing because most of the challenges nursing faces are related to these issues. Some way of understanding, responding to, or acting upon these economic forces must be developed or acquired. Some may believe that nurses are underpaid without ever having examined salary schedules or other related information for nurses or other professionals; others may reach the same conclusion (or a different conclusion) only after extensive study of the situation. On any particular issue, individual opinions, knowledge, or beliefs may be highly varied: vague or explicit, correct or inaccurate.

Relatively few health care professionals have had formal coursework in economics, business administration, accounting, finance, or related fields that would enable them to better assess the impact of economic issues on them and their profession. As a result, too many health professionals—not just nurses—may have difficulty in confidently developing appropriate understandings of, responses to, and action upon those economic concerns.

In the early decades of nursing in the United States, it was common practice to develop nursing texts dealing with the knowledge base of a particular discipline recast in a way believed more understandable to student nurses. Thus, many books were published on such topics as anatomy for nurses, bacteriology for nurses, mathematics for nurses, and even English for nurses. This, however, is not a book on economics for nurses.

Rather, this book is about the economics of nursing—a topic that will not be taught in a department of economics or by those educated primarily in the discipline of economics. Today, nursing is within the mainstream of higher education. Nurses, either as undergraduates, graduate students, or in adult education experiences, can enroll in general courses in economics at a local college or university.

The Economics of Nursing is intended for general use by nurses in several contexts. It should serve as a useful reference for practicing nurses in both clinical and administrative positions. The book is written to be used as a text in graduate and undergraduate nursing programs. Certain adjustments and compromises have been made because of this broad focus and intended readership. Economic concepts and their applications have not been explained with the detail, completeness, or precision found in the leading textbooks; however, the level of precision is sufficient for an adequate understanding of their applicability to nurses and nursing. At the same time, other concepts are discussed in more detail. These include nursing employment, salaries and their determinants, and nursing costing concepts. Inclusion of these topics reflects their economic importance to nursing. Throughout, efforts have been made to relate economic concepts and principles directly to nursing and to health care. To place the practice of nursing in an economic context is the responsibility of nurses.

Part I provides an overview of the book. Chapter 1 places the economics of nursing in the context of the professionalization of nursing, explores the work force of nursing, and describes an economic model of health services delivery. Chapter 2 introduces economics as a science, describes key concepts and principles, and discusses representative economic data and research tools.

Part II describes economic markets and nursing. Chapter 3 is a description of the market system including supply and demand analysis, resource allocation, price determination and behaviors involving choice. Special attention to the market for nursing care is provided in Chapter 4.

Part III pertains to the economics of nursing employment. Chapter 5 examines the general characteristics of wage and salary structures and the underlying theory of wages. Chapter 6 is devoted to employee benefits, and Chapter 7 considers the major determinants of nurses' salaries and benefits.

Part IV describes health care expenditures, financing, and the cost–quality exchange. Chapter 8 describes the level of health care expenditures in the United States and the economic issues surrounding the financing of health care. Chapter 9 discusses the payment sources and mechanisms for the nation's health care providers. Chapter 10 is devoted to the interrelatedness of cost, quality, and standards of care. Quality assurance is approached as an exchange relationship between the quality of health services that technically can be provided and the quantity of health services for which society is willing to expend the nation's time as well as financial and physical efforts.

Part V considers the macroeconomic relationships of government programs and policies as they pertain to health care, including their effects upon nurses and nursing. There is also a concluding chapter on nursing, economics, and the health care system.

The book provides nurses with sources of information and assistance in developing economic perspectives and seeing economic alternatives. It contains a synthesis of material drawn from economics, nursing, health care policy, financial management, and wage administration. *The Economics of Nursing* is intended to help nurses understand issues that surround and affect their practice.

Acknowledgments

The early chapters were written while I was on sabbatical leave as a Professor at the College of Nursing, Wayne State University, Detroit. My move to the University of California, San Francisco, slowed completion of the book; however, I am indebted to faculty and students on both those campuses for providing useful ideas and content. Particularly, it was years of recurring questions from graduate students which convinced me that a book outlining explicit economic issues within nursing is needed.

I owe special words of appreciation to Richard C. McKibbin, Ph.D., economics consultant, who read the book in progress, and who wrote Chapter 11 in its entirety. In many other areas, Dr. McKibbin provided examples and explanations to clarify important points.

Special gratitude is due my husband who waited patiently for the book to be completed, for the clutter of paper in our study to diminish and a clean desk top to reappear. He is an architect, and he understands that whether the basic commodity is shelter or health care, a clear economic basis is requisite for the practitioner to serve the consumer effectively.

Virginia S. Cleland

Part I

Overview

Chapter 1

An Introduction to the Economics of Nursing

Economics is a science of choices from scarce or limited resources. The scarcity of the resource and the extent of the demand usually determine the economic value. It is difficult to imagine a field of practice characterized by so many choices and challenging decisions as nursing. Entry into nursing practice is available through alternative types of nursing programs of differing length, character, and expense. There are many employment options nurses can then elect. At the entry level, nursing positions are not so unlike initial positions in other fields, except there are more alternative employment settings for beginning nurses. For nurses willing to invest in self by acquiring appropriate additional education and relevant experience, there are an array of employment opportunities in advanced clinical practice, management, education, quality assurance, and research. The fact that nurses can work in hospitals, ambulatory care facilities, long-term care facilities, community agencies, and educational institutions in almost any city, state, or country provides broad choices.

In slightly more than 20 years (from 1965 to 1988) the number of registered nurses has expanded from 621,000 to nearly 2,033,000 (Moses, 1989). The nation's nearly two million nurses make nursing the largest category of employees in health care and one of the largest groups of employees in the nation's work force. Since World War II, there has been a continuing demand for more nurses than have been available—a nursing shortage. Employment options have been so broad and prevalant that many nurses have not understood that market demand, and thus salaries, in nursing as in other fields reflects a *quid pro quo*. That is, the greatest employment choices and highest salaries are enjoyed by those who acquire the requisite education, experience, and competence.

Throughout nursing history, the leadership of professional nursing has had three paramount goals: (1) to bring about the professionalization of nursing, (2) to control preparation of all categories of personnel that make up the work force of nursing, and (3) to influence supply, demand, utilization, and evaluation relative to the market for nursing care. Nursing's long-range goals have not differed, essentially, from those of any other profession. When the nursing leadership fails to agree, disagreement generally centers on the methods to be used to promote one or another of the three goals, and does not involve disagreement about the goals themselves. Each of these goals has a fundamental economic basis that nurses need to understand and utilize in their own career choices and professional decisions.

The balance of this introductory chapter has been divided into three sections, each relating back to the three paramount goals for nursing: professionalism, control of nursing education for all personnel in the nursing work force, and influence over the utilization of nursing personnel.

Nursing as a Profession

It would seem unusual to an economist to devote an early section of a book on economics to professionalization. It is not inappropriate, however, when considering the economics of nursing. The attainment of professional recognition, status, privileges, and professional-level salaries has dominated much of nursing's activities, literature, and attention for many years. Attainment of professional recognition for nursing has historically been hindered by various factors: the predominance of women in nursing, the lack of uniformity in educational preparation for nursing practice, a traditional view that nurses were physicians' "handmaidens," or occupied a subservient role, and the view that women at work were there only temporarily, eventually to leave the work force for childbearing and child-rearing responsibilities.

The drive for professionalization in nursing has important economic consequences. Workers regarded as professionals are more independent in the conduct of their work, and better able to control their own practice activities than are other workers, and are generally more highly paid. Professionals are also able to take advantage of more meaningful career advancement, both in terms of responsibilities and remuneration, than are other employees. The nature of professionalization and its impact on the economics of nursing is therefore appropriate to consider.

Friedson (1973) distinguished between workers who are organized on the basis of administrative principle and those who are organized through professionalization of their field of work. The former are hired, trained, assigned, supervised, and evaluated through the process of administration. Control is by persons employed in management positions. Production workers, such as laborers, sales, office, and clerical persons are organized to do the work that administration wants done. Today it is common for members of professions, including the majority of professional nurses, to be employed by organizations rather than being self-employed. It is common for management to control the terms and conditions of the professional's work while the content and standards of work are controlled through standards developed by the profession.

Pavalko (1971) summarized writings on the characteristics of professions and concluded that little is gained by evaluating occupations in relation to absolute criterion achievement. Rather, it is helpful to focus on the concept of professionalization of the field as a dynamic, evolving process. Using commonly accepted criteria, it is possible to consider the degree of professionalization by a specific group or to track the history of its progress. Occupations both advance and diminish over time in relation to these commonly accepted criteria. The process of professionalization may be rapid or slow. An occupation such as nursing may be advanced in the professionalization process on certain characteristics and less advanced on others. Pavalko's criteria will be reviewed briefly, and it may be instructive to consider in more detail how these criteria apply to nursing.

Theoretical Knowledge and Intellectual Technique

According to Pavalko, a profession's body of knowledge is organized around theory derived from philosophical inquiry and research. Preparation for professional practice is intellectual and abstract, and includes a major skill component in which theoretical knowledge is applied to the problems of clients.

The discipline of nursing is evolving this dimension in its academic and research centers. The creation of the federally financed National Center for Nursing Research in 1987, within the National Institutes of Health, is a major development to further research activity. Nursing knowledge undergoes continuous modification, and the individual professional nurse must engage in life-long learning to keep abreast of knowledge development.

Relevance to Basic Social Values

Each profession has as its focus some social value that is its reason for being. For example, clergy focus upon moral values and behaviors; lawyers, upon justice; teachers, upon education; and the military, upon defense.

Medicine has been construed by the public as focusing upon health. Rather, close observation would lead to the conclusion that medicine's focus has usually been upon the control or elimination of disease. Nursing's goal is promotion of clients' personal health, independent functioning, and well-being.

Extended Training Period of a Specialized Nature

Professions, over time, tend to lengthen their educational process and develop courses of study unique to their particular group. Socialization of professionals involves considerable time to enable them to learn the "subculture" of that profession, that is, learn the values, norms, and work role expectations of the profession. Most professions provide a transition experience, such as an internship or residency for physicians, for learning these values from designated role models. Clerkships in law and clericships in the ministry are other examples, as is employment of a graduate student, who may eventually become a professor, as a teaching assistant. In nursing, academic nursing programs, employment experiences with preceptors, and professional organizations fulfill these functions, in part.

Service Ideal

The focus here is upon the *motivation* of the group. For a profession to focus its contribution upon a service needed by society does not mean that personal self-interests must be ignored. It is important that the public have confidence, and it must, in fact, be true that the professional practitioner has clients' interests uppermost. This is the basis of trust in the practitioner–client relationship. From an economic perspective, the expected future income of potential professionals must be sufficient to attract an adequate supply of competent practitioners to provide those services in appropriate amounts for the requirements of society.

Autonomy Recognized by Society

Autonomy relates to the self-regulation, self-control, and self-discipline of members of the professional group by the profession itself. Perhaps the most important facet of autonomy is the extent to which the public recognizes this autonomy and permits members of the profession to define in law their scope of practice, their educational programs, and their supervision, in relation to the work content, by members of their profession. These are important issues for nursing with major economic consequences.

Autonomy derives from the public's respect for a profession's specialized or unique knowledge. Society, in effect, empowers a profession (Hall, 1982; Styles, 1982). Professional nurses distinguish between the dependent functions of nurses (activities associated with medical diagnosis and treatment) and the independent functions of nurses (activities associated with the "diagnosis and treatment of human responses to actual and potential health problems" [American Nurses' Association, 1980]).

Personal Commitment

A profession generally evokes from an individual a major, if not life-long commitment to work in that field. While members of a profession may be employed in diverse positions, they remain members of the profession. For professional workers, the work content itself is perhaps the most important source of motivation, as opposed to pay, hours, administrative situations, personal power, or other factors.

Professional Community

The professional community serves as the major reference group for its members. In nursing there is a shared sense of identity that provides the major influence for the socialization of new members of the nursing staff. Professional organizations, such as the American Nurses' Association, and its affiliate State Nurses' Associations, are influence agents for the professional community; they represent the nursing profession in many arenas involving economic and political activity.

In fact, support of a profession's political positions may be regarded as one key measure of the internalization of the profession's values. The professional community has power to reward its members and, in this way, is able to influence their adaptation into the system of shared beliefs and common concerns held by the profession.

Ethical Practices

Professions such as nursing establish a standard of expected behavior that includes relationships among or between professional members and between professional members and the public. This code serves to enforce the "service ideal" and can be used in courts to identify acceptable—or unacceptable—behaviors. To have a code of ethics is one characteristic of a profession, which tends to have greater influence as an educational instrument than as a professional judicial device.

These criteria reflect the process of professionalization. It is apparent that there is a central, well-developed *profession of nursing* that is rapidly evolving a credible body of scientific and humanistic knowledge as its base. There is also a large number of associate nurses whose work is controlled administratively, as Friedson (1973) defined. These distinctions need to be recognized economically, politically, and, in time, legally.

The Work Force of Nursing

The work force of nursing may be categorized with a model of concentric circles (Fig. 1–1). Not all nurses will agree with this model. As stated above, this will probably represent agreement with the professional goal for nursing

Figure 1–1

The work force of nursing.

that underlies the model but may reflect lack of agreement about the way in which the categories of the nursing work force have been defined. If the model were viewed in cross section, it would form a cone with the profession at the top. The *profession of nursing* (center) is composed of registered nurses possessing a baccalaureate or higher degree with a major in nursing. The major in nursing is stressed because the actual degrees have many different names. The presence of upper division (junior and senior college years) nursing knowledge is essential in order to be a professional nurse as defined by the criteria discussed in the previous section. Professional nurses include most members of nursing job categories such as practitioner, clinical nurse specialist, educator, researcher, consultant, and administrator. Large numbers of these nurses hold masters or doctoral degrees. The occupation of nursing (center and middle) includes registered nurses prepared in associate or technical (associate degree and diploma) nursing programs and licensed practical nurses (LPN or LVN). Thus *occupation of nursing* refers to nurses prepared at the professional level as well as at the associate/technical and licensed practical nurse levels. The *work force of nursing* (all circles) includes not only professional nurses, associate/technical and licensed practical nurses, but also assisting personnel such as nursing assistants, aides, or orderlies who are not registered and who are most commonly trained on the job by the institution employing them. Ward clerks and other clerical personnel, who are often employed by nursing departments, are not part of the work force of nursing because they do not provide direct nursing care services to clients or patients.

The outer border of the model is defined with a broken or "semipermeable" line to indicate that individuals are able to move rather freely in and out of nursing employment at the assisting level. The other two circles are represented by solid lines because licensure, regulations, and professional considerations define these groups. In each instance additional formal education is required to move to the next level.

Future changes in the licensure of nurses will not affect this model since professional nurses will be unaffected. Nurses prepared at the associate or technical level already are considered as part of the occupation of nursing but not of the profession of nursing. Proposed licensure changes would "grandfather" (leave unaffected) the registered nurse status of these nurses. Although they would complete their careers licensed as registered nurses, these nurses will be ineligible for professional positions with qualification requirements of the BSN degree. The lack of uniformity in nursing education has produced many problems, disagreements, and situations difficult for nursing to resolve in a reasoned manner. The model of associate nurses and professional nurses used in this book recognizes that the process of correction is starting to take place in the employment arena without regard for licensure status.

The leadership for nursing is provided by professional nurses whether one is considering nursing practice, administration, education, or research. For this reason the conceptual perspective for this book derives from nursing as a health profession. Within nursing, however, as with most other professions, paraprofessional personnel provide large amounts of day-to-day services.

Nursing Administration

Executive-level nurse administrators in hospitals, long-term care, ambulatory care, and home care agencies have significant influence over the utilization of nursing personnel. It is nurse administrators who determine which nursing resources will be utilized and for what purposes. The book *Magnet Hospitals* published by the American Academy of Nursing (1983) illustrates that where institutions have strong, competent, professionally-oriented nursing leadership, there can be marked improvements in the quality of nursing care received by patients and the work satisfaction of nurses. The employment of professional, associate, and assisting personnel by nurse administrators has a direct effect upon the educational market in nursing.

It is the responsibility of nurse administrators to evaluate and to be accountable for the effectiveness of care and the efficiency of the nursing delivery system in achieving the expected standard of nursing practice in that health care facility. The quality of nursing care as perceived by the public, as well as the importance that society places on its need for nursing care, reflects and affects nursing's professional reputation, regard, respect, and power.

Nurse administrators must be able to "translate" the language of professional nurses into the language of financial officers, personnel managers, executive administrators, and members of institutional boards and public bodies. The more effective nurse administrators are in this process, the more effective and efficient nursing becomes. Nursing administration exists, in part, to narrow the gap between patients' nursing care needs, as defined by the profession, and the demand for nursing care that is defined by health service administrators as the willingness of patients and third-party payers to pay for that care.

An Economic Model of Nursing Care Delivery

A simple economic model of nursing care delivery is presented in Table 1–1. The model indicates that nursing care is produced by combining selected factors of production to produce hours of nursing care that are sold in the health service market to consumers. As nursing care is utilized, there are both consumer and nurse outcomes.

Table 1–1 General, Health Service, and Nursing Care Market Models

General Market
Inputs + Production Processes → Process Outputs + Market → Consumer Utilization

Health Service Market
Factors of Production + Health Service Production → Health Services + Health Service Market → Patient/Client Utilization

Nursing Care Market
Personnel, Facilities, Technology, Financing + Nursing Service Production → Nursing Care + Nursing Care Market → Patient/Client and Nurse Outcomes

In health care, as in most other fields, the most important inputs used in production include personnel, facilities, technology, and financing. In health care these factors are highly specialized: nurses, physicians, physical therapists, medical technicians, dietitians (personnel), and hospitals, nursing homes, clinics of various types (facilities), for example. The technology utilized in the provision of many forms of health services as well as the financing for health services is also specialized. With financing coming primarily from sources other than an individual's own personal funds, the nature of the financing characteristics of the health services delivery market first became an important economic issue in the 1970s and will continue to be a serious societal problem. Movement toward a free market in health care has brought loud protests from those who believe health care should be planned and financed as a human right of all members of our society. The model in Table 1–1 does not distinguish between a free market or a centrally regulated health care economy. This issue is considered in detail in Chapter 11.

In any health services delivery setting, some particular configuration of personnel, facilities, technology, and financing are combined in a production process from which services are provided for patients. Take the example of a surgical procedure: Over time, considerations based on patient safety, effective treatment, efficiency, economy of time, and expense have evolved into a pattern of care for a patient undergoing a particular surgical procedure that can be described fairly readily by someone familiar with health care delivery. Staff members involved conduct specific activities prior to, during, and following the surgery. Specialized facilities, including both pre-operative and post-operative (recovery) rooms, may be required as well as the surgical suite itself. It is highly likely that the way in which the procedure will be paid for has been ascertained and verified in advance. The entire set of services, from pre-admission evaluation to post-discharge monitoring, surrounding this surgical procedure are part of the production process.

What is the output? In a trivial sense, it is the fact that the surgery was performed and hours of nursing care provided, but output really refers to results or outcomes. Production processes in health services delivery are goal oriented: from the nurse's perspective, the appropriate outcome from the surgical procedure is the restoration of the patient's optimal, independent functioning in a timely fashion.

The provision of nursing services as a critical part of the production process in health care delivery settings relates to their ultimate efficiency and effectiveness in achieving desired results for clients. Thus, a critical responsibility of nursing and the health care delivery system is to make available to the public an appropriate grouping of factors of production that can combine to provide production processes that create efficacious, efficient, and safe health care services at reasonable costs.

In this model, economic factors are evident. Personnel, facilities, and technology must be financed. Those who pay for health services expect them to be rendered at a reasonable, if not minimal, cost. Economically, it is possible to organize the production of health services in more than one way—an obvious example is the shift in recent years of many in-patient services now provided on an ambulatory basis. The organization of nursing services also changes, as in the growth in popularity of primary nursing over the earlier team nursing approach. Different ways of organizing the production processes in health care delivery have consequences for the costs of services provided and for other aspects of services as well.

Another economic consideration implicit in this model of nursing care delivery involves distinctions between *needs*, *wants*, and *demands* for health services. The failure to recognize the differences between these concepts as they relate to health services delivery is one source of frustration for many practicing nurses and a source of dissatisfaction for many patients. In terms of health care requirements, *needs*, refer to objective professional assessments and judgments about the level of service that, optimally, could be provided to the patient. *Wants*, economically, refer to the level of care that would be desired if no cost were involved. Patients may want more nursing care than they in fact need, and nurses may want to do more for a patient than objective need dictates.

Health professionals sometimes have a tendency to believe that a patient's needs and a practitioner's wants for the patient are the same. Within service institutions, nursing care needs (or wants) become modified by the institution's administrative decisions relative to the economic environment. The service requirements accepted by the institution are generally those for which there is an economic *demand*, that is, the level of service for which someone or some agency is in fact willing to pay.

Considerable stress and anxiety is experienced by nurses who do not understand that the nursing profession, in its academic research centers, develops the knowledge base or science of nursing and teaches nursing students appropriate interventions for meeting clients' needs. This does not mean that society is willing or able to purchase everything that the profession may have identified as part of the appropriate nursing interventions.

Health service institutions can only provide the care for which society is willing to pay. No health profession, be it medicine, pharmacy, dentistry, social work, clinical psychology, or nursing is ever fully satisfied with the nature of the support it receives from society. Every profession is scientifically and technically able to meet client needs that, in fact, often are not fully met because the institution involved is able to commit only the level of resources to the production processes of health services delivery that reflect economic demand (i.e., the willingness of someone to pay for the services rendered). Thus, it is apparent that economic considerations have important effects on both the profession and all members of the work force of nursing.

References

American Nurses' Association. 1980. *Nursing: A social policy statement.* Kansas City: Author.

Friedson, E. (Ed.). (1973). *The professions and their prospects.* Beverly Hills, CA: Sage Publication.

Hall, R.H. (1982). The professions, employed professionals, and the professional association. In *Professionalism and the empowerment of nursing.* Kansas City: American Nurses' Association.

Moses, E. (1989). Selected findings from the 1988 sample survey of registered nurses. Washington, D.C.: Division of Nursing, Department of Health and Human Services.

Pavalko, R.M. (1971). *Sociology of occupations and professions.* Itasca, IL: F.E. Peacock Publishers, Inc.

Styles, M. (1982). Society and nursing: The new professionalism. In *Professionalism and the empowerment of nursing.* Kansas City: American Nurses' Association.

Task Force on Nursing Practice in Hospitals. (1983). *Magnet hospitals.* Kansas City: American Academy of Nursing.

Chapter 2

Economics as a Science

Economics, like other major social sciences, has as its goal the theoretical explanation of certain phenomena and relationships characteristic of society. Economics, and its major subfields, derives from a body of knowledge and established principles. To assist nurses and other health professionals in understanding and utilizing economic concepts and principles, this chapter focuses on the major divisions of economics, key economic concepts, economic data sources, and certain research tools common to this field. By necessity, the discussion that follows is brief and omits a number of the concepts, principles, complexities, and interrelationships that are characteristic of economics. A fuller description of these can be found in any of the leading textbooks on economics.

Discipline of Economics

The discipline of economics is built upon two fundamental concepts: scarcity and choice. *Scarcity* is defined as a limited supply, that is, all persons cannot have as much as they might wish to have of something or other. Scarcity is this constraint on the availability of the resource, product, or service that gives it worth or economic value. Personal relationships may have high value to the persons involved, but there is no marketplace in which they can be bought or sold, so their economic value can not be expressed well in terms of money. Most people would not agree with the old song, "The Best Things in Life are Free," when they try to balance their budget or arrange the financing for a new house or car. Even the air we breathe has taken on economic value as the cost of keeping the air clean increases.

Choice involves selection among alternatives. When consumers' choices are aggregated, the resultant demand encourages business firms to produce those goods and services that consumers are willing to purchase. Employers choose employees from an existing pool of potential workers. A fundamental difference between a primarily free market economy (as in the United States) versus a government-planned economy (as in the Soviet Union) is the extent of reliance on free choice and free markets. In a free market society, not only do consumers have the freedom to choose what they will buy but enterprises have considerable freedom in choosing which marketable products or services to produce, and in what way to produce them.

Economics as a Behavioral Science

Since economic choices are made by people, economics is a behavioral science. As a science, economics is concerned with the allocation of resources, the methods of production, and the ways in which goods and services are distributed, enabling consumption. Each of these decisions involves scarcity and choice. Thus economics can be defined as the science of choice among scarce and competing alternatives, involving decisions about the use of resources, what to produce, and how to distribute the goods and services that are produced. Although economics, like other social sciences, has limitations in the predictability of its theories, the assumptions economics makes about human behavior are among the most reliable among all behavioral sciences.

Those assumptions, which have been tested repeatedly and have become fundamental to the science of economics, include:

Human desires for goods and services are insatiable. When individuals satisfy specific wants, they develop new ones. As individuals' incomes increase, the houses they live in, the cars they drive, the clothes they wear, and so forth, all tend to become more expensive. Those who do not spend more and more save their earnings—trying to satisfy the desire for financial security.

Human beings are rational maximizers. This means that individuals select ways to achieve their maximum satisfaction from the goods or services they purchase for the minimum effort or cost. Individual choices differ significantly, but economic behavior is determined rationally in order to maximize the individual's perceived well-being from the consumption of goods and services.

Human beings respond in predictable ways to changes in economic incentives. As the economic advantages associated with the choice of a particular behavior increase, more persons choose that behavior. The opposite is also true: greater economic disadvantages result in decreased levels of that behavior. Changes in the tax laws provide examples of changes in economic incentives that may affect the behavior of individuals or businesses.

Major Divisions of Economics

Economics is divided into two major areas: microeconomics and macroeconomics.

Microeconomics

Explored more thoroughly in the next chapter, microeconomics pertain to the activity of individuals and businesses with regard to the allocation of resources and the production and distribution of goods and services. In microeconomics, the focus is upon the fundamental and critically important economic concepts of *supply* and *demand* and their functioning in the *marketplace*. The marketplace may reflect the purchases of all consumers, it may reflect this for a segment of the economy (e.g., the market for health services), or it may indicate the behaviors of an individual economic agent (e.g., an individual nurse deciding whether or not to accept a position at a particular wage or an individual hospital deciding whether or not to purchase a new technological device).

Macroeconomics

Based upon a broad view of the economy as a whole, macroeconomics pertains to the interrelations of the subsystems to the entire system. Attention is directed to the interdependence of the major components of the economy and the total, or aggregate, influences upon them. Macroeconomics involves the totality of business activity and focuses on economic concepts such as describing and predicting changes in the gross national product (the value of all goods and services produced in the nation in a year), inflation or deflation, the distribution of income, the consumer price index, and employment and unemployment. Generally, data are aggregated across economic sectors to reflect trends in geographic areas or the nation as a whole. Macroeconomics also examines the performance of the economic system over periods of time, frequently over a few to 10 years but sometimes may examine the performance of economic variables over a period of 50 years or more.

Using macroeconomics data, the federal government has two major instruments for influencing the economy. One of these is *fiscal policy*, which involves (1) increasing or decreasing government spending and (2) raising or lowering taxes. Fiscal policy decisions are reflected in the annual federal budget enacted by Congress and signed into law by the president. Fiscal policy decisions have important consequences for the amount of money available to pay for health care services in the nation because health care programs such as Medicare are major components of the federal budget. The second major instrument of economic influence by the federal government is *monetary policy*, which relates to the supply of money available and the price (the rate of interest) at which one can borrow money. The money supply is controlled to a considerable degree by the Federal Reserve Board, charged by Congress to be a quasi-independent agency. The Federal Reserve adjusts the availability of money by: (1) stipulating the percentage of their assets that member banks (most major banks are members of the Federal Reserve System) must hold in reserve, (2) changing the discount rate (an interest rate at which member banks may borrow from the Federal Reserve), and (3) engaging in open market operations (i.e., the buying and selling of U.S. government bonds). To illustrate, the Federal Reserve can decrease the availability of money by increasing the amount of funds member banks borrow from the Federal Reserve, or by selling government bonds, which means that the private purchasers of the bonds transfer money to the government's account, reducing the amount of money in private hands. The importance of both fiscal and monetary policy is that they can profoundly influence the levels of consumption and investment spending on the economy. A more restrictive fiscal policy (less government spending) or a "tighter" monetary policy (less money available to the public) both tend to restrict private spending for consumption and investment. If the government severely curtailed its contribution to the Medicare program as part of an overall fiscal policy, some elderly who would otherwise have received health services would not obtain them. Similarly, a more restrictive monetary policy implies higher interest rates, at which consumers and businesses will restrict purchases financed by debt—such as the construction of a new hospital facility or treatment unit.

Clearly both microeconomics and macroeconomics are related to nursing. In the organization of this book, those elements of microeconomics as they relate to nursing are described first, in Parts II and III. The more general, macroeconomic elements of economics as they relate to nursing are generally confined to Parts IV and V of the book. As with any social science, however, these distinctions sometimes "blur" in the discussion that follows.

Economic Concepts

Several major concepts that have evolved in the field of economics are important for nurses and other health professionals to understand. These concepts or relationships are a fundamental part of economic science and are often used in decision making relative to the provision of health services. These concepts are described fully in economic texts such as those by

Heilbroner and Thurow (1984) and Mansfield (1983). The following are brief explanations.

Ceteris Paribus

This Latin phrase means "other things being equal." It is used extensively in economic research because, in fact, economic relationships are influenced by myriad variables that are constantly changing. To study the relationship between economic variables, it is useful and often necessary to assume that other influences not of immediate interest are constant. In describing the resultant effect, one would qualify the statement by stating, "other things being equal" or *ceteris paribus*. Comparing current levels of health expenditures to amounts spent in earlier years makes little sense due to inflation. Thus the comparison should be made *ceteris paribus,* as if the purchasing power of the dollar had not changed from year to year. Or, as a hypothetical nursing example, suppose a hospital has reduced staff, closed a medical–surgical unit, reorganized administratively, and opened a burn unit—all of which may have affected nurse staffing levels. It might be of interest to know, *ceteris paribus,* what was the effect of opening the burn unit on nursing staff. These are only two examples, but the concept has broad application in economics to enable economists to explore the unique effects of a particular change, when in fact many if not most economic variables are regularly changing. Since economic variables are interdependent, the effect of a change in any one is otherwise difficult to specify without the simplifying assumption of *ceteris paribus.*

Opportunity Cost

When resources are used for a specific purpose, economists are also interested in the best alternative choice that was not selected. What was, in fact, given up because the first option, rather than the second best option, was selected? An example with which most nursing students can relate has to do with income *not* earned while attending school. The cost of advanced education includes not only the direct expenses for tuition, books, and so forth, but also the loss of income that could have been earned if one had been working instead of pursuing the additional education.

Still another example: If a hospital adds an expensive new service such as heart transplant capabilities, the hospital's administration or board of trustees must consider not only the anticipated capital costs, annual expenditures and revenues, but also opportunity costs associated with the new service. What other alternatives does the hospital have to forego in order to use its money for the new heart transplant service? What would the expenditures and revenues be for a different type of service? Would the hospital "do better" to establish a perinatal center instead? Often economic decisions are very difficult when opportunity costs are considered. Sometimes the value of "the path not chosen" cannot be known with certainty. It is, however, important to recognize that virtually *all* economic decisions involve opportunity costs. By reading this book now, there is something else that you might have done but cannot do now. By becoming a professional nurse, there is another profession that you will not enter. Life is full of situations involving opportunity costs. According to economics, the point is to be aware of them and to choose those opportunities that are of the greatest value compared with the next best alternative.

Diminishing Returns

An increase in resources used as inputs does not result in steady increases in outputs indefinitely. At some level, output starts to decrease due to the quality of the inputs, space crowding, impaired technology, or other factors. Production cannot be expanded indefinitely, and when the relative output decreases, that is the point of diminishing returns. Diminishing returns do not relate to cost of the increased inputs but rather to the quality of the effectiveness with which they can be utilized. In terms of Table 1–1, diminishing returns occur when the inputs used in production (personnel, facilities, technology, and financing) can no longer be combined as efficiently as before into production processes to provide health services.

As an example, nurses may have experienced the concept of diminishing returns when working on hospital units with too many patient beds. Even when appropriately staffed, a nursing unit can sometimes be so large that it becomes less efficient due to problems in staffing and communication. Likewise, certain hospitals have expanded their physical plant and services to the point of diminishing returns. Excessive physical distance between units of the hospital can increase costs, such as excessive time for patient transport, and impair services, such as difficulty in delivering hot meals to the bedside.

Economies of Scale

A basic assumption is that there are efficiencies associated with large scale enterprises, such as in mass production, and that larger scale operations can produce goods or services at a lower cost per unit—at least up to the point of diminishing returns. The Hill–Burton Act provided federal funds for hospital construction, enabling many small hospitals to be built in the decades after World War II. Many of these hospitals are now, however, too small to maintain an adequate staff with the range of competencies needed for efficient utilization; thus, they suffer from problems related to a scale of operation that is economically too small. Years ago many rural school districts consolidated into "unified school districts" in order to benefit from economies of scale. Should a number of the nation's smaller rural hospitals do something similar in order to benefit form economies of scale?

Marginal Effects

Marginal is an economic term that refers to small amounts of change, or incremental variance (plus or minus). The term is frequently used in economics to indicate or measure change: For example, *marginal cost* refers to the cost of one additional unit. Initially at low levels of production, the production of more units decreases the marginal cost per unit. As some point, however, there are labor or physical plant increases associated with increased production. Then, the marginal cost of that next unit becomes higher. The concept of marginal cost is used extensively in determining the optimal size of a production operation.

Marginal benefits may also be identified. In health care, additional services or expenditures on behalf of particular patients tend to have smaller extra benefits than the initial services provided; this is only logical because what is most essential (beneficial) should be that service or treatment which is done first. Marginal costs may also be compared with marginal benefits, an exercise that has important implications for the quality of care. This subject is pursued in Chapter 10. There is also *marginal utility*, which refers to the additional value received by consuming one more unit of a good or service within a defined time period. The concept can be applied to anything that is consumed, be it health care, automobiles, hamburgers, coats, or televisions. In each instance, the total utility (subjective personal benefits) may increase with each additional item consumed but the marginal utility provided by each additional item actually decreases. This is called the *law of diminishing marginal utility*, that is, the second, third, and fourth of anything tends to produce less utility for the consumer than the previous item although total utility continues to slowly increase. The law of diminishing marginal utility therefore helps to explain why some families have two or three cars or televisions but few have four or five of either. It implies that after some amount of good or service has been purchased, the opportunity cost of purchasing any more of it becomes too high and something else is purchased. Thus, there is an interrelationship between the law of diminishing marginal utility and the concept of opportunity costs.

Indifference Analysis

Since the actual marginal utility of a product to a consumer is often difficult to measure, economists are likely to make these comparisons using the hypothetical construct of indifference analysis. For someone who likes apples and oranges equally, a choice between having six apples or only one orange may be obvious but, at some point, a consumer becomes indifferent and the choice becomes immaterial (e.g., three apples versus two oranges, if the individual slightly prefers oranges to apples).

As a simple application of indifference analysis to health care, assume that an employer pays for hospital/medical insurance for employees, but family coverage is charged to the employee. Would the employee rather have higher insurance premiums or larger deductibles? At what point is the consumer indifferent? Not all consumers react in the same fashion, and the insurance company might therefore sell policies with $200 deductibles (at a higher price) and policies with $300 deductibles (at a slightly lower price). Some employees prefer one option, others the alternative. Some employees have difficulty deciding—they are really indifferent in the sense that each alternative is of equal value or utility to them. Suppose, however, the insurer offers policies with $1000 deductibles. Few, if any, purchase this policy despite its much lower price. This policy involves such a high level of individual risk that few purchasers are indifferent to the trade-off between the price (premium charged) and their individual financial responsibility for a large deductible payment should an illness occur.

Positive and Normative Economics

The nature of this book makes it important for the reader to understand the difference in these two terms. *Positive* economics refers to *what is,* to the scientific use of economics. Positive economics includes descriptive statements of fact, propositions, and statistically derived statements about relationships, plus predictions about the future. "In 1986, the United States spent $458 billion on health services, which was equal to 10.8 percent of the value of the Gross National Product that year," would be an example of a positive economic statement.

Normative economics involves the use of economic concepts and data to make statements about what *should be* or what *ought to* take place. As economics is so closely involved in all policy decisions, it may be necessary to go beyond the science of relationships and predictions and recommend a normative or political position. It may be appropriate to advocate a position, but it is important to label the assertion properly. "To properly care for the health of Americans, it is desirable for the government to provide adequate health insurance for those who lack adequate coverage or have none at all. This might cost $30–40 billion annually . . . " This would be an example of a *normative* economic statement. Statements about the economics of nursing will involve both positive and normative economic statements.

Efficiency

Economists distinguish between *technical* and *economic* efficiency. Combining units of production in such a way as to obtain the maximum possible number of units of output is technically efficient. This may not be economically efficient, in which efficiency may be measured by seeking the least-cost method of production or the maximum benefit for the least possible effort. For example, a staff nurse and a clinical specialist may both perform the same procedure. If the clinical specialist can complete it in 20 minutes compared to 30 minutes for the staff nurse, then the clinical specialist is technically more efficient. If the staff nurse is paid $14 per hour and the clinical specialist $24 per hour, then the value of the specialist's 20 minutes is $8.00 while the staff nurse's 30 minutes is $7.00. The staff nurse is therefore more efficient, economically, for performance of that procedure.

Interdependence

All parts of the economic system are interrelated, and changes in one section of the economy generate effects elsewhere. The complexity of these interrelated effects is, to a considerable extent, beyond the scope of this book. This is one reason why is was indicated early in the chapter that readers may wish to consult a standard economics textbook in connection with this material on economics as a science. Interdependence of economic events occurs both in microeconomics and macroeconomics. In physics an action generates a reaction. In economics an action may cause a whole series of reactions, some of which may be recognized and intended, others of which may not be known or expected. This complexity is why economists often utilize the simplifying assumption of *ceteris paribus*.

Logical Fallacies and Economics as a Science

No discussion of the science of economics would be complete without a description of several logical errors, or fallacies, that often slip into economic arguments. Such errors can lead to incorrect conclusions about economic relationships, trends, and effects. As each economic fallacy is explained, an example from health care or nursing is provided. The purpose of this section is to help readers avoid committing such errors in thinking about the economics of nursing.

Post Hoc Ergo Propter Hoc

This Latin phrase simply means "after this, therefore, because of this." It implies causation, that a cause and effect relationship exists between two events simply because one occurred first in time. Errors in attribution of causality are not unique to economics, but they do occur with some frequency and should be questioned. The critical problem in economics, as with other social sciences and behavioral phenomena in general, is that there are so many variables.

Prospective payment based on diagnosis-related groups was introduced in 1983 as major economic and health policy reform for the Medicare program. Average lengths of stay declined markedly in 1984 in the nation's hospitals. Is this a result of the prospective payment system (PPS) and its incentives—a fixed payment per stay rather than a per diem accumulating for each additional day in the hospital? Almost certainly it was important for the Medicare population, but average lengths of stay declined for *all* age groups hospitalized. This general trend cannot be explained simply by the introduction of PPS. A complete explanation is much more complex.

As a second example, consider the fact that nursing school enrollments began to decline in 1984. In 1986 a shortage of nurses reappeared. An immediate temptation to attribute the shortage, at least in part, to reduced nursing school enrollments and graduations, *post hoc ergo propter hoc*. In reality, the number of nurses who graduate each year continues to exceed the number who withdraw from nursing practice due to death, retirement, or other reasons. The explanation of the current shortage lies elsewhere. (Of course, if enrollments continue to decline, there will be a serious adverse effect on the *future* supply of nursing personnel.)

The Fallacy of Composition

Understanding the logical error in economic thought requires recognition of the fact that "what is true for one is not necessarily true for all." For example, suppose a hospital in a metropolitan area wants to increase its occupancy rate. It introduces a successful marketing campaign and achieves a greater share of the region's patient population. Yet if all the hospitals in that metropolitan area introduce equal campaigns, similarly favorable results would not occur for all—the region's patient population is essentially constant. What is true for one is not necessarily true for the group.

As another example, suppose a nurse in a metropolitan area desires to increase her income and becomes an entrepreneur by establishing a temporary nurse staffing agency. If the area is not currently served by such an agency, the business may be successful and profitable. If a large number of nurses attempt the same thing at more or less the same time, however, the supply of temporary services could far exceed the demand for them, and few if any of these nurse entrepreneurs would control successful and profitable business ventures.

The fallacy of composition in economics is essentially the argument that "what's true for me must be true for everyone as a group." It is simply not true.

Economic Reality Depends on Economic Conditions

Suppose all nurses who want to work are fully employed—a period of prosperity for nursing. Then suppose the government introduces a new health care program significantly expanding home health care benefits for the elderly and disabled. Where can the additional nursing personnel necessary for these new services be obtained? Since all nurses willing to work are already doing so, the extra home health nurses can only be secured by hiring nurses away from other health settings, creating a shortage of nurses in those areas.

Under different economic conditions there may be a surplus of nurses. The new government policy expanding home health care benefits could then be implemented and staffed without disrupting nursing care in other settings. Therefore, economic "truth" or reality depends on underlying economic conditions. What occurs in one setting or situation, as in prosperity, may have very different effects if it were to occur during a recession or depression.

Unconscious Preconceptions and Value-charged Terms

Aware of it or not, most people have preconceived ideas about economics, economic relationships, and economic principles. Many people hold opinions, often strong opinions, about government spending, debt, taxes, the role of labor unions, and the appropriateness of wages earned by people in various professions. In nursing there are many economic-related issues about which nurses often hold strong views: appropriate role and salary differentials (if any) for nurses with different educational preparation, collective bargaining for nurses, the lack of adequate economic status afforded the nursing profession, and the appropriateness of high levels of spending for heroic measures for terminally ill patients are examples. While everyone has opinions and personal points of view, in considering the economics of nursing it is important to be aware of one's own preconceptions and perhaps, in some cases, reject or revise them.

Another common problem in economics is the use of value-charged or "loaded" terminology. It sounds very different to speak of "socialized medicine" as opposed to a "national health program," both of which may amount to the very same thing. Preconceptions are often revealed in the terminology used to describe economic principles or policies. Effort has been made in this book to avoid using terms with meanings beyond that which they are in fact intended to convey.

Representative Economic Data and Research Tools

Economic Data and Their Sources

Most data used by economists for research purposes are collected initially by federal and state governments or by trade associations representing a specific segment of the economy. Government departments regularly publish a variety of documents derived from data that firms or organizations are required to report annually, quarterly or monthly. In this country probably the single most comprehensive data summary is the *Statistical Abstract of the United States*, which is prepared annually by the Bureau of the Census in the Department of Commerce and published by the U.S. Government Printing Office. In the *Statistical Abstract* nurses and health professionals can find accurate data on population, vital statistics, health and nutrition, education, health and human services, the labor force, and employment and earnings, along with information on many other topics.

In one of the appendices of the *Statistical Abstract* there is a guide to primary statistical sources of data collected and published by government agencies. For example, under the heading "Health and Medical Care" it is noted that the Health Care Financing Administration publishes four types of statistical guides:

Annual Medicare Program Statistics, descriptive program data (published annually)

Health Care Financing Program Statistics, Medicare and Medicaid data (published annually)

Health Care Financing Research Reports, special research reports on particular topics (published intermittently)

Health Care Financing Review, research and demonstration projects and statistical information in health care (published quarterly)

After each topic heading in the *Statistical Abstract* appendix there is a listing of government agency documents, followed by reports prepared by private professional or trade associations. One can learn that, for example, (1) *Medical Economics* magazine publishes an annual review of physicians' earnings and expenses; (2) the American Nurses' Association publishes *Facts About Nursing*, a statistical summary of nursing data, about every two years, and that (3) the American Hospital Association publishes an annual document called *Hospital Statistics*. The documents listed above represent important sources of economic data on health care and nursing in the United States.

Many federal government agencies publish selected monographs that are widely utilized. The Department of Health and Human Services annually publishes *Health, United States,* which provides current data on health status (population, fertility, mortality, and various selected measures of the health of the population), utilization of health resources (ambulatory and inpatient services), and health care resources (manpower, facilities, and health care expenditures).

The Bureau of Labor Statistics of the Department of Labor publishes the *National Survey of Professional, Administrative, Technical and Clerical Pay* (annual) and *Employment and Earnings* (monthly). The latter is an excellent source of information for comparing labor costs for various occupational groups across metropolitan statistical areas or by census regions of the country.

In a similar fashion, the Bureau of Economic Analysis of the Department of Commerce publishes monthly the *Survey of Current Business*. The Bureau of Economic Analysis is responsible for data pertaining to the gross national product, national income, disposable personal income, households at or below the poverty level, and similar indices or counts.

Descriptive Indicators

Most of the data sources reviewed above provide descriptive statistics. Economists, like health professionals, are involved in a field in which there is broad interest by the general public. For this reason there is a great deal of economic data that are descriptive of the current status of various indicators for the status of the American economy. One important contribution of economists specializing in macroeconomics has been the development of indices that are used to reflect overall changes in the level of economic activity in the nation. Several important examples follow.

Gross National Product

The total U.S. output of all goods and services produced during a given year, valued at their market prices, is the Gross National Product (GNP). It includes total expenditures for goods and services by private consumers and government, gross private domestic investment (capital investment and the inventories of business), and the net balance of exports of goods and services. From this definition one can see why a negative balance of trade (as a nation, importing more goods than are exported) can have a serious effect on the GNP.

The GNP in the United States is now in excess of $4 trillion annually, and some 11 percent—more than $500 billion at current rates—is spent on health care. The health care services industry is one of the largest in the country. Thus it stands to reason that macroeconomic policies—monetary and fiscal policies—have important effects on health service delivery. This is particularly true because government at federal, state, and local levels has substantial responsibility for the payment of health services.

National Income

This represents another key measure of economic activity. National income represents the total amount of income being received in the nation, that is, the sum of all wages, rents, interest payments, and profits. It is important to note that national income, after certain adjustments have been made, is always equal to the GNP. The adjustments are necessary for two principal reasons. First, the GNP does not take into account that equipment and buildings depreciate. Depreciation is not income or production, so it is subtracted from the GNP to obtain a net national product. Second, businesses collect some taxes as part of the price for which goods and services are sold. The gasoline tax added to the price at the pump is an obvious example. Once these indirect business taxes are removed as well, then the GNP equals national income. The importance of this is that GNP represents the total value of all goods and services produced, as measured by expenditures. Expenditures may represent revenues to others and, thus, necessarily the national income equals the GNP after the adjustments described. All our incomes depend on spending by others; in turn, their spending depends on income derived from our expenditures. Income equals expenditure for the nation.

Consumer Price Index

The Consumer Price Index (CPI) is sometimes referred to as the cost-of-living index, or as the nation's principal measure of inflation. It is a weighted average of prices for a fixed and typical "market basket" of goods and services commonly purchased by urban consumers. The sample on which the CPI is based is representative of about 80 percent of the non-institutional, civilian population. In preparation of the CPI, prices are obtained in over 32,000 establishments in 85 areas of the country each month. The CPI is weighted by the relative importance of each item in the typical consumer's budget. The multitude of items included in the CPI represent expenditures for things such as housing, utilities, furnishings, fuel, food items, clothing, personal care articles, and services, medical care, and entertainment. For example, it is known that in the fuel grouping 2 percent of total consumer expense is for electricity; therefore, electricity represents 2 percent of the base or "market basket" of goods and services on which changes in prices that affect the CPI are calculated.

Wages in many labor contracts and social security payments have been tied to the CPI with increases for inflation in the form of cost-of-living adjustments, protecting recipients against loss of purchasing power. These adjustments may, at the same time, tend to exacerbate inflation to some degree because they raise incomes without necessarily being associated with any increase in the production of more goods and services.

With the purchasing power of the dollar generally changing and economic studies involving comparisons of money values over time, it is often necessary to adjust the value of the dollar to constant or "real" terms to take away the effects of inflation. In Table 2–1, the level of the CPI is shown since 1967, representing the rate of inflation experienced in each year. The CPI was 100 in 1967 because this was the base year in which the value of the index was arbitrarily fixed.

An example is shown in which the dollar values of a nurse's salary at two points in time are compared in constant dollar or "real" purchasing power terms. From such an example, one could determine whether or not purchasing power has been maintained; in other words, had the nurse's pay kept up with inflation?

General Analytic Techniques

The science of economics utilizes a variety of analytic techniques in order to explain and predict economic behavior and relationships. The most fundamental analytic technique used is supply and demand analysis, which is of such importance that it is explained in Chapter 3; a brief explanation of this basic tool for analyzing economic behavior in this chapter would be inadequate. Apart from supply and demand, a number of other analytic techniques represent significant tools for economists. Two of the more useful are cost-effectiveness analysis and cost-benefit analysis. Both of these have applicability to nursing and health care. Cost-effectiveness and cost-benefit are often used (and misused) as if they were interchangeable concepts in discus-

Table 2–1 The Consumer Price Index

Year	Index	Annual change[a]	Example
1967	100.0		A sample computation using the CPI:
1970	116.3	5.9	The average salary for a hospital
1971	121.3	4.3	staff nurse in 1976 was $12,000. In
1972	125.3	3.3	1986 it would have needed to be
1973	125.3	6.2	$23,113 for that staff nurse to have
1974	147.7	11.0	"stayed even" over that period—to
1975	161.2	9.1	have maintained equivalent
1976	170.5	5.8	purchasing power in the face of
1977	181.5	6.5	inflation.[b]
1978	195.4	7.7	
1979	217.4	11.3	
1980	246.8	13.5	$12{,}000 \times \dfrac{328.4}{170.5} = \$23{,}113$
1981	272.4	10.4	
1982	289.1	6.1	
1983	298.4	3.2	
1984	311.1	4.3	
1985	322.2	3.6	
1986	328.4	1.1	
1987	342.9	4.4	
1988	357.9	4.4	

SOURCE: Consumer Price Index, *Statistical Abstract of United States: 1988.* Washington, DC: U.S. Printing Office.

[a]The most commonly accepted measure of inflation is the annual percentage change in the CPI.

[b]Salary studies suggest that hospital staff nurse salaries in 1986 averaged around $24,000. Thus, while they have kept up with inflation, their increase in real terms has been minimal.

sions pertaining to health-related matters. They are therefore good examples of general analytic techniques in economics for further examination.

Cost-effectiveness analysis deals with evaluation of alternative means to obtain the same result or outcome. In health care it is well known that persons with certain conditions may be treated in more than one fashion, often with significantly different expense, but not necessarily with significantly different outcomes.

Two examples are coronary artery disease and end-stage kidney disease. Coronary artery disease treatment might involve bypass surgery or consist of a continuing medication regime without surgery. In the case of kidney disease, an individual may be treated by dialysis or by transplant.

How can economics contribute to the making of appropriate decisions in such cases? Through the use of cost-effectiveness analysis, costs are calculated for each alternative approach and are compared in terms of their relative abilities to achieve a specific set of results. In the past several years, the prevalence of coronary bypass surgery has declined because it has been learned through studies by the Veterans Administration and others that treatment with medication alone is often as effective and costs much less than surgical intervention. This is an application of cost-effectiveness analysis.

As another application consider a study of kidney transplant versus dialysis conducted in the 1960s. This study was a relatively early but classic example of the application of cost-effectiveness analysis in health care (Smith, 1968). This study was undertaken by a group of physicians, statisticians, and economists. The study compared the cost and effectiveness of two alternate ways of prolonging the lives of persons with end-stage renal disease. New technological capabilities at the time of the study (1966) and the obvious consequences of no action (death) made this investigation unusual.

The two possible means of prolonging life, kidney transplant and use of dialysis equipment, can be used in various combinations, such as repeated dialysis followed by transplant. Effectiveness is measured in a straightforward comparison of the number of years of life expected to be added, on the average, through transplantation or dialysis. This comparison originally assumed that a gain in years of life by one mode of treatment was the same in quality as that from another treatment method. The study group, however, could not accept this because of the volume of evidence suggested a difference in the value of the added time.

Patients dependent on mechanical dialysis equipment must limit their actions to some extent—a geographic limitation, for example—because they must be able to get to the equipment when it is needed. Also, certain dietary restrictions apply, restrictions that do not affect those with a transplant.

Although the committee did not go so far as to suggest that their weighting factor was the result of rigorous economic analysis, they did accept a factor of 1.25 to weight the value of a year of life gained after transplantation more heavily than a year of life gained by hemodialysis. They stated that this factor was for illustrative purposes, but even so it seems extremely significant that a committee of this status publicly went on record as accepting the difficult premise that life under some conditions could be 25 percent more valuable than under other conditions.

The philosophical point to be emphasized is that this in no way implies that some people's lives are more important than others. This is not the issue here, and it would be unfair to so imply. The concept of different values of time, however, is an important and controversial one to many researchers because of the various uses to which time can be put.

On the cost side of the ledger, the computations were made more complex because the cost of failures as well as successes must be included on the presumption that all medically suitable patients will be treated. A further complication with dialysis is the large difference in cost, depending on whether treatment is done at a center or in the home. In making the calculations, life tables were constructed to show the life expectancies under each treatment mode. A further example of the committee's need for innovation was that not enough time had elapsed to permit reliable estimates of long-range life expectancies in this new field; estimates therefore had to be based on speculation and the best testimony then available.

The results from computing effectiveness showed that an average marginal life expectancy of 9.0 years could be expected for a person on dialysis treatment compared to 17.2 years for one in the transplantation group (actually 13.3 added years from a successfully transplanted kidney followed by 3.9 more years on dialysis after eventual failure of the transplant). After adjustment at 13.3 × 1.25 + 3.9, an estimate of 20.5 quality-adjusted years of life is obtained—more than twice as much as that for a person under dialysis treatment (Table 2–2).

The cost-effectiveness computations indicated that the transplantation method provided the lowest cost per year of added life expectancy for end-stage renal patients. Fortunately, it also appeared to offer the greatest prospect for length of added life.

One early conclusion of the study group was reached, not as a direct result of the cost-effectiveness analysis, but because of the incidental gain in program understanding due to the study process. This conclusion was that there were not enough available kidneys for transplant and that many were lost after transplantation due to problems with organ storage, preservation, and tissue typing. The group recognized that these problems ought to be high on the priority list of kidney disease research.

Adding another column (not in the report) to show the ratio of effectiveness to cost, using years of life gained as the effectiveness measure, yields the following figures:

Treatment	Years of life gained (Costs in $10,000s)
Dialysis:	
Center	0.9
Home	2.4
Transplantation:	
Unadjusted	3.8
Adjusted for quality	4.6

A recent study of end-stage renal disease (ESRD), by the National Center for Health Services Research (NCHSR) (1986) provides a current example of the application of cost-effectiveness analysis. This new report evaluates the cost-effectiveness of a new ESRD technology that is being recommended for

Table 2–2 Cost Per Year and Years of Life Gained by Two Treatments for
Kidney Disease

Treatment	Cost	Years of life gained	Cost per year
Dialysis:			
Center	$104,000	9	$11,600
Home	38,000	9	4,200
Transplantation:			
Unadjusted	44,500	17.2	2,600
Adjusted for quality	44,500	20.5	2,200

SOURCE: *Report of the Committee on Chronic Kidney Disease* (1967). Washington, DC: U.S.
Printing Office.

coverage under Medicare. Roughly 105,000 ESRD patients—more than 90
percent of the total number with the condition—are enrolled in Medicare. In
the study, NCHSR's Office of Health Technology Assessment (OHTA) found
that hemofiltration, which mimics the kidney's normal filtration process, is a
safe and effective substitute for the more costly and time-consuming hemodialysis. Traditionally, dialysis has been used for removing urea and other
toxic substances from ESRD patients' blood, while filtration has been used
primarily to siphon the excess fluid. According to OHTA, hemofiltration
appears to be particularly advantageous when used on high-risk, unstable
patients, such as elderly persons with heart disease or diabetes, because it
produces fewer side effects. The precise advantages or disadvantages of
filtration relative to dialysis, however, remain to be defined in long-term,
follow-up studies. Thus cost-effectiveness studies in health care may lead to
important modifications in treatment.

While cost-effectiveness compares two methods of achieving the same goal,
cost-benefit analysis involves comparison of the relative desirability of two or
more programs or projects. At the national level, an example might be the
relative desirability of spending an additional billion dollars for the health
care of the poor or a similar sum of money on low income housing. A rational
economic decision between, or among, alternatives can be made only when
the economic value of benefits per dollar of expense can be determined for
each; the rational economic decision would be to choose the program with
the highest rate of benefits to costs, *ceteris paribus*.

At an institutional level, a hospital may be considering two very different
projects; for example, a home health care program and a helicopter service,
but can only afford to pay for one of them. The home health care service will
produce moderate income but it will also enable the hospital to discharge
patients sooner and thus shorten the average patient stay. This will make

more of the hospital's Medicare admissions profitable. The helicopter service will provide considerable media publicity that will keep the institution's name before the local citizenry. Patients arriving by helicopter tend to require high charge, intensive services. But it is true that many of the acute trauma patients are young people who are inadequately insured. Also, many hospitals have had multiple problems in staffing a helicopter service and maintaining it accident free. Again, reliance on cost-benefit analysis may enable the hospital to make a more reasoned decision than would be possible without attaching cost figures to the probabilities of various potential happenings.

Statistical Techniques

Analytic techniques based on statistical principles are commonly utilized in economics. Described here are regression analysis, correlation, and multiple regression.

The statistical tool used most frequently in economics is that of regression analysis. *Simple* regression involves a hypothesis about the relationship between two variables in which the statistical model being tested is that of an equation for a straight line, in the form:

$$Y = a + bX$$

By tradition X is the independent variable and Y the dependent variable. In the formula, a is the intercept of the line on the vertical axis, and b is the slope of the line. If the line slopes upward from left to right, the relationship is positive. If the line slopes downward from left to right, the relationship is negative. A negative slope is associated with a situation in which increases in the independent variable produce decreases in the dependent variable: an inverse relationship.

In utilizing regression analysis, an economist hypothesizes the slope of the line, obtains relevant measures of the variables, and tests the regression of the independent variable upon the dependent variable. Remember that the null hypothesis (the hypothesis that there is no relation between the two variables X and Y) is rejected on the basis of the probability that the difference between b and zero could not have occurred on the basis of chance alone. If the null hypothesis can be rejected, the research hypothesis has been supported.

The *degree* of relationship between two variables is called a simple correlation coefficient. *Correlation* is high or low depending upon how closely the observations of the one variable lie along the regression line. When observed data are located closely along the regression line, the correlation is high. Conversely, when the observations are quite scattered and at varied distances from the line, correlation is low. Note that a high level of correlation indicates that the two variables are related in *some* way (they both may be related to a third variable): high correlation does not indicate that there is a causal relationship, that is, that one variable is causing the changes in the other variable. Recall the concept of *post hoc ergo propter hoc.*

Another analytic technique commonly used in economic research is that of multiple regression. Here the interest is in determining to what extent several independent variables individually have effects of varying extent on the dependent variable. Once again the goal is to find the equation for the line that provides the best fit, or is most representative, of the data.

For example, suppose a researcher wishes to determine which of three possible influences has the greatest effect on the attrition rate among hospital staff nurses. The economist may hypothesize that the reason is low starting salaries (S); the hospital administrator may believe it is related to family responsibilities (F); and the director of nursing might be convinced that the

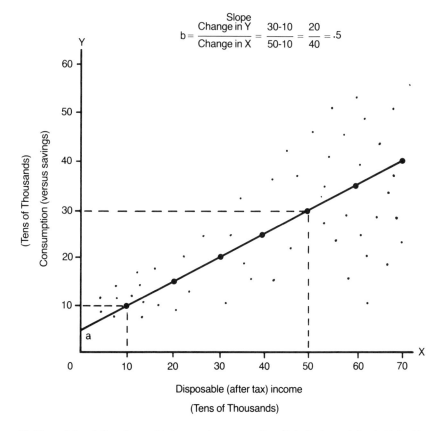

Slope
$$b = \frac{\text{Change in Y}}{\text{Change in X}} = \frac{30\text{-}10}{50\text{-}10} = \frac{20}{40} = .5$$

Fictitious data relating disposable income to consumption. Note that correlation is high at low levels of income and low at high levels. Why?

attrition rate is closely correlated with inadequate economic recognition for merit (*M*). The multiple regression equation would therefore be:

Attrition = a + b_1S + b_2F + b_3M

From the sample data, the researcher computes *a* (the vertical axis intercept) and the values of b_1, b_2, and b_3. These regression coefficients indicate how each of the independent variable effects the dependent variable, attrition. From the regression coefficients the correlation coefficients are obtained. If *R* is the correlation coefficient, R^2 is the coefficient of determination, which measures the proportion of variance accounted for by that independent variable. It is then possible to determine which variable or combination of variables has the greatest influence; that is, accounts for the most variance.

Economics as a science also involves the creation of elaborate statistical models that combine many variables into complex multiple regression equations. Models that are found, with repeated testing, to include the best mix of relevant variables become the basis for testing economic relationships and for making economic projections about future trends in economic activity, both at microeconomic and macroeconomic levels.

References

Heilbroner, R.L., & Thurow, L.C. (1984). *The economic problem* (7th ed.). Englewood Cliffs, N.J.: Prentice Hall.

Mansfield, E. (1983). *Principles of microeconomics* (4th ed.). New York: W.W. Norton.

National Center for Health Services Research, Health Technology Assessment Reports. (1986). *Hemofiltration as a substitute for hemodialysis in the treatment of end-stage renal disease* (No. 4). Washington, D.C.: U.S. Printing Office.

National Center for Health Statistics. (1987). *Health, United States.* Washington, D.C.: U.S. Printing Office.

Smith, W.F. (1968, November) Cost-effectiveness and cost-benefit analyses for public health programs. *Public Health Reports,* 83.

U.S. Bureau of Census. (1987). *Statistical abstract of the United States: 1988* (108th ed.) Washington, DC: U.S. Printing Office.

Part II

Economic Markets
and Nursing

Chapter 3

The Market System

The market system, the circular flow of economic activity in markets, and the functioning of supply and demand to determine prices in the market system are critical economic concepts. They are fundamental to an understanding of economics and to the economics of nursing. Concepts associated with the market system and how it functions as an organizing device for the economy need to be examined in some detail, which is the purpose of this chapter. Examples of how the market system relates to nursing are also provided. The reader can find these concepts described more fully in books by Heilbroner and Thurow (1984), Albrecht (1983), Mansfield (1983), Shepherd, Putallaz, and Anderson (1983).

Components of the Market

Imagine a trip to a farmers' produce market. This provides an opportunity to examine the complex functions of the market system in a simple format. The farmers rent space in the market to offer their produce for sale. Members of households (potential consumers) come to the marketplace to compare, in terms of price and quality, the produce available for purchase and to make purchases according to their personal preferences and income. The items in the market have been produced with land, labor, and capital provided by each farmer. Capital includes intermediate products of production, such as farm equipment, tractor fuel, seeds, and fertilizers. As purchases occur, money is exchanged for goods by households (consumers) and farmers (producers). Prices will fluctuate depending on the available amount of produce (supply) and the willingness of consumers to make purchases at particular prices (demand). If the various farmers notice early in the day that there is a large supply of tomatoes available, they may reduce their prices from the outset. Alternatively, if few purchasers come to the market that day, prices are also likely to fall because demand will be less than usual. As farmers' goods are highly perishable, prices may fall towards the end of the day as the farmers' attempt to sell their remaining produce; otherwise it may spoil and be worthless. Even in this simple example, households and producers interact by making exchanges in a market system in which prices are determined by the forces of supply and demand.

Markets are much more complex in industrially developed nations. Where elements utilized in production and consumer goods and services purchased by households are multitudinous in number and variety, much more elaborate systems of production and distribution have evolved. The market system is depicted in Figure 3–1. It involves circular flows of real, tangible items in the outer circle in exchange for payments and receipts in terms of money in the inner part of the circle. The constituent parts of the market system and how it functions are now examined.

Households

The standard unit for analyzing consumer behavior is the household. Typically this includes persons living at a single address who act together as an economic unit. Consumer decisions always involve choice behaviors that reflect preference for one item over another; these purchasing decisions are made to satisfy human wants in the effort to maximize the satisfaction, or utility, derived from the consumption of goods and services.

In addition to purchases, households make choices about household resources, including labor services and decisions about their sale in the labor market (i.e., the type of employment at which household members work and whatever investment in training or education household members engage in to prepare for the labor market). Households also make decisions regarding savings or how to use assets not needed immediately for consumption spending. Savings can be invested and, along with accumulated interest, utilized for purchases at a later date. In this model, households own the labor, capital, and land that are the basic resources utilized in the production of goods and services.

This model may seem unrealistic because business firms seem to own most of the productive resources in the economy except labor. Businesses, however, are owned by individuals who are members of households—either

Figure 3–1

The market system.

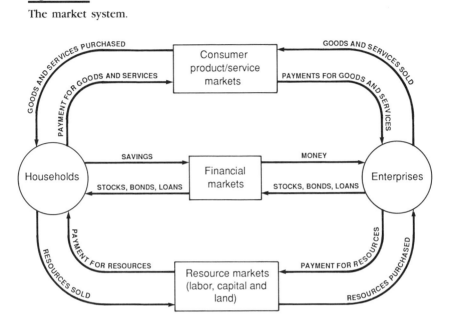

directly (as in a sole proprietorship, where the business is owned by one individual) or through ownership of shares of stock (such as in Humana, Inc., which is owned by literally millions of individuals through direct ownership of stock or through mutual funds and pension plans that hold part of the corporation's stock in their portfolios). Households ultimately *do* own these resources.

Within households there are many productive activities that have value to the members of households but have no assigned, monetary economic value in our society. Examples include individual time spent in shopping, washing, ironing, sewing, child care, cooking, or cleaning. These productive functions have no defined value because exchanges for these activities do not occur in the formal marketplace, and formal prices for their values are not assigned. Of course it is possible to determine these activities' potential value as such services are available for purchase in the marketplace.

Enterprises

Enterprises (businesses) are organized legally as individual proprietorships, partnerships, or corporations. By purchasing labor, capital, and materials, enterprises produce products or services that are subsequently sold to other enterprises or to households (consumers). For any enterprise, the difference between total revenues and all costs of production determines profit. Private enterprises attempt to maximize profit. This requires them to produce products for which there is a demand in the marketplace and to closely monitor their costs of production so that products can be sold profitably at prices consumers are willing to pay.

In addition to individual and other privately owned firms, there are also public (government) enterprises. For these, the primary goal is provision of needed services (e.g., nursing and health care services, teaching, and public mass transportation) or needed facilities (roads, universities, hospitals). Complementing the private and public sectors, there is a third sector of the economy called the private, not-for-profit sector where organizations are privately owned but profits are not distributed to owners. Instead, profits (technically called surpluses under not-for-profit tax laws) are used to further the organization's goals, such as expansion of facilities or services. Many hospitals, universities, and museums are private, not-for-profit organizations.

Mansfield (1983, p. 21) reports that there are about 15 million private firms in the United States that together produce 90 percent of the nation's goods and services. The other 10 percent are produced by the public and not-for-profit institutions.

Enterprises of all types utilize *factors of production,* resources for production, that are purchased from individual households. In the traditional economic model, the factors of production are land, labor, and capital.

Land consists, for economists, not only of physical space on the earth but also the natural resources associated with that land, such as timber, water, coal, oil, and other minerals. Land, therefore, includes products made or formed by nature. The income received by the owners of land for its use by enterprises is called rent.

Labor includes both mental and physical effort by persons whose labor services are purchased for specific periods of time (hour, day, or year). Labor includes unskilled workers as well as highly skilled professionals and is paid on the basis of hourly wages, annual salaries, fees-for-services, or commissions.

Capital refers to man-made productive resources: buildings and equipment, including machinery and devices such as the wide assortment of technical equipment found in any hospital. Capital goods are durable, that is, the item is not rapidly worn-out or depreciated and can be expected to be useful for a period of years. Households that supply money to enterprises for the acquisition of capital receive in exchange interest, dividends on stocks, or interest payments on bonds.

Market Exchange

A market is composed of the buyers and sellers of related goods or commodities within a relevant geographic area. Some markets are geographically clearly defined, like that of a hospital in an isolated rural community. It may be the only hospital for 100 miles in any direction. The market it serves consists of all persons residing in the surrounding area.

On the other hand, the retail market for Coca Cola is widespread, the product being sold in more than 100 countries around the world. Further, Coca Cola is but one part of a larger, related market: the market for soft drinks.

Exchange Goals

Before describing the actual exchange process, it is important to consider the exchange goals of households and enterprises. The economic view is that households and enterprises try to *maximize utility*, or satisfaction, subject to their income limits as a constraint. Self-interest motivates both buyers and sellers. The ability of a good or service to satisfy a want as determined by the satisfaction received from its consumption is called the utility of the good or service. Necessities provide higher utility than luxury items until basic needs are met. Even so, within the market for food there are great differences in the composition of purchases in people's "market baskets" according to income. In addition, even if a specific household can afford caviar with every meal, it does not mean that taste preferences and choices regarding expenditures for food versus other goods and services does not impact on food purchases.

Enterprises, like households, make decisions based on self-interest and a desire to maximize satisfaction (profits) within the constraint of resource limitations. The desire to maximize profits motivates the organization's management to purchase productive resources at the lowest possible cost and to sell its products at the highest prices consistent with selling most, if not all, of what the enterprise has produced.

While self-interest and utility or profit maximization are the theoretical assumptions that economists use to study market behavior, this does not mean that each individual decision to buy or sell is so motivated. Sometimes purchasers have insufficient information on which to make the best possible decision (a common problem in health care). The economist is not concerned with individual errors based on poor judgment or lack of knowledge. The self-interest and maximization assumptions relate to factors underlying the motivation of participants in the market process.

Value, Price, and Cost

The *market value* of a good or service is equal to its *market price*. If an ~xchange takes place in the market, the price obtained by the seller is the vaiue accepted by the purchaser. When only a few items exist or can be exchanged, for example, rare "old master" oil paintings, market values and prices may vary a great deal due to subjective or random factors. When many similar items can change hands, however, the effect of supply and demand causes these objects to be exchanged at relatively stable market prices that reflect their value to a large group of households.

While value and price are the same, *production cost* and price are quite different. Cost, here, refers to the expenses incurred by the enterprise in producing the product or service and making it available on the market. If there are few purchasers who demand only small amounts of the product, the seller may have to dispose of the product with minimal mark-up or at a loss. If quantity demand is very high, the price may be much higher than the actual cost of production. The market defines the relationship between cost and price.

Market Processes

Returning to Figure 3–1, one can see that all markets are divided into three general types: (1) consumer products and services markets, (2) financial markets, and (3) resource or commodity markets. Interactions between households and enterprises may be by way of all three of these markets. Households sell labor and other resources and, in turn, receive wages, interest, and rent. They dispose of money in the consumer products and services market. Unspent income may be placed in savings or used to purchase financial instruments such as stocks or bonds, but, in any case, this money enters the financial market. An enterprise may sell stock or borrow funds to finance production or to expand production capacity. Notice in the figure that every market involves supply and demand.

Demand

Demand relationships in markets focus upon the behavior of buyers of resources or products. Both households (which demand goods and services) and enterprises (which demand resources for inputs in production) have demand relationships in markets. *Demand* reflects the amount of something that buyers are willing and able to purchase at various prices during a particular period of time.

Factors that Affect Demand

In addition to being affected by buyers' *ability to pay* and *product preferences,* demand is also influenced by the existence of *substitutes* and *complements* in the market. Chicken can be a substitute for beef. If scarcity causes the price of beef to rise, households may elect to consume more chicken. Sales of used cars can increase when new cars increase in price. Complements are items that are used together. Changes in the market for one extends, in a similar fashion, to the other. The demand for boating accessories is complementary to the sale of boats: if more boats are sold, more boating accessories (e.g., waterskis, life jackets) are likely to be sold. When a new surgical specialist is added to a hospital staff, the institution must provide many new products and services to enable that surgeon to practice.

Population changes, including changes in the birth rate, median age of the population, the age distribution of the population, and overall population growth have effects on both the general market and market segments. Overall population growth will increase the demand for health services of all types, *ceteris paribus.* A higher birth rate will increase the demand for maternity services and baby food. Likewise, income distribution within the population affects demand. High income areas are likely to have more luxury car dealers, more furriers, more physicians relative to the population, and more plastic surgeons. Poor inner city neighborhoods, on the other hand, are likely to have more secondhand shops and too few physicians, nurses, and other health professionals practicing there.

Demand is also influenced by the household's expectations regarding future prices and future income. If households expect mortgage interest rates to rise, they may purchase more new houses now. Similarly, if employees are fearful of layoffs and reduced future income levels, they may defer purchases of various kinds.

Demand Curves

The relationship between the price of a commodity and the quantity of that commodity sought by consumers can be shown with a *demand curve.* Economists usually illustrate the demand curve using a standardized product well-defined by quantity and quality and for which there is a broad market. A finished consumer service such as patient day in a hospital involves many variables that make discussion of demand schedules much more complex. For simplicity, Figure 3–2 shows a hypothetical demand schedule and its associated demand curve for disposable syringes, which are assumed to be useful for various purposes. The relationship described is a general one, however, and can be thought of as applying to the demand for any product or service.

Notice that there is an inverse relationship between the price of these syringes and the number of units hospitals are willing to purchase. When hospital purchasing departments consider the disposable syringes to be relatively expensive, they may be restricted to IV use, for example, and many hospitals substitute a re-sterilizable product for other injectibles. As the price decreases, usage expands and the number of disposables demanded by hospitals increases.

The data can be plotted graphically and shown as a demand curve. The demand curve for virtually any commodity generally has a left to right, downward or negative slope because households, in the aggregate, buy less as the price of any good increases even though any one individual household may not alter its own buying patterns. What is naturally a curve may become a straight line when only a few points are plotted.

It is important to notice that demand refers to the overall price–quantity relationship for a good or service, that is, it refers to the entire demand curve

Figure 3-2

Hypothetical demand schedule and demand curve for disposable syringes.

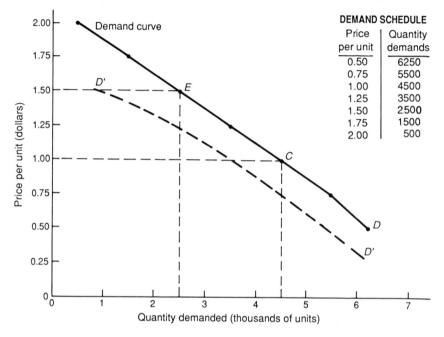

DEMAND SCHEDULE	
Price per unit	Quantity demands
0.50	6250
0.75	5500
1.00	4500
1.25	3500
1.50	2500
1.75	1500
2.00	500

or relationship at all possible prices. The quantity demanded refers to a particular point on the demand curve associated with a specific price. Point *C* shows the quantity of syringes demanded at $1.00 and Point *E*, the quantity demanded at $1.50. This change in price reflects movement along the demand curve. Discovery that the syringe may be prone to blood spills when withdrawing blood samples for laboratory tests would produce a shift or movement of the demand curve to the left (*D* to *D*¹). This reflects a decreased quantity demanded at any price.

Elasticity of Demand

The quantity demanded of a good or service has been shown to be responsive to changes in prices. The extent to which changes in prices affect the amount demanded is referred to as the *price elasticity of demand.*

If a relatively small change in price produces a relatively large change in quantity, the demand for the item is considered to be *elastic.* If a relatively large price change produces little relative change in quantity, demand is *inelastic.* Elasticity is a relative measure, the formula for which is:

$$\text{Price elasticity of demand} = \frac{\text{Percentage change in quantity demanded}}{\text{Percentage change in price}}$$

In the formula for computing price elasticity, the cause (here, a change in price) is placed in the denominator and the effect (a change in the quantity demanded) in the numerator. Since the demand curve almost always slopes downward (higher price leading to decreased quantity demanded), the elasticity ratio generally is negative, but by convention the sign is ignored. Economists define the price elasticity of demand so that if the computed ratio is greater than 1, demand is elastic; if less than 1, demand is inelastic.

The degree of elasticity in demand is predictive of the effect of price change on quantities demanded. When price changes, other things being constant, quantity moves in the opposite direction, that is, if price decreases, quantity demanded increases. If the price demand ratio is inelastic, however, price has little effect upon demand.

Two hypothetical examples from health care illustrate the concept of the price elasticity of demand. Consider the demand for two types of health services: emergency appendectomies and home health services. For simplicity, assume that persons in need of such services must pay for them with their own funds. It is reasonable to assert that the demand for an emergency appendectomy is highly inelastic with respect to price, while demand for home health services is elastic. Demand curves associated with these two types of services are illustrated in Figure 3–3.

The demand for emergency appendectomies is highly inelastic because they entail an immediate, usually painful, life-threatening situation. An increase of 100 percent in the price of this procedure, say from $5000 to $10,000, might reduce demand by only 5 percent. This would represent, using the formula presented earlier, a price elasticity of demand of only .05, showing a demand curve of nearly a vertical line.

Alternatively, the example of home health services in Figure 3–3 suggests that the demand for these services is elastic. If prices increase by 50 percent, from $40 to $60 per visit, the graph indicates that home health visits (assuming these are paid for with personal funds, not by a third party payer) might decline from 450,000 per year to as few as 340,000 per year in the service area. At the higher price many individuals using these services would reduce their frequency or eliminate them altogether in an attempt to manage their health situation in some other fashion. The 50 percent increase in price creates a 75 percent decline in the quantity demanded, a price elasticity of demand that is 1.5, or highly elastic.

In general, the price elasticity of demand of any specific good or service is dependent upon:

The necessity of the product or service

The availability of alternative goods or services (substitutes) serving a similar function

The percentage of income spent on the product

Figure 3–3

Price elasticity of appendectomies and home health visits.

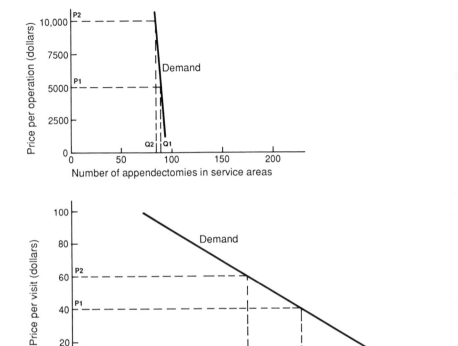

The amount of time since the price change occurred (more time allows for searches for alternatives to the purchase of a particular good or service)

In the case of emergency appendectomies, demand is inelastic because the procedure is often of absolute necessity, and there are no substitutes for it. For home health services, demand is elastic because certain visits (at least many of those by home health aides) have alternatives: care by a family member or friend or a live-in companion hired to assist with activities of daily living.

The concept of the price elasticity of demand is one that most people encounter in everyday life on a regular basis. Many people who like apples eat very few in the late winter when they are out of season and prices are high. Demand responds to the change in price; this price responsiveness is what the price elasticity of demand is useful to explain. It affects not only households but also business enterprises: If demand is inelastic with respect to price, increased prices lead to high revenues and profits for the enterprises, but if demand is elastic, raising prices may reduce sales so much that the revenues and profits decline.

Economists also define an elasticity relationship between income and demand, the *income elasticity of demand.*

$$\text{Income elasticity of demand} = \frac{\text{Percentage change in quantity demanded}}{\text{Percentage change in income}}$$

For this computation, the average income of the area served by the market is used. It is possible to compare the amount spent on automobiles from year to year within a geographic area. If average annual income decreases, one would expect declines in the amount spent on automobiles as well. Thus, when income levels and the quantities of goods or services purchased change in the same direction, this is called *positive income elasticity.* Goods or services that have positive income elasticity are called *normal goods.* When people purchase more of a good or service while they are receiving higher incomes, this is the typical response and the product is a normal good or service.

When less of a good or service is purchased as a result of higher income levels, the product, in economic terms, is an *inferior good.* Goods that experience less demand and show negative income elasticity are called inferior because people free to choose without income constraints tend not to buy them. Powdered milk is, in economic terms, an inferior good. It is important to note that inferior goods reflect consumer choices that may or may not coincide with the quality of the product or service. Margarine was once considered an inferior good, but, with current cholesterol concerns, low cholesterol margarines show much less adverse income effect upon demand. Nurse midwifery has long been regarded as an inferior good by the general public although the record is clear that for normal births, nurse midwives offer a superior service.

Supply

Supply refers to the producers' or sellers' side of the market exchange. It is a relationship expressing the quantity of a good or service that sellers are able and willing to make available at various prices at a given time and geographic location. Various sellers do not have identical production costs and can make profits when prices are at different levels than is possible for other business enterprises. *Ceteris paribus,* the supply of a good or service in the market increases when the price increases and decreases, or even ceases to be supplied at all, if the price falls below producers' abilities to recover their costs of production.

Producers' Factors that Affect Supply

Obviously, price is the most important influence on the quantity of goods and services that is supplied, but there are other relevant factors. The cost of producing a good or service is influenced by (1) the *cost of the resources* (land, labor, and capital) used as inputs in the productive process and (2) the *cost of the productive process* necessary to combine the resources into a finished good or service. Management expertise in organizing the productive process as well as technology, as long as they are used efficiently and effectively, can reduce costs per unit and enable producers to offer larger supplies of goods and services in the marketplace at given price levels.

Changes in *other dependent markets* can also affect supply. To illustrate, if grain is cheap, farmers may withhold it from the market and instead feed the grain to additional livestock with the hope of recovering their costs of producing the grain through the sale of more beef. As a result, however, livestock producers may find prices depressed when the increased supply of cattle reaches the marketplace.

Finally, considerable fluctuations in supply can be traced to the *time interval* needed by producers to increase or decrease production in response to price changes. Nursing provides a good example. If the prices paid for nurses' services (salaries) were to rise dramatically, more college students would choose nursing instead of other professions. It would take years, however, for nursing schools to graduate enough new nurses in order to affect supply significantly. The time interval is long and is even longer in other fields such as medicine.

Supply Curves

Analogous to the earlier discussion of demand, an example of a supply schedule and supply curve may be illustrated (Fig. 3–4). Supply responds positively to price, that is, as price increases, the supply increases, therefore the supply curve slopes upward, moving upward from left to right when graphed. Note that these quantities reflect the amount the producers are willing to sell at various prices during a specified period of time. A supply curve does not indicate amounts actually sold, just as a demand curve does not indicate quantities actually purchased.

The supply curve in its entirety refers to the entire relationship between quantity and price, and quantity supplied refers to a specific point on the supply curve associated with a specific price and quantity. This distinction was also noted in terms of the demand curve and the quantity demanded. When prices increase, the supply available in the market increases along the curve itself. If there are factors other than price that come into play, for example some event that tends to increase supply at any given price, these non-price

Figure 3–4

Hypothetical supply schedule and supply curve for disposable syringes.

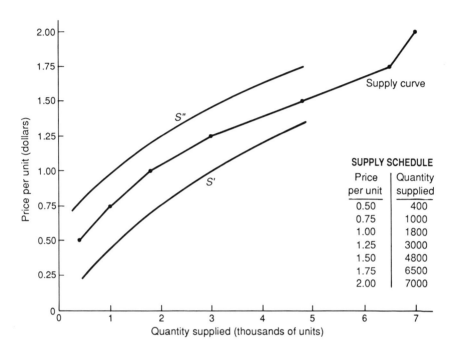

SUPPLY SCHEDULE	
Price per unit	Quantity supplied
0.50	400
0.75	1000
1.00	1800
1.25	3000
1.50	4800
1.75	6500
2.00	7000

influences cause the supply curve to shift to the right (*S'*). It then follows that when non-price factors that tend to decrease the supply at any given price occur, the supply curve shifts to the left (*S"*).

Elasticity of Supply

As was true with demand, economists are interested in the *price elasticity of supply,* which can lead to predictions about the responsiveness of supply to price changes. The formula is similar to that for the price elasticity of demand.

$$\text{Price elasticity of supply} = \frac{\text{Percentage change in quantity supplied}}{\text{Percentage change in price}}$$

If the price elasticity of supply is greater than 1, the good or service is considered to exhibit an elastic supply; if the value is less than 1, the supply is inelastic.

Supply tends to be inelastic or non-responsive to price change when production requires long time lags. The available supply of disposable syringes in the demand example can be assumed to be able to be increased in a few weeks. Expensive, complex diagnostic equipment (CT scanners or MRIs), however, requires time and large capital investment for increased supply and responds relatively slowly to price changes, unless producers have excess stock or capacity (plant and equipment not now being used for production). As has been indicated, it takes years to produce (educate) nurses and physicians so that the supply of both groups changes slowly in response to price (salary) changes. On the other hand, it is relatively easy for a hospital or other employer to secure additional minimally trained workers in the labor market in a short period of time by offering higher wages.

How Markets Function

Now it is possible to combine demand and supply schedules (Fig. 3–5) to show how markets function and how prices are determined. It can readily be seen that the hypothetical supply and demand curves for the disposable syringes intersect at a price of $1.25 a unit. At that price, about 3,350 units will be sold during a given period of time. The price is stable at $1.25, hospitals are able to purchase exactly the amount of the disposable item that they wish to purchase at that price, and suppliers are able to sell all of the

Figure 3–5

Demand and supply curve with equilibrium price and quantity.

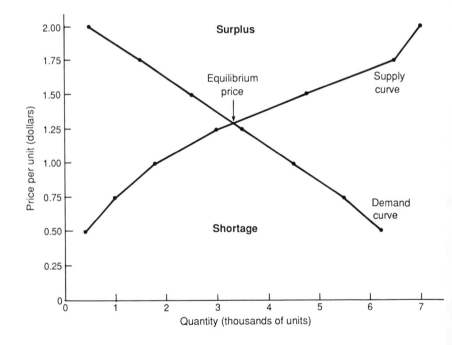

item that it was appropriate for them to produce at that price. The market satisfies both buyers and sellers.

Markets are rarely characterized by equilibrium, however. The usual situation is that buyers, sellers, or both are unable to obtain precisely what they want. Typically markets are adjusting: supply and demand schedules are shifting to the right or left, and both the prices of goods and services and the quantities sold change as well. The market system involves literally hundreds of thousands of specific markets, few of which are in a state of equilibrium. Rather, markets adjust so as to tend toward equilibrium. This is known as the *market adjustment process.*

To illustrate this process, suppose initially that the price of the disposable syringe is $1.00. Hospitals are willing to purchase 4,500 units according to their demand schedule, but suppliers only offer 1,800. A *shortage* of the disposable soon becomes apparent. The market adjustment process then comes into action. Recognizing that they cannot fill all the hospital orders at $1.00, suppliers begin to produce more and offer their output for sale at higher prices. If they had perfect knowledge of the market, suppliers would recognize that they should offer exactly 3,350 units for sale, but complete knowledge is a rare commodity. Besides, it is unlikely that suppliers would inform one another to what extent production at their enterprises was being increased. As a result, rapid attainment of an equilibrium situation is far from guaranteed.

It is quite possible that producers might supply 4,800 units during the next time period, at a price of $1.50. Again, the market is not in equilibrium. A *surplus* of 2,550 units exists and cannot be sold at $1.50 (the size of the surplus is equal to 4,800 syringes supplied minus the 2,250 actually demanded at that price). Market adjustments again occur. Excess inventories encourage producers to accept lower prices and production; at lower prices hospitals demand and purchase larger quantities. Eventually, equilibrium could be established at the price and quantity associated with the intersection of the supply and demand curves.

Other factors, in addition to price, have been identified that may affect either demand or supply. These influences—changes in incomes, changes in consumers' tastes or preferences, changes in technology—cause the demand or supply schedule and curve to shift. Different amounts are demanded or supplied at any given price. Demand curve shifts were illustrated in Figure 3–2 and supply curves in Figure 3–4. How do these shifts affect market function, the market adjustment process, and prices and quantities?

One final time, return to the market example for disposable syringes. Suppose the market attained equilibrium at a price of $1.25, and supply and demand are equal at 3,350 units, as in the intersections of the supply and demand curve in Figure 3–5. What happens if the government decides to provide disposable syringes to drug addicts to control the spread of AIDS? Economists would interpret this as a change in preferences in favor of the disposable syringe, a shift in the demand curve itself, not a movement along the curve. Examine Figure 3–6 and follow the numbers on the graph with those in the text.

1. The demand curve shifts from the original demand curve D to the new demand curve D^1 due to the expanded use of disposable syringes. This increases the quantity to be purchased at any given price. At a price of $1.25, hospitals now want to purchase 5,500 units, up from 3,500. This creates a major shortage.

2. Hospitals bid against each other for the limited supply of disposable syringes, which causes the price to rise to $1.50. At this higher price, the quantity demanded on the new demand curve D^1 moves back to 4,800, and the quantity supplied increases from 3,500 to 4,800,000. An initial market adjustment process has occurred, and the market is in an interim equilibrium position. The market adjustment process, however, is not complete.

3. At the new price of $1.50, producers find that this product is significantly more profitable. Existing producers expand output, and more producers

Figure 3–6

Market adjustment due to changing conditions.

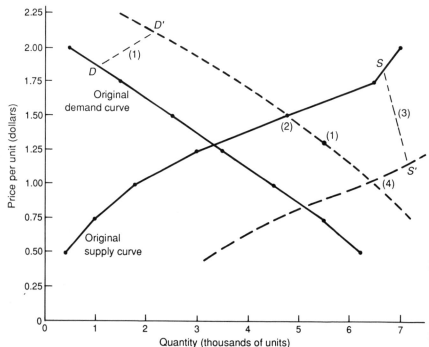

may start producing this item. Each business enterprise that expands production or begins to produce the item increases total market supply somewhat. Taken together, producers' responses shift the supply curve to the right, from S to S^1. Prices begin to fall as well.

4. Supply increases result in declining prices. In this case so many additional producers entering the market have shifted the supply curve enough that the new equilibrium position is established. It is at the intersection of D^1 and S^1, with a price of $1.00 and 6,500 units sold each time period. Is this the end of the adjustment process? Not necessarily, because the new price is less than the original price in this market. Producers may discover that their profits have declined or even disappeared. If profit erosion is significant, some producers may either reduce the quantity they supply to the market or may withdraw altogether from the production of this item. Thus a final possible effect may occur. The supply curve may shift somewhat back to the left if producers reduce production or exit the market. So many producers might leave the market that the original $1.25 price would be reestablished at the intersection of another supply curve (not shown in the figure) and the new demand curve, probably with quantity demanded and supplied of about 7,000 units.

All of these changes occurred as a result of only one initial change in the marketplace. That change was the decision to make disposable syringes available to drug addicts to control the spread of AIDS. It should be evident that the market adjustment process is complex. Changes in demand and supply occur in most markets on a regular and ongoing basis. These affect both the prices and quantities of items supplied and demanded in the marketplace. Thus the market involves a continuing adjustment process seeking equilibrium.

To summarize, it should be recognized that economists' market model relies on the forces of supply and demand in the market process to determine the prices and quantities of all goods and services. When markets are not in equilibrium, surpluses or shortages occur and adjustments take place that tend to move the market towards equilibrium through the price mechanism. Prices therefore play a critical role in the economy in helping to determine market behaviors and in influencing both households and enterprises relative to their purchasing and production decisions.

Market Problems

The real world is much more complex than the market model described above. The assumption has been made up to now that the marketplace works relatively freely, without interference and without significant problems. There are, however, major problems with the functioning of markets. Some of these are inherent while others have been intentionally created to avoid potential abuses that may occur in a freely functioning market. Significant limitations such as these cannot be ignored. They take a variety of forms, which are discussed below with their implications for the standard free market model of the economy.

Information Problems

The free market model described assumes that information or knowledge is readily available to both consumers and producers and that they base their decisions on complete information about the market. Obviously this is not necessarily the case. Health care is an excellent example. Consumers may have certain health problems but may have limited understanding about the nature of the problems or of the interventions that may be necessary. Patients therefore rely on the advice of physicians, nurses, and others. Physicians frequently act, in effect, as purchasing agents for consumers who have health problems, making health decisions on the patients' behalf. This is an interesting situation in terms of a market: physicians are supplying services and are also controlling the demand for those services by recommending to patients what course of treatment to pursue. Even physicians, of course, are dealing with limited information. The exact nature of a health problem may be unclear.

Seeking information or knowledge about a possible purchase is costly in terms of time, effort, and, sometimes, consultation or appraisal fees. Some individuals do explore various alternatives before making a large purchase, such as a major home appliance or an automobile. Expensive purchases tend to receive more careful scrutiny than others. Even so, when buying a house most individuals spend a relatively limited period of time (a week or less) in making what is usually the largest expenditure that they will ever make. Individuals relocating for a job provide a clear example. It is not unusual for people to spend only one day in house hunting. In a city it is fairly evident that a one day search and decision is based on very incomplete information. As a result the household may end up purchasing a dwelling that is less than satisfactory.

The Disadvantaged

The free market system in its pure sense provides no safety net for persons with physical or mental problems that make them unable to compete effectively in the marketplace. Since the marketplace fails to provide a minimal living standard for all, it becomes government's role to provide for the disadvantaged through social programs, such as welfare, food stamps, and Medicaid. There is disagreement, however, about the level or degree of support to which the disadvantaged should be entitled. For example, should persons on Medicaid receive precisely the same type and quantity of health services as those who have private health insurance coverage or sufficient wealth to purchase whatever health services they desire? If the same services are not made available, the result is a two-tiered health care system that is unacceptable to many care providers.

Monopolies

The model of the freely functioning market process described earlier ignores the fact that in certain circumstances there may be only one supplier of a good or service. The most common situation associated with a monopoly is the supply of utilities to individuals' houses (i.e., electricity, water, natural gas, and other types of services involving the installation of overlapping sets of poles, lines, and other supply systems). A single supplier of each service generally serves a particular market area.

These so called natural monopolies are invariably regulated by government. Regulation is appropriate because when there is only one supplier of a good or service that supplier has significant market power and can, if not regulated, solely determine what quantities to offer for sale in the market and what prices to charge. Government therefore establishes public utility commissions and other rate review boards to ensure that the behaviors of these natural monopolies are not inconsistent with the interest of the public that they serve.

Other industries may develop monopoly-like situations. A town of 25,000 persons may have but one hospital. If it is a significant distance to the next town, the hospital exerts some monopoly effect on the population base that it serves. If it raises prices, most people in the area will still use that hospital because there is no viable alternative. In this situation the hospital also has monopoly market power relative to the wages that it pays nurses and other employees. Nurses in that town may have little opportunity to be employed anyplace but at that hospital. If there were another hospital in a nearby town, however, then the proximity of the two hospitals would make it much more difficult for either hospital to engage in monopolistic policies. Patients and nurses could utilize either facility, placing the two hospitals in competition, *ceteris paribus.*

Public Goods

There is a class of goods and services that provides benefits to a large group of individuals and has the characteristic such that no one person can be specifically excluded from enjoying the benefits of these goods or services. Government provides many of these services such as national defense, police protection, park systems, and education. Many of these services would not exist if they were not provided by government. In other words, the marketplace would fail to provide them because the market cannot be defined in such a way as to prevent someone from enjoying or benefiting from the existence of the good or service. All income-earning adults pay for national defense as part of their income taxes. That is because in the case of war it would not be possible to defend only those persons in the country who choose to pay for defense.

Emergency medical services are an example of a public good. These services should not be denied to individuals unable to pay for them. Therefore tax-supported services are made available to all within a geographic area.

Externalities

This term refers to side effects of production that may be either good or bad but are not taken into account in the marketplace when prices or quantities are determined. Examples of negative externalities include water, air, and soil pollution; the ecological damages of strip mining and defoliation; and even noise pollution. Although historically these have not been taken into account in the marketplace, in many instances government now intervenes and requires producers to clean up the undesirable consequences of their production processes.

There are also positive externalities. If all home owners in an area maintain their houses and lawns in an attractive fashion or have a regular anti-crime patrol, this may be pleasing or beneficial to these residents. It may not, however, increase the value of an individual house in this neighborhood.

Where negative externalities exist, it is important for the government to intervene for the protection of the environment and to make sure producers pay for the cleanup of the pollution. Hospitals have been required by various governmental agencies to develop expensive disposal programs for hazardous waste materials. These costs are then added to the traditional costs of producing health care services.

Governmental Market Adjustments

Federal, state, and local governments impose controls upon the marketplace, most involving regulations that affect either price or quality.

Price controls are instituted when government fears inappropriate economic consequences may result from the functioning of the marketplace. In the 1970s, after the Oil Producing and Exporting Countries (OPEC) increased oil prices significantly, the United States imposed a Windfall Profits Tax on producers. This had the effect of taking away part of the increased profits that oil producers were enjoying simply because of the price increase for oil imposed by OPEC. As another example, price ceilings exist for housing in various cities. In Berkeley, California, rent controls have been in effect for a number of years with the intention of protecting residents from excessively high rents. While controls such as these may initially protect the renter, the long-term effect is to make investors unwilling to construct more housing or maintain the existing stock of rental apartments. Thus prolonged price controls disrupt the marketplace by restricting supply and may exacerbate the very problem they were designed to resolve. New York City, for example, has used rent stabilization to control the rate of rent increases but still protecting owners' ability to earn an adequate return on investment.

Health care is another major area in which government sets or influences prices. Since 1983, under the Prospective Payment System the federal government has fixed the prices it pays for the treatment of Medicare beneficiaries. The primary intent of this program is to help control the rate of increase in expenditures for the Medicare program. Hospitals' interest in knowing the costs of various services that they provide, hospital employment, and hospital length of stay for the elderly have all been affected.

A second type of government control in the marketplace involves quantity. Certain substances such as cocaine and marijuana are illegal and, in the eyes of the law, the quantity supplied to the marketplace of either of these commodities should be zero. Of course the market for such substances does not cease to exist. Instead, both cocaine and marijuana are supplied through an undercover or black market for much higher prices.

During the 1920s, the United States, through an amendment to the Constitution, prohibited the supply of alcoholic beverages. Prohibition of alcohol was not successful and ultimately the amendment was repealed. It is an interesting note that during prohibition the amount of wine produced for "religious purposes" increased in a spectacular fashion.

Another form of quantity control is rationing, common primarily in wartime. This can be effective even on a national level when there is a feeling of unity of purpose. During World War II a whole host of items, from milk to automobile tires, were rationed. Some people would circumvent the rationing directives, yet, overall, the program was a success. Water rationing for a fixed duration in a drought area can also be successful. When a strong sense of unity or purpose is missing, however, price or quantity controls imposed by government tend to promote black market activities.

Suppose the government, for public health reasons, were to ban the sale of cigarettes. Would there be no further smoking of cigarettes in the United States? It is highly unlikely. Cigarettes would be smuggled in from abroad. Individuals would grow or import tobacco and roll their own cigarettes. Perhaps a more effective policy to stop smoking would be to increase the cigarette tax to $1.00 or $2.00 per pack. The more a pack of cigarettes cost, the more people would weigh the utility of maintaining a smoking habit.

Indirect quantity controls also exist through the mechanisms of licensure and registration of professional and technical workers. These mechanisms are designed to protect the public's welfare, yet, in controlling entry standards, they can control the quantity of personnel in a field. In California for many years it appeared that the dental licensing board wished to restrict the movement to California of dentists trained in other states. The purpose, apparently, was to control the patient–dentist ratio and protect the incomes of dentists trained in California. All dentists were required to take a licensure exam that included, in its practical phase, a rarely done procedure. Graduates from California dental schools had been trained in this because it was known that this would be part of their exam. Thus, although licensure is designed to protect the public, it may also serve the self interests of a profession.

Another consequence of licensure may be an increase in price for the services of licensed professionals. Does protection of the public from possible incompetent practitioners justify the possible increase in the cost of those services to the public? In any case, licensure and registration requirements are another form of government-imposed controls on quantity in the marketplace; their existence is another example of actual situations that deviate from the free market model.

All national economies have developed some mechanism for interfering with market forces. The number of special market characteristics that cannot be adequately dealt with simply through the function of free markets have brought about for all nations a variable degree of control and planning in market decisions. Most economies can be described as mixed, that is, they involve both private and public decisions. The United States is one of those nations that has considerable reliance upon free markets and the least reliance upon government decisions. The Soviet Union traditionally has exhibited the most government control over economic matters and market decisions and the least free market decision making by its citizens.

In the United States, health care is less controlled by government than in other nations, which generally have some form of national health systems. Roemer and Roemer (1982) have written a classic paper opposing the free market system in health care and advocating more government involvement. Where there are national health systems most health care workers are government employees, and the government controls prices, wages, construction of new hospitals or other facilities, and all administrative decisions for the system. Such a system has little appeal for many persons in the United States. At the same time, in the United States there is government intervention in health care relative to licensure, regulation, price and quantity controls, assistance for the disadvantaged, the provision of public hospitals and other aspects of health services delivered. All of these are examples of the way in which an economy develops its market system uniquely to it own needs and social preferences.

References

Albrecht, W.P., Jr. (1983). *Microeconomic principles* (2nd ed.). Englewood Cliffs, NJ: Prentice Hall.

Heilbroner, R.L., & Thurow, L.C. (1984). *The economic problem* (7th ed.). Englewood Cliffs, NJ: Prentice-Hall.

Mansfield, E. (1983). *Principles of microeconomics* (43rd ed.). New York: W.W. Norton.

Roemer, M.I., & Roemer, J.E. (1982). The social consequences of free trade in health care: A public health response to orthodox economics. *International Journal of Health Services, 12*(1), 111–129.

Shepherd, W.G., Putallaz, A., & Anderson, W.L. (1983). *Microeconomics.* Englewood Cliffs, NJ: Prentice Hall.

Chapter 4

The Market for Nursing Care

In an economic sense, nurses represent the critical "input" in the process of producing nursing care. Nursing care, or nursing care services, are a major component in the production of the health services delivered in the United States. The market for nursing care focuses on the demand for and supply of nursing services as a component of health services delivery. In that capacity, it would be useful from an economic perspective to be able to measure the "output" of nursing care in terms of units of improved health, through measures of health status. In fact, such a measurement goal may not be achievable because health status is complex, and it is influenced by many variables in addition to nursing care. Generally, improvement in health is equated with reduction in the presence or the effects of disease, but health status involves much more than merely medical criteria. Relating health status changes to the productive contributions of any particular health care provider group is a very complex problem. It is apparent that many kinds of health care providers may contribute to the improved patient outcomes. Thus, it is most common for the production of health care services to be measured in terms of the volume of services rendered (e.g., hours of care, number of home visits, hours of client instruction) rather than as a single identifiable or quantifiable outcome.

The development of valid and reliable quality care indicators and productivity measures appropriate for nursing is an important task for nursing in order to demonstrate the basis of the demand for nursing care in the health services delivery market. Research in this area is needed, and, as meaningful criteria evolve, it is the responsibility of the profession to establish acceptable standards for those measures of the contributions of nursing care to health care outcomes.

A Model of Nursing Care Services Market

In order to understand the economic relationships that operate within this occupation, a model of the supply and demand forces affecting the nursing care services market is reviewed. In Figure 4–1, a model of the health care

Figure 4–1

An overview of health care markets.

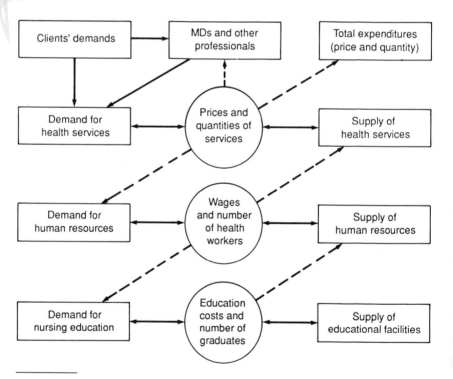

SOURCE: Adapted with permission from P. Feldstein, *Health Care Economics* (2nd ed.). Copyright © 1983, John Wiley & Sons. Adapted by R.C. McKibbin in *Economic and Employment Issues in Nursing Education* (1983, p. 4). Kansas City: American Nurses' Association.

markets adapted by McKibbin (1983) is presented. The diagram shows the demand and the supply sides of the markets and is further divided into the services market, the nursing resources or factors of production market, and the educational market.

From a professional view, it may be logical to describe first the education market and the preparation of the nurse; however, from an economic perspective, it is more appropriate to begin with the service market. For what nursing care services is there an economic demand? The health services market, which creates the need for all nursing services, involves interactions among consumers, physicians, health service institutions and agencies, and third-party payers. Although all demand for health services is initiated by consumers, they are often uncertain, due to lack of knowledge, about the specific health services that are appropriate. The clients' demand for treatment is therefore influenced by providers and payers. The demand for nursing services is similarly influenced by non-nurse providers. This is a fundamental reason why nursing leaders must be prepared to negotiate with other providers and third-party payers about how, and by whom, certain health services are provided in the health services market. Physicians may believe they can meet the educational needs of their patients; most patients' inquiries about their health are presently directed initially to physicians. In fact, physicians' time may be too costly, or they may be insufficiently skilled as teachers, to provide this needed service except for a small proportion of patients. In many cases, referrals to nurses who specialize in patient education would be a more efficient and cost-effective means of providing that service.

Individual nurses often do not appreciate the critical nature of their contribution to health care. The activities of nurses position them in the location, nearest to the patient, with a responsibility to assess and intervene in ways that reflect the totality of the patient's well-being. Professional nurses are thus able to integrate the services of individual providers into complete, appropriate, efficient, effective, and safe health care services. Administrators of hospitals, long-term care facilities, and home care agencies are heavily dependent upon clinical nurses for much of the technical information fundamental to the planning and provision of appropriate services.

Since 1965 there has been almost continuous expansion of the demand for nursing personnel. This is reflected in nursing employment, expressed here in terms of nurse–population ratios (Table 4–1). In 1965 there were 275 full-time equivalent (FTEs) nurses per 100,000 population; in 1975 there were 384, and in 1985 the figure had reached 533. Thus even when the effects of population growth have been removed, the demand for nurses has continued to increase (American Nurses' Association, 1987).

The demand for nursing services within a freely operating health service market determines the wages and the numbers of nurses employed in the nursing resource market. In this market, nurses' employment levels are

Table 4-1   Employed Registered Nurses in the United States: 1965–1985

Year	Total No. of Nurses	FTEs	RNs per 100,000 population	FTEs per 100,000 populatio
1985	1,531,200	1,271,400	641	533
1980	1,272,900	1,068,000	560	470
1975	961,000	821,650	449	384
1970	750,000	642,000	366	313
1965	621,000	543,500	319	275

SOURCE: *Facts about Nursing* (1983, 1985, 1987). Kansas City: American Nurses' Association. R{ printed with permission.

determined by the types of positions available (demand), the available number of nurses (supply), and their respective salaries (prices). Nurses' wages and employment levels in turn influence the educational market for nurses. The interrelatedness of the service, resource, and educational markets can be shown in this example: Suppose an epidemic (such as AIDS) creates an economic pattern of new or increased demand in the service market. This will generate additional demand in the human resources market for nurses that, in turn, creates a greater demand for nursing students in the education market; nursing schools attempt to recruit more students in order to respond to the requirements for more nursing personnel created by the epidemic.

Educational institutions, however, are slow to respond in a similar fashion to decreases in health service market demand. It is the student who must beware of preparing for a field of practice or specialty in which the market may be declining in size (employment opportunities) or where high levels of current demand may represent only a brief, temporary increase.

Economic Influences on the Demand for Nursing Services

Nurses, as providers of nursing care, are inextricably linked to the economics of health care and most particularly to medicine. Nursing leaders should be careful to distinguish between autonomy in the practice of nursing, which is a legitimate goal, and total independence from medicine, which could be suicidal, economically. Outside of nursing education there is little organized demand for nursing services that is not currently related to physician practice.

Nurses as Complements and Substitutes for Physicians

Physicians diagnose and treat pathology. Professional nurses diagnose and treat human responses to actual or potential health problems (American Nurses' Association, 1987). Generally, members of each profession work autonomously within their own scope of practice, but they also recognize areas of mutual interdependence. Considering particular health problems, the role of a physician may involve 99 percent or only 1 percent of the total health service contribution. Similarly, nursing contributes 1 percent to 99 percent of the health service. At this time, in the United States, most health problems that require no involvement of a physician nor a delegated responsibility from a physician, are generally excluded from the economic system of health care; they are not paid for by private insurance, government funds, or other third parties. The inadequate development of services for health promotion and wellness reflect this fact.

Nurses believe that clients should be able to contract for nursing care (e.g., home health care, nursing home care, health education) without a referral from a physician. Today, this is possible only if the patient is able and willing to personally pay for the service. In general, government program administrators and health economists express concern about the financial consequences of expanding entitlements such as these as this might cause increased health care expenditures.

On the other hand, nurses point out that nursing care can decrease the need for the more expensive services of physicians, hospitals, and nursing homes. Home health care has clearly been shown to be less costly in comparison to hospitalization. Clearer evidence, through controlled studies of diverse population groupings, is needed to document potential value of a community-based nursing service for health education and home health care having economies relative to the need for physician and nursing home services among high-risk clients.

In 1987, bills were introduced in the House of Representatives (H.R.1161) and the Senate (S.1010) at the urging of the American Nurses' Association that would permit community-based nursing and ambulatory care services to be paid for under Part B of Medicare. Excluded from coverage would be physician, x-ray, laboratory, and other designated services. The community nursing organization would be paid at a rate equal to 95 percent of the average adjusted per capita cost, similar to how Health Maintenance Organizations (HMOs) are paid under Medicare risk contracts (Human Resources, 1987). Out of that sum, the nursing agency would have to arrange for all necessary covered services and assume the financial risk if utilization of these services was far higher than expected. Congress passed the first stage of the bill, which provides for several demonstration projects. Broadest appeal may be to potential clients who are elderly, as well as mothers, children, and those with chronic illnesses who need services in the home. The fact that Congress passed this legislation over the protests of organized medicine is an indication that changes may occur in the future in the traditional means of organizing and financing nursing services in the United States.

In many states, legal efforts are being directed to change state laws or regulations to permit nurse reimbursement for services that are (1) within nursing's legal scope of practice and (2) covered by private insurance or governmental funding sources. Such efforts to obtain reimbursement are generally limited to nurse midwives, nurse anesthetists, and nurse practitioners qualified for advanced practice (those with graduate preparation in nursing). Here the goal is to make it easier for nurses in advanced practice to become *substitutes* for physicians, that is, to take the place of the physician in providing the service (Gibson, 1984). Such legal changes would make it possible for service institutions, Health Maintenance Organizations and Preferred Provider Organizations to utilize, as an economic asset, the full capabilities of nurses qualified for advanced practice as an alternative or substitute for a physician.

Professional nurses will argue, and can demonstrate, that their services are quite different from those of physicians, but economists will continue to view the types of nursing service described above as being physician substitutes because a portion of the nursing service does in fact substitute for physician care (Griffith, 1984). To control administrative costs and to preserve their own political neutrality, third parties will wish to limit service payment to approved agencies which, in turn, will pay the nurse provider a salary,but, perhaps, based upon a productivity measure. Fee-for-service reimbursement to individual nurse providers is, generally speaking, an unrealistic political and economic goal for most nurses.

A significant exception has been the success of the American Association of Nurse Anesthetists in obtaining direct reimbursement for professional services from Medicare, Part B. This arrangement began in January 1989. This is the first time Congress has designated that Part B be used to pay nurse providers. When diagnosis-related groups (DRGs) were implemented, starting in 1983, nurse anesthetists' services were included within the hospital's lump sum payment. This created an incentive for hospitals to use services of anesthesiologists instead because those costs would be billed and paid separately. In legislation, Omnibus Budget Reconciliation Act of 1986, Congress agreed that it did not make economic sense to eliminate Certified Registered Nurse Anesthetists inadvertently as competitors with MDs. Cromwell and Rosenbach (1988) in a review of economic questions surrounding payments to nurse anesthetists and anesthesiologists conclude that greater competition is unlikely as long as hospitals and surgeons have no economic stake in the choice. Surgeons will refer to anesthesiologists.

It will continue to be much more common for registered nurses to function as *complements* to physicians rather than as substitutes for them. Physicians, such as burn specialists, heart surgeons, neonatologists, and neurosurgeons, greatly increase their institutions' demand for nurses because of the physical and emotional dependence of their patients and the complexity of the technology of care. These physicians' patients have extensive nursing care needs. With shortened hospital stays, increased patient acuity, and advances in the technology of care, there is increased demand for nurses as complements to physicians' services: Nurses' services are required to be provided jointly with physicians' services in the production of health care services.

It should not go unnoticed that when nurses serve as substitutes for physicians, as do nurse midwives, nurse anesthetists, and nurse practitioners, they have had a much more difficult time in procuring appropriate professional acceptance and payment for their services. Here there can be little question of expanding entitlements and total health care expenditures. Women will not have more babies because nurse midwives are reimbursed; patients will not elect to have more surgery because nurse anesthetists are being reimbursed, and the teaching-type visits of nurse practitioners will never be more expensive than the total cost of the procedure/test-type office visits typical of most fee-for-service physicians. When nurses substitute for physicians, there are positive economic gains to the health care system in terms of cost effectiveness.

When nurses are complements to physicians, legal and economic questions are not raised. Yet it is as complements to high technology services where nursing may be associated with increased total health care expenditures. The latter situation may be associated with questions about the cost effectiveness of heroic, expensive technological procedures that may have little prospect for extending life.

The issue of reimbursing nurses in expanded practice roles is controversial because these nurses are recognized as competitors of physicians and economic substitutes. Physicians, therefore, use their well-organized political power both at state and national levels to attempt to prevent this increased competition for their own services.

Effects of Health Care Financing Upon the Demand for Nurses

Changes in the financing of health care services produces modifications in the ways in which services are organized and delivered. Such changes also affect the demand for nursing services. The movement to finance health care on a capitation basis (HMOs and PPOs) or on the basis of DRGs rather than fee-for-service, are examples of economic changes in the health care system with direct effects upon the demand for nurses in health care employment.

Economic pressures created by third-party payers have decreased the occupancy rates of hospitals by requiring that many services be provided on an out-patient basis. The length of the average hospital stay is decreasing and the average acuity level, therefore, of patients remaining in the hospital is, by definition, increasing. The shortened stay necessitates that some nursing activities be provided as pre-hospital or post-hospital care services. Individual teaching is being replaced by more cost-effective group teaching where possible. As the acuity levels of patients and the technological levels of care increase, there are fewer patient activities that can be properly delegated to licensed practical nurses and ancillary nursing personnel. Where nursing divisions have reduced personnel expenditures (generally in small community and rural hospitals), it appears to be non-registered nursing staff who have been let go or not replaced following normal attrition. The increased acuity of patients has increased the demand for nurses with advanced specialty skills who are prepared to work in critical care, intensive care, operating room, oncology, and management positions (Selby, 1986).

Dramatic evidence of this shift in staffing can be seen in Table 4–2. LPN staff, on a full-time equivalency basis, was virtually unchanged per 100 patients from 1977 through 1983, but declined from 27 to 23 per 100 patients from 1984 through 1986. RN employment, on the other hand, has expanded throughout the period shown in the table. This is true both for total numbers and for RN FTEs per 100 adjusted average daily census.

Since passage of Medicare and Medicaid legislation in 1965, there has been a steady decrease in the funding by city, county, and state governments of community-based health programs so fundamental to the activities of public health nurses. These reductions were deemed appropriate because Medicare and Medicaid had taken on new and expanded financial responsibilities for personal (individual) health care services. Increasingly, nursing services in the community are provided by home care agencies based upon an order from a physician. Many traditional public health programs have been eliminated at the federal level. Traditional health promotion programs, particularly for home visits to high-risk families have suffered. It is an unfortunate fact that most community health nurses involved in providing health promotion and disease prevention services to high-risk families failed to document the outcomes of their visits in ways easily communicated to public officials. Favorable evaluation of, and continuing funding for, service programs often have not had a high priority in settings other than acute care where outcomes are easily understandable and apparent.

Home care following hospitalization is viewed as an economical arrangement, a less expensive and intensive "step-down" arrangement for care. This may also be true of home care services provided to the elderly, which may enable them to avoid expensive nursing home care. Home care is promoted where it is an apparent, less expensive alternative to institutional care. Home health services for those who do not now receive them, however, tend to be viewed as adding more expenditures to the nation's health care bill and would likely be opposed by most politicians. Expansion of services, to win political approval, must be seen as reducing costs.

Another example of health care financing affecting the demand for nurses can be seen in the Medicare prospective system of payment for hospital

Table 4-2 Changes in Staffing Mix in Acute Care Facilities

Year	Number of Hospitals	Adjusted Average Daily Census[a]	Number of FTE Registered Nurses	RN, FTE per 100 AADC[b]	LPN, FTE per 100 AADC[b]	Total Personnel FTE per 100 AADC[b]
1974	5,977	793,195	418,034	53	25	289
1975	5,979	805,747	447,481	56	26	298
1976	5,956	815,513	474,386	58	26	304
1977	5,973	820,122	504,221	61	27	315
1978	5,935	825,212	530,867	64	27	323
1979	5,923	841,330	559,996	67	26	328
1980	5,904	861,206	623,148	72	27	334
1981	5,879	875,943	630,459	72	27	347
1982	5,863	881,883	673,005	76	27	376
1983	5,843	868,701	699,303	80	27	357
1984	5,814	824,319	698,915	85	25	367
1985	5,784	779,546	710,511	91	24	385
1986	5,728	773,697	737,269	95	23	392
1987	5,611	775,910	758,973	98	22	401

SOURCE: *Hospital Statistics* (Annual editions, 1975–1988, Table 3). Reprinted with permission. Chicago: American Hospital Association.

[a]Adjusted average daily census is inpatient census plus an equivalent outpatient census.

[b]FTE per 100 AADC is the number of full-time equivalents (full-time plus ½ part-time) for each 100 adjusted average daily census.

services. When DRGs were introduced in 1983, many hospitals discontinued intravenous therapy teams and ceased to replace respiratory therapists who resigned. These activities have often been reassigned to the professional nursing staff. Earlier, when hospitals could bill separately for therapist services but could not bill when that service was provided by a staff nurse (whose services were already being paid for as routine nursing care), there was economic incentive to create new categories of health service providers. With lump-sum payments, it may be more economical to reassign such services to the unit nursing staff. Such reassignments increase the nurses' workloads, increase the hospital's willingness to hire additional nurses, or both.

There is considerable concern that this country may be preparing too many physicians (Lewis, 1982). Significant surpluses of physicians in most specialties are forecast for the 1990s. Petersdorf, president of the American Association of Medical Schools, has advocated (1) decreasing residency opportunities for foreign medical school graduates, (2) federal "decapitation grants" to help medical schools withstand the economic costs of decreasing enrollment, and (3) strengthening the accreditation standards for both medical schools and residency programs (Inglehart, 1986). There has also been a shift away from medical school traineeships to loan programs. Loans now comprise 85.5 percent of all medical student assistance with an average indebtedness upon graduation of $33,499 (Inglehart, 1986). It is also likely that medical specialty boards may decrease the numbers of residencies in their respective specialties to prevent overcrowding in the practice arena. If these efforts to reduce the supply of physicians are successful, individual hospitals will not be able to recruit their usual numbers of house officers. Actually, the high technology of hospital care requires more, rather than fewer, house officers. The dilemma for medicine is that eventually house officers become practicing physicians and competitors in the same market as those who taught them their specialty skills.

Community hospitals will wish to keep their attending physicians satisfied. Over time, this type of shift in demand and resources may provide opportunities for experienced professional nurses to be employed as case managers or as nursing house officers where they can assume responsibility for a broad spectrum of nursing care, including the patient's nutrition, ambulation, exercise, skin care, analgesics, sedatives, cathartics, and so forth. All of these concerns were at one time nursing responsibilities and, in many settings, will be again. A nursing conceptual framework can help establish practice boundaries and an institution-based, limited formulary can enable professional nurses with appropriate preparation, to prescribe common medications for which the clinical data for decision making is usually obtained by nurses rather than by physicians.

Professional nurses employed as nursing house officers can substitute for some physician services. More importantly, from a professional perspective, such practice could reclaim for nursing more of the relevant human responses to illness and permit closer coordination of care between physicians and nurses. The boundary between medicine and nursing in the clinical sphere has been variable and will continue to be so in the future. Boundary decisions ultimately are made on the basis of cost effectiveness in the work setting.

Politically, it is wise for nursing to claim the broadest possible scope relevant for its practice. Other professional, technical, and clerical workers can be employed to carry out non-nursing activities for which nursing is administratively responsible. Professionally, nursing should claim or reclaim all that can theoretically be considered nursing. Finally, from an economic perspective, whenever a responsibility is returned or assigned to nursing, it is essential that appropriate budgetary support accompany that activity.

Estimating Demand

Periodically there are major national studies of nursing and nursing resources. Without exception, these studies have been sought by nursing leaders in order to develop consensus within nursing and within its relevant arenas (such as hospitals, community health, medicine, and public agencies) regarding (1) anticipated demand for nursing services and (2) types of educational programs and numbers of students needed to meet the projected demand. Major studies relating to needs and resources of nursing are listed in the bibliography at the end of this chapter. There also have been a multitude of statewide studies, and from these have evolved a few state plans for nursing education within particular states. Too often the plan is not accepted by nursing's relevant arenas, and nursing itself has lacked the professional unity and the political power to enforce a plan independently.

To estimate demand, several methodological approaches have been developed (*Health Manpower,* 1975; Kriesberg et al., 1975). Each method has advantages and disadvantages and the choice is dependent, in part, upon the size of the budget, the "cost" of being wrong, and whether one is estimating demand in an institution, a state, or for the nation.

Manpower/Population Ratio Method

The most commonly used method is to relate manpower needs to population. Here the formula becomes:

$$\text{Estimated nursepower requirements} = \frac{\text{Nurse power}}{\text{Population}} \times \text{target population}$$

The ratio between the type of nurses (registered nurses, licensed practical nurses) and the population is based upon determining the ratio in an area or community that seems adequately supplied with this type of worker. Expert opinion may be used to estimate the proportions of these nurses needed. Such estimates can then be extrapolated to a metropolitan region, a state, and so forth. A common example would be the number of employed nurses per 100,000 population. As shown earlier in Table 4–1, there were 275 FTE nurses per 100,000 population in 1965. If the population increased 25 percent over a period of time, there would be need for 25 percent more nurses to maintain the status quo. In truth, the technology of care and the numbers of services provided increased so rapidly that in 1985 there were 533 FTE nurses per 100,000 people and still a shortage.

This method is relatively inexpensive to use, simple to understand, but may have considerable error if the ratios do not reflect appropriate quantities of health personnel and if the demand for nurses is not similar throughout the region studied. Projections based upon population can be useful if there have not been significant changes in the technology of care or in demand.

Service Targets Method

This is similar to the population method, but demand is not related to the number of people but rather to the volume of service. Demand is related to the utilization associated with some number such as 100 hospital beds or 1000 clinic visits. These models generally are based upon the number of nurses needed or currently utilized in relation to some health service characteristics (e.g., beds, visits, patients, morbidity). Planners then extrapolate (trend forward in time) the number of nurses needed as the projected characteristic changes. It is a common practice to look at the number of registered nurses per 100 hospital patients.

In Table 4–2, hospitals in the United States employed 80 registered nurses (FTEs) per 100 patients in 1983. From this one could have projected the number of registered nurses needed with a 15 percent decrease in the national average daily hospital census, similar to that which occurred between 1983 and 1985. One would probably have been wrong. The demand for registered nurses remained strong, despite significant declines in census, as hospitals shifted to more RN-intensive staffing in response to higher patient acuity levels and increased technology of care.

With the service target technique, it is necessary to (1) define the service demands for the area, (2) determine the staffing need for each service demand, (3) decide on a level of productivity (e.g., a home health nurse might average five visits per day), (4) adjust demand for average hours worked per week and the hours the service is available (e.g., the average nurse in ambulatory care might work 24 hours per week and such clinics may be open 48 hours per week), and (5) combine the demand for this category of worker with similar care delivery institutions or systems in the service target area.

It is easy for the health planner to get bogged down in masses of data if a large service target area (e.g., metropolitan New York) is being defined. All of the assumptions are based upon normative estimates, which can change markedly and quickly if the technology or financing of health care is modified.

Health Needs Approach

This method is based upon study of the health status of a local population, and estimates are made of the need for personnel to assist that population to attain and maintain its health. Thus estimates of the need for maternal and newborn health services can be based upon the birth rate and the incidence of complicated births in a county. Estimates of the need for long-term care nurses are based, in part, upon estimates of the population over 65, 75, and 85 years of age since persons in each of these age groups by decade are considerably different in terms of their demand for long-term nursing care services.

Estimates based upon defined needs or "what ought to be" for optimal services have considerable appeal for health care providers. While this method supports the ethical value system of providers, there is little agreement among providers about the types and amounts of services theoretically required. More serious is society's lack of agreement, particularly over health care services to be purchased for others.

Economic Demand Approach

This method focuses upon effective demand, that is, the actual willingness of someone to pay for specific goods or services at particular prices. For example, there has been a great reduction in the use of registered nurses in doctors' offices in the past 20 years, but increased demand for workers with different skills and at less cost. Licensed practical nurses, technicians, and clerical staff with abilities in bookkeeping and insurance forms have become more critical in physicians' offices. When registered nurses now are employed in physicians' offices, they must be providing billable professional services to clients that enable the physicians to perform other billable services. If not, professional nurses are not cost effective. The typical office nurse of 20 years ago has virtually disappeared: The demand has changed.

Estimates of demand for nurses are generally regarded as the sum of the existing filled positions (FTEs) and the number of budgeted, unfilled positions, that is, total budgeted positions, filled and unfilled, are equal to economic demand. Economic demand cannot be used to estimate the impact of a proposed health service program: Until the program is authorized and budgeted, there is no real demand for nurses' employment expressed in the health services market place.

Estimating demand by budgeted positions in a particular area of practice at the beginning levels is useful, but it does not work well for higher-level positions. Organizations do not carry budgeted, unfilled positions at advanced levels for very long. The position may be filled by a non-qualified nurse, be modified, or be eliminated—each considered a better solution than an on-going vacancy. It is also true that when an organization has the opportunity to hire a nurse with superior qualifications, management often creates a position where none previously existed.

An approach related to the method of economic demand was tested by the American Nurses' Association (1985). It involved a composite index of the volume of help-wanted Sunday newspaper advertising for registered nurses in 22 major metropolitan areas. This approach was analogous to a general help-wanted advertising index reported monthly by the Conference Board, a prestigious New York-based economic analysis firm. Using this technique, 1982 was selected as the base year in which the index of advertising volume was arbitrarily assigned to be 100. For the succeeding years, higher or lower amounts of advertising led to numbers above 100 or below 100, reflecting percentage changes in the amount of ads for registered nurse positions. While the possible usefulness of this method appeared good in an overall sense and in specific locations, the project was unfortunately eliminated due to budget cuts.

When expert nurses make projections about the need for nurses at various competency levels, there may be a tendency to enlarge the estimates because of a professional bias toward provision of a superior quality of care. This tendency to overestimate is probably a more significant problem in occupations that are still attempting to establish professional status. In nursing, studies of projected demand may be used to advance the cause of upgrading the occupation's professional standing. This is less of a problem in studies of medicine, law, and similar groups. In such fields, professionals in private practice are very sensitive to overproduction of new professional graduates because they would crowd the field and reduce the future potential earnings of all those already in that field.

The Bureau of Labor Statistics calculates unemployment rates based upon interviews of the civilian labor force and from this data computes the rate of unemployment, including among registered nurses. The rate is always negligible: In 1986 it was 1.6 percent (American Nurses' Association, 1987). When a nurse is unemployed, it generally reflects either a period of transition between jobs or a temporary inability to obtain desired employment conditions rather than the lack of any nursing employment opportunities whatsoever. In 1987 unemployment among LPNs was 3.3 percent and among nursing assistants it was 9.4 percent.

Changing health care requirements alter the demand for nurses: more or fewer nurses may be needed for health care delivery, the needed level of educational preparation of nurses may change, and the appropriate distribution of nurses among different geographic and practice settings may also change. Thus confusion may occur in the nursing care market because there are, in fact, many markets for nurses. It is possible to consider demand and supply of nurses in more specific ways only in relation to more precise definitions of the personnel categories within the work force of nursing.

Supply of Nurses by Selected Characteristics

The most complete compilation of statistics about the supply of nurses in the United States can be found in *Facts About Nursing*, which is published every two years of the American Nurses' Association. The data reported were originally collected by federal and state agencies and by a variety of professional and health care organizations. The Interagency Conference on Nursing Statistics (ICONS) is a group of statisticians representing these organizations (ICONS, 1986). ICONS meets periodically to refine definitions of categorical descriptors (e.g., "part-time"), to delete duplicative reporting in the nursing data (e.g., licensure held by a nurse in more than one state), and to prepare estimates of the nursing population. The U.S. decennial census is rarely used in nursing studies since its data have been shown to contain considerable over-reporting (e.g., many LPNs reported as RNs and many individuals listed as RNs when, in fact, they do not possess current licenses).

Demographics

For the years 1977, 1980, and 1984, there have been extensive national sample surveys of registered nurses conducted under contract for the Division of Nursing, Bureau of Health Professions, of the Department of Health and Human Services. An additional survey was conducted in 1988; its results are to be published in 1989. These surveys have generally been conducted at the request of Congress to determine if, and where, federal intervention is indicated to assure the nation an adequate supply of nurses. The surveys involve a mail questionnaire, and, from the sample, data are extrapolated to the nurse population as a whole.

There have been concerns about shortages of nurses since World War II. Only during brief periods of severe economic recession, when nurses often became the primary economic providers for their families due to unemployment of a spouse, have there been seemingly adequate supplies of nurses. Registration of nurses provides an unusual amount of current data for tabulation of a well-defined occupation. A few selected tables are presented here to provide a basic understanding of the size and composition of nursing's work force.

In the 1988 survey, it was shown that in the United States there were 1,627,035 employed registered nurses, over 2 ½ times the total number in 1965. This is an astounding growth rate, particularly for an occupational category that is so large in absolute size (2,033,000). In the second column of Table 4–1 full-time equivalents are computed on the basis of two part-time nurses equaling one full-time worker, a standard assumption used by ICONS and others. This may overestimate the number of FTEs because many part-time nurses work only 1 to 2 days a week. The last two columns show the numbers of nurses in relation to the population. Per 100,000 population, which has the effect of holding population constant, the number of RNs actually increased 2.01 times and FTEs increased 1.94 times between 1965 and 1985.

Table 4–2 shows two interesting trends based upon hospital statistics. The employment of RNs per 100 patients has shown a 62 percent increase between 1977 and 1987. As the acuity of hospitalized patients increases with shortened stays and advanced technology, the numbers of registered nurses required to provide their care has increased. Also, between 1981 and 1987 almost 106,000 beds were removed from use. This reflects improved economic efficiency.

Table 4–3, shows the sex, race, and ethnic characteristics of the nurse population. Males represent only 3.0 percent of all nurses, but the number of males in the nurse population more than doubled between 1977 and 1984 (from 27,300 to 57,200) (Registered Nurse Population, 1986). Significant progress also has been made in opening nursing to racial and ethnic minorities. Minorities make up about 8.2 percent of the nurse population, but the number of nurses with minority background increased 78 percent between 1977 and 1984. It should be noted that higher proportions of male registered nurses and racial/ethnic minority registered nurses are *employed* in nursing than is true of white female registered nurses.

Education

In Table 4–4, a breakdown of registered nurses by highest nursing-related educational preparation is shown. While 45.3 percent of all registered nurses hold a diploma as their highest educational level, that proportion has decreased from 85.8 percent in 1965. RNs with baccalaureate degrees have increased from 10.4 percent of all RNs in 1965 to 25.5 percent in 1984, and preparation at the master's level or higher has increased during that same time period from 2.5 percent to 5.9 percent. Diploma graduates in the RN

Table 4–3   Sex, Race, and Ethnic Background of Registered Nurses

Groupings	Proportion in Nurse Population	Proportion Employed in Nursing
Male	3.0%	86.8%
Female	97.0%	78.5%
White	90.3%	77.9%
Black	3.9%	90.7%
Asian	2.6%	81.3%
Indian	.3%	91.1%
Hispanic	1.4%	89.8%
Unknown	1.4%	60.3%

SOURCE: *Registered Nurse Population, 1984* (1986, p. 19). Washington, DC: Division of Nursing, Health and Human Services.

Table 4–4 Highest Nursing-related Education of Employed Registered Nurses

Highest Nursing-related Education	1965	1970	1980	1984
Diploma	85.8	80.4	50.7	45.3
AD	1.3	3.7	20.1	22.8
Diploma or AD	87.1	84.1	74.4	68.1
BS	10.4	12.9	23.3	25.5
MS or Doctorate	2.5	3.0	5.3	5.9

SOURCE: *Facts About Nursing* (1982–1983, p. 15; 1986–1987, p. 24). Kansas City: American Nurses' Association. Reprinted with permission.

population have been partially replaced by associate degree graduates: combined these groups represented 87.1 percent of the registered nurses in 1965 and 68.1 percent in 1984. The proportion of diploma graduates in the work force can be expected to fall rapidly in the next 10 years because a significant proportion of these nurses will retire by the year 2000.

Employment

In Table 4–5 it is possible to see the influence of age on the employment rates of registered nurses. The table shows two frequently observed patterns: a decrease in employment during the prime childbearing years, followed by higher labor force participation between ages 40 and 50; and another em-

Table 4–5 Proportion of Registered Nurses Employed in Nursing by Age

Year	25	25–29	30–34	35–39	40–44	45–49	50–54	55–59	60–64
					Age				
1966	86.9	67.4	57.7	60.3	66.1	71.7	74.1	74.1	70.2
1977	88.2	78.3	68.9	67.9	70.4	71.2	68.9	64.7	54.1
1980	95.2	87.7	80.7	77.2	78.5	78.3	75.1	66.7	51.3
1984	94.9	91.1	84.7	82.3	82.1	80.8	77.5	69.8	53.3
Percentage change between 1966–1984	+8.0	+23.7	+27.0	+22.0	+16.0	+9.1	+3.4	−4.3	−16.9

SOURCE: *Facts About Nursing* (1970–1971, p. 17; 1980–1981, p. 13). Kansas City: American Nurses' Association. *National Sample Survey* (1984, p. 19). Washington, DC: Division of Nursing, Health and Human Services. Reprinted with permission.

ployment decrease after age 55. Over half of all nurses, however, are still employed at age 65.

A new pattern of much more interest is the great increase in employment activity among nurses under age 45. This change is probably due to (1) the interrelated influences of better birth control, the women's movement, and increased interest in long-term careers; and (2) maintenance or improvement of standards of living that are increasingly dependent upon two incomes. While there has been a great increase in employment under age 55, much of this is by nurses who work part-time.

In general, the employment of nurses over age 55 has been decreasing. Some of this decrease might be attributable to spousal retirement and improved pension plans. It also is possible that many nurses find the physical stresses of employment in direct care positions too demanding and are electing to cease employment at an earlier age. There has been no research to provide an explanation for this decrease in employment after age 55.

Finally, Table 4–6 presents information on the types of positions held by employed nurses according to their educational preparation. One must recognize that many nurses are "over-employed" relative to their academic preparation. When personnel shortages exist, persons without otherwise acceptable education levels may be promoted based on work experience. This is less true now with associate degree graduates than in the past with diploma graduates: As health care management becomes more complex over time, incumbent nurse managers are likely to be replaced by nurses with advanced academic preparation. One might also question the statistic that 14,800 nurses with master's degrees are employed as staff nurses; this is almost certainly an error which reports clinical nurse specialists as staff nurses because they are not employed in management positions.

A fundamental problem with equating supply to demand in the market for nursing care is lack of correspondence between the location of the position and the location of the nurse. Associate nurses, for the most part, are not geographically mobile. These nurses could find employment in any state but for personal reasons they choose a local community college followed by local employment. Their services are available only in the immediate area in which they live. Therefore, there is a host of *local* markets for associate nursing care in which the local forces of supply and demand determine local wages. Professional nurses, particularly those prepared at the master's and doctoral levels, are most mobile and are considered a national resource (Institute of Medicine, 1983).

Nursing Education Market

Returning to the McKibbin model in Figure 4–1, it can be seen that the demand for nurses in the marketplace for health services creates, in turn, a demand in the educational market. This demand is influenced by many factors including salaries, occupational image, and job opportunities.

Table 4–6 Type of Position and Highest Nursing-related Educational Preparation of Registered Nurses.

Type of position	Estimated number	Total %	Diploma %	Associate degree %	Baccalaureate %	Master's %	Doctorate %
Administrator or assistant	77,177	100.0	37.2	14.3	27.2	19.2	1.5
Consultant	11,491	100.0	36.7	15.6	28.6	17.3	1.8
Supervisor or assistant	89,542	100.0	50.4	20.8	23.5	5.0	—
Instructor	65,935	100.0	17.1	7.0	32.7	38.7	4.5
Head nurse or assistant	94,060	100.0	45.6	21.6	29.1	3.3	—
Staff nurse	992,956	100.0	43.0	29.1	25.9	1.5	—
Nurse practitioner/ midwife	18,642	100.0	30.4	11.8	30.1	27.4	—
Clinical nurse specialist	23,698	100.0	30.9	16.7	21.1	30.8	.6
Nurse clinician	14,731	100.0	37.9	16.9	37.3	6.9	—
Certified nurse anesthetist	18,530	100.0	43.2	19.9	30.4	6.6	—
Researcher	3,009	100.0	16.7	13.7	42.5	27.1	—
Private duty nurse	22,675	100.0	55.3	19.8	20.6	3.1	—
Other	53,188	100.0	41.1	18.0	31.7	8.7	.2
Not known	93	100.0	—	44.3	55.7	—	—
Total	1,485,725[a]	100.0	41.8	25.1	26.6	5.8	.3

SOURCE: *Registered Nurse Population, 1984*, (1986). Washington, DC: Division of Nursing, Health and Human Services.

[a]Includes an estimated 6,495 nurses for whom no information was available on highest nursing-related educational preparation. Estimated number and percent may not add to total due to rounding.

Economic Model of Demand for Nursing Education

Richard McKibbin (1983) has proposed a conceptual model of the demand for nursing education programs by prospective students. It would be necessary to operationalize the terms to be able to test it but the model serves a useful purpose in describing the relevant influences.

$$D = f(P^d, P^i, Y^e, W^e, N^e, P^{18}, S^e, T^e)$$

Where

D = the demand of a group of individuals for nursing education a function (f) of the following influences or variables:

P^d = the direct costs (e.g., tuition, books) of the nursing education program (net of those alternative possible program, if relevant). (−)

P^i = indirect (opportunity) cost of undertaking a nursing education program (i.e., these being primarily earnings that are foregone in order to undertake the program). (−)

Y^e = expected lifetime annual average earnings from the practice of nursing. (+)

W^e = actual or expected wealth holdings (here McKibbin assumes that nursing students are not commonly of upper socioeconomic class with significant inherited wealth). (−)

N^e = expected employment prospects in nursing relative to other alternative possible occupations. (+)

P^{18} = population of 18- to 24-year-old females. (+)

S^e = expectations regarding personal satisfaction variables associated with health and helping occupations. (+)

T^e = a composite variable reflecting other expected factors such as personal preferences independent of those above. (+)

McKibbin shows that the model may be used in general terms by assigning plus or minus signs to each of these variables; one can then hypothesize specific relationships. Thus the model suggests which conditions, *ceteris paribus,* increase the demand for the study of nursing, if they increase or improve (+), and which decrease the demand for the study of nursing, if they increase or improve (−). From the model it is also possible to hypothesize what the profession would need to do to make nursing a more attractive, sought-after career.

Nursing is entering a difficult recruitment period in which there is a greatly decreased population of 18- to 24-year-old females. As this population is the principle source of nursing students, the model indicates that this factor alone will lead to a decline in the number of nursing students. At the same time, young women have many more occupations from which to choose. As the numbers of female medical, law, and engineering students increase, there is a decrease in the number of nursing students (Buerhaus, 1987). It has been difficult to recruit sufficient numbers of males to offset the loss of females because nursing has been an occupation stereotyped by sex.

If nursing schools attempt to recruit the same numbers of females as in earlier decades, it can probably be done only by accepting students with lower test scores and lower levels of academic achievement. To do so in order to maintain class size would be short-sighted and could have long-term deleterious effects on nursing. It is far better to allow the numbers of nursing students to decrease. A decreased supply of nurses, coupled with increasing employer demands for nurses, will lead to increased nursing salaries and elimination of non-nursing job duties. Such changes will make the profession more competitive and attractive.

Types of Programs

Persistently strong demand for nurses in the health care market has been a double-edged sword for the nursing education market. While there has been an abundance of positions available, the magnitude of the number of nurses utilized has made health care industry administrators protective of an adequate supply of nurses to restrain the costs of nursing care. Nursing leaders have believed that the public would support the cost of better prepared, better selected practitioners, but the public does not directly make that decision. Rather, the decision evolves from the actions of health service administrators and third-party payers. All nursing program data in this next section are taken from *Nursing Data Review, 1987* (NLN, 1988).

Mainstream Nursing Preparation

Increasingly, entry into professional nursing practice requires a baccalaureate degree with a major in nursing (BS or BSN). There were 280 nursing baccalaureate programs in 1966, 336 in 1976, and 455 in 1986. This is the foundation for graduate nursing education, leading to a master's degree in nursing (MS, MN or MSN) with advanced preparation for clinical practice. In 1986 there were 189 such programs. Finally, a doctorate in nursing (PhD or DNS) provides emphasis on the development of research skills and the knowledge base of nursing. In 1986 doctorates were offered in 38 programs in 25 states.

Technical nursing preparation obtained in community colleges leads to an associate degree (AD or ADN). There were 776 programs in 1986, up from 632 in 1976 and 198 in 1966. Practical nursing programs will merge, over time, with associate programs, and graduates will be licensed as associate nurses (Selby, 1985) or licensed practical nurses depending upon state laws. Associate nurses will work under the general direction of professional nurses, who will be responsible for nursing's total scope of practice (American Nurses' Association, 1987).

Alternate Routes

To maintain the supply of nurses needed, it is important to provide entry points that can accommodate early or late decisions for entrance into the nursing work force. Students who, for economic or personal reasons, are unable to commit themselves to a 4-year baccalaureate program can complete an associate degree program. Employment in technical nursing can be a career goal, or it can be used to finance a BSN completion program (the 2 + 2 format) for entry into professional nursing. Even with well-articulated programs, however, there is a certain waste of time as well as money (e.g., duplication of course work and effort) to the individual and to society. This pattern should not be elected if it is possible to go directly to the BSN program, but it is an important alternative for students who must work to defray some of the costs of education.

For the college graduate who makes a late decision to enter nursing, a few special nursing programs exist. Generic preparation at the graduate level, similar to the pattern utilized in medicine, dentistry, and law, leads to an ND degree. There are other programs for college graduates that combine generic nursing and graduate specialization leading to the MSN degree. With these special curricula, the level of teaching can be developed appropriately to take full advantage of such students' prior academic preparation.

Inefficient Alternatives

The traditional practical nursing program must be classified as a wasteful alternative because graduates have no potential for educational mobility except by starting over. Economically, LPN programs once were a good buy for applicants, but the technology of care has advanced so much that hospitals, in particular, are no longer electing to hire LPNs in any substantial numbers.

In 1984, The National Federation of Licensed Practical Nurses approved a move to an 18-month associate degree program by 1990 (Griffin, 1985). Of the LPN programs, 32 percent are in community colleges, existing side by side with an ADN program, and many members of the nursing faculty teach in both. Since there is little vocational education monies for LPN programs and no federal capitation monies for ADN programs, institutional administrators are likely to be supportive of the profession's efforts to merge the LPN programs with the associate degree programs. LPN programs in technical schools will cease to exist. In 1985 there were 599 programs in technical schools, almost 100 having closed since 1975.

There is no educational reason for hospital diploma programs to continue to operate. It is exploitative to recruit students into programs that the nursing profession formally rejected in 1965 when baccalaureate preparation was initially endorsed as the preferred route for preparation as a professional nurse. For the graduates of diploma programs, the lack of transferable credits means that they must remain in school an excessively long time to earn a baccalaureate degree. Some short (one year) BSN-completion programs have developed for diploma graduates, but these are not accredited. The number of diploma schools has decreased from 788 in 1966, to 390 in 1976, to 238 in 1986.

A final wasteful pattern is that of AD or diploma program graduates who

Table 4–7 Annual Admissions to Basic Registered Nurse Programs and Percentage of Change from Previous Year

Academic year	All basic RN programs		Baccalaureate programs		Associate degree programs		Diploma programs	
	Number of admissions	Percent Change	Number of admissions	Percent change	Number of admissions	Percent change	Number of admissions	Percent change
1966–67	58,021	−3.6	14,012	+6.9	11,137	+30.3	32,872	−14.7
1967–68	60,673	+4.6	14,813	+5.7	14,577	+30.9	31,283	−4.8
1968–69	63,408	+4.5	15,901	+7.3	18,536	+27.2	28,971	−7.4
1969–70	74,598	+17.6	18,942	+19.1	25,142	+35.6	30,514	+5.3
1970–71	78,524	+5.3	20,299	+7.2	29,433	+17.1	28,792	−5.6
1971–72	93,344	+18.9	27,228	+34.1	36,454	+23.8	29,662	+3.0
1972–73	103,789	+11.2	30,348	+11.5	43,733	+20.0	29,708	+0.1
1973–74	107,344	+3.4	32,461	+7.0	47,940	+9.6	26,943	−9.3
1974–75	109,020	+1.6	34,956	+7.7	49,368	+3.0	24,696	−8.3
1975–76	112,174	+2.9	36,320	+3.9	52,232	+5.8	23,622	−4.3
1976–77	112,523	+0.3	36,670	+1.0	53,610	+2.6	22,243	−5.8
1977–78	110,950	−1.4	37,348	+1.8	52,991	−1.1	20,611	−7.3
1978–79	107,476	−3.2	35,611	−4.7	53,366	+0.7	18,499	−10.2
1979–80	105,952	−1.4	35,414	−0.5	53,633	+0.5	16,905	−8.6
1980–81	110,201	+4.0	35,808	+1.1	56,899	+6.1	17,494	+3.5
1981–82	115,279	+4.6	35,928	+0.3	60,423	+6.1	18,928	+8.1
1982–83	120,579	+4.6	37,264	+3.7	63,947	+5.8	19,368	+2.3
1983–84	123,824	+2.7	39,400	+5.7	66,576	+4.1	17,848	−7.8
1984–85	118,224	−4.5	39,573	+0.4	63,776	−4.2	14,875	−16.7
1985–86	100,791	−14.7	34,310	−13.3	56,635	+11.2	9,846	−33.0
1986–87	90,693	−10.0	28,026	−18.3	54,330	−4.1	8,337	−15.3

SOURCE: *Nursing Data Review, 1987* (1988). New York: National League for Nursing. Reprinted with permission.

Table 4–8 Graduations from Basic Registered Nursing Programs and Percentage Change from Previous Year, by Type of Program: 1966–1967 to 1985–1986

Academic year	All basic RN programs		Baccalaureate programs		Associate degree programs		Diploma programs	
	Number of graduations	Percent Change	Number of graduations	Percent change	Number of graduations	Percent change	Number of graduations	Percent change
1966–67	37,931	+8.7	6,122	+11.5	4,639	+38.5	27,170	+4.2
1967–68	41,245	+8.7	7,132	+16.5	6,163	+32.8	27,950	+2.9
1968–69	41,801	+1.3	8,355	+17.1	8,578	+39.2	24,868	−11.0
1969–70	43,103	+3.1	9,069	+8.5	11,483	+33.9	22,551	−9.3
1970–71	46,455	+7.8	9,856	+8.7	14,534	+26.6	22,065	−2.2
1971–72	51,304	+10.4	10,968	+11.3	18,926	+30.2	21,410	−3.0
1972–73	58,881	+14.8	13,055	+19.0	24,497	+29.4	21,329	−0.4
1973–74	67,061	+13.9	16,957	+29.9	28,919	+18.0	21,185	−0.7
1974–75	73,915	+10.2	20,170	+18.9	32,183	+11.3	21,562	+1.8
1975–76	77,065	+4.3	22,579	+11.9	34,625	+7.6	19,861	−7.9
1976–77	77,755	+0.9	23,452	+3.9	36,289	+4.8	18,014	−9.3
1977–78	77,874	+0.1	24,187	+3.1	36,556	+0.7	17,131	−4.9
1978–79	77,132	−1.0	25,048	+3.6	36,264	−0.8	15,820	−7.7
1979–80	75,523	−2.1	24,994	−0.2	36,034	−0.6	14,495	−8.4
1980–81	73,985	−2.0	24,370	−2.5	36,712	+1.9	12,903	−11.0
1981–82	74,052	+0.1	24,081	−1.2	38,289	+4.3	11,682	−9.5
1982–83	77,408	+4.5	23,855	−0.9	41,849	+9.3	11,704	+0.2
1983–84	80,312	+3.8	23,718	−0.6	44,394	+6.1	12,200	+4.2
1984–85	82,075	+2.2	24,975	+5.3	45,208	+1.8	11,892	−2.5
1985–86	77,027	−6.2	25,170	+0.8	41,333	−8.6	10,524	−11.5
1986–87	70,561	−8.4	23,761	−5.6	38,528	−6.8	8,272	−21.4

SOURCE: *Nursing Data Review, 1987* (1988). New York: National League for Nursing. Reprinted with permission.

later obtain a non-nursing baccalaureate degree. Such programs can contribute to a student's general education, but the graduate receives no upper-division courses in nursing, does not meet minimal standards for professional nursing, and, in most instances, cannot be admitted to a graduate program in nursing without taking additional prerequisites. At a minimum, every nursing education program should provide the student, if otherwise qualified, with the necessary preparation to move to the next level of professional education.

Students

The number of students entering schools of nursing has decreased since 1983–1984 as shown in Table 4–7. This is true of baccalaureate, associate degree, and diploma programs. This decrease is generally believed to be related to the decreased number of 18- to 24-year-old women, who, at the same time, because of societal changes, have many more fields of study from which to choose.

Beginning with 1985–1986, there also has been a decreased number of students graduating from schools of nursing (Table 4–8), yet that number is almost identical to the numbers graduated in 1976, 1977, 1978, and 1979. In fact, the largest number ever graduated in 1985. It is likely that admission and graduation data have received excessive attention because of the "nursing shortage." Over time, student numbers certainly will affect the supply of nurses; however, the shortage identified in 1986 and the years following relates to an increased demand for nurses within hospitals rather than to major shifts in enrollment patterns in schools of nursing. What is probably most helpful to learn from enrollment data is that the nursing supply cannot be markedly increased by recruiting more students into schools of nursing. Increased utilization of part-time nurses and more efficient utilization of full-time nurses have more potential for success.

References

American Nurses' Association. (1983, 1985, 1987). *Facts about nursing*. Kansas City: Author.

American Nurses' Association. (1987). *The scope of nursing practice*. Kansas City: Author.

Buerhaus, P.I. (1987). Not just another shortage. *Nursing Economics, 5*, 267–279.

CRNAs score one for nurses: Congress OKs billing rights. (1986). *American Journal of Nursing, 86*, 1419.

Cromwell, J. & Rosenbach, M.L. (1988). Reforming anesthesia payment under Medicare. *Health Affairs, 7*(4) 5–19.

Gibson, R. (1984). Nurse midwives and competition: Testing an assumption. *Nursing Economics, 2*, 42–46.

Griffin, S. (1985). LPNs see AD as key to their survival. *The American Nurse, 17*(1), 5.

Griffith, H. (1984). Nursing practice: Substitute or complement according to economic theory. *Nursing Economics, 2*, 105–112.

Health manpower planning process. (1975). Washington, DC: Division of Planning Methods and Technology (DHEW Publication No. 74–14013).

Human Resources, (1987). Community nurses' organizations: The new HMOs? *Hospitals, 61*(13), 69–70.

ICONS: Interagency conference on nursing statistics. (1986). *Nursing Economics, 3,* 127.

Inglehart, J.K. (1986). Data watch: Trends in health personnel. *Health Affairs, 5*(4), 128–145.

Kriesberg, H.M., Wu, J., & Hollander, E.D., et al. (1975). *Methodological approaches for determining health manpower supply and requirements.* Washington, DC: Division of Planning Methods and Technology (DHEW Publication No. [HRA] 76–14511).

Lewis, C. (1982). Nurse practitioners and the physician surplus. In L. Aiken (Ed.), *Nursing in the 1980s: Crises, opportunities, challenges.* Philadelphia: Lippincott.

McKibbin, R.C, (1983). Economic and employment issues in nursing education. *Economic and employment issues for registered nurses.* Kansas City: American Nurses' Association.

National League for Nursing. (1988). *Nursing data review, 1987.* New York: Author.

Registered nurse population, 1984. (1986). Washington, DC: Division of Nursing, Health and Human Services, (HRP–0906938).

Selby, T.L. (1985). House votes "Associate" as second title. *The American Nurse, 17*(8), 1.

Selby, T.L. (1986). Demand surges for specialty nurses. *The American Nurse, 18*(10), 1.

Special Bibliography
Some Major Studies of Nursing and Nursing Resources (Listed in Chronological Order)

Goldmark, J. (1923). *Nursing and nursing education in the United States.* New York: Macmillan.

Burgess, M.A. (1928). *Nurses, patients, and pocketbook.* New York: Committee on the Grading of Nursing Schools.

Committee on the Grading of Nursing Schools. (1934). *Nursing Schools—Today and tomorrow.* New York: National League for Nursing Education.

Brown, E.L. (1948). *Nursing for the future.* New York: Russell Sage Foundation.

West, M., & Hawkins, C. (1950). *Nursing schools at the mid-century.* New York: National Committee for the Improvement of Nursing Services.

Surgeon General's Consultant Group on Nursing. (1963). *Toward quality in nursing: Needs and goals.* Washington, DC: Department of Health, Education, and Welfare.

National Commission for the Study of Nursing and Nursing Education. (1970). *An abstract for action.* New York: McGraw–Hill.

National Commission on Nursing. (1983). *Summary report and recommendations.* Chicago: American Hospital Association.

Institute of Medicine. (1983). *Nursing and nursing education: Public policy and private action.* Washington, DC: National Academy of Sciences.

Secretary's Commission on Nursing. (1988). *Final Report*, (Vol. 1) and *Support studies and background information* (Vol. II) Washington, DC: Department of Health and Human Services.

Part III

The Economics of Employment in Nursing

—

Chapter 5

Wage and Salary Principles

Organization–Worker Exchange

In the market system, many individuals from households sell their labor to enterprises or business organizations and, in exchange, receive payment for their work effort expended. Generally, payment rates are hourly wages or annual salaries. When wages or salaries are combined with other employment benefits having economic value, this is the worker's total *compensation*.

While this chapter focuses upon direct financial rewards (positive utility of employment) received by employees from employer organizations, no administrator can afford to forget that non-financial rewards associated with work are also an important part of the exchange process. Henderson (1985) believes that to the extent possible, management must strive to design jobs and provide work settings that:

Enhance dignity and satisfaction from work performed

Enhance physiological health, psychological well-being, and emotional maturity

Promote constructive social relationships with co-workers

Require adequate attention and effort

Allocate sufficient resources to perform work assignments

Grant sufficient control over the job to meet personal demands

Offer supportive leadership and management

The employee expects (1) job security, (2) a basic standard of living, (3) some luxuries (always changing wants) commensurate with job requirements and personal investment and, (4) in recent years, it has become clear that the worker expects to have influence in the workplace.

In exchange for financial compensation, organizations employ labor to assist with the production of the products or services that reflect the organization's purpose and to engage in activities necessary for organizational maintenance. To accomplish these broad purposes, organizations expect employees to be competent and dependable, to perform work assignments at stated times, and to do so while maintaining acceptable standards. Employees who attempt to improve the quantity and quality of output, reduce costs, and minimize wasteful use of resources (including employees' time) are generally highly valued. Many employees increase their value to their employers by obtaining additional education and training, making upward mobility more likely. Thus, it is logical to design compensation programs to influence employee behavior in ways that are beneficial to the organization. Employees have their own ideas, however, about what they will or will not accept as just reward for their efforts. For these reasons, plus a myriad of external influences, compensation programs are constantly evolving as the marketplace for labor becomes increasingly complex and as reward systems become more sophisticated.

Societal Objectives

Governments as Social Agents

Governments act as agents of society in establishing social policy. Policies enacted by state and federal governmental bodies have had considerable influence on the amount of compensation workers receive and the way in which such programs are administered. These efforts can be categorized into two broad public missions.

Role Model

In the first type of activity the government acts as a role model and says, "We will do the right thing and other private organizations will follow our example." Government agencies initiated the practice of putting their personnel policies in writing and sharing these with employees. The federal civil service made the earliest corrections of policies violating the civil rights of minorities and, as a result, minorities have found job opportunities in government employment denied to them in the private sector. The nature of the election process makes it politically rewarding for elected officials to take action to improve the quality of life for significant components of their electorate.

Minimum Standards

The second broad purpose of governments has been to establish minimum standards for employee practices by businesses engaging in interstate commerce (federal laws) or intrastate commerce (state laws). The rationale of minimum standards is that anything less than the minimum leaves a worker (and society) vulnerable. The worker, without adequate protection, may be forced to become a welfare recipient at a later time. Private companies should not profit from an inadequately compensated work force whose members become dependent upon public support systems.

Henderson (1985) has recounted the history of early legislation in the area of minimum employment standards. President Martin Van Buren in 1840 issued an executive order establishing the 10-hour day for government workers. Until the Civil War, the 12-hour or 13-hour day was commonplace and until the early 1920s still existed in many segments of the American economy. Within industrial settings the 10-hour work day was well-established by 1890. Many of the legal efforts at the turn of the century were directed at shortening the work week for women and children.

In 1912 Massachusetts passed a minimum wage law, the first in the United States, mainly designed to protect women and children from both long hours and inadequate wages. In 1923 the U.S. Supreme Court in the case of *Adkins versus Children's Hospital*, overturned as unconstitutional the District of Columbia statute stating that it was illegal to deprive individuals of the right to take any job offered that was acceptable to them. This decision provided court sanction to minimum wage laws.

The earliest national legislation relating to minimum wage was the Davis-Bacon Act of 1931 that required construction contractors with federal contracts to pay construction workers a wage comparable to those prevailing in the area. While this act continues to have considerable influence within the construction industry, it has broader significance because the act requires the Secretary of Labor to determine the prevailing wage in all areas of the country. Through the years these data requirements have been expanded until today the Department of Labor provides extensive sets of data on labor costs in all fields, including health services, by metropolitan areas, states, regions of the country, and for the nation as a whole.

Major Federal Laws Relating to Compensation

There are many federal laws that may affect direct income. For example, during wartime Congress would likely enact various kinds of wage control legislation. Without wage control severe inflation would likely develop because of stimulation of the economy by greatly increased federal expenditures. Another example of federal influence upon compensation is income tax legislation, particularly laws affecting withholding taxes and taxes on benefits. Only a few major laws directly affecting compensation will be considered here.

Fair Labor Standards Act (FLSA)

The FLSA was enacted in 1938 and established minimum wages for all employees whose employers engage in interstate commerce. This original legislation has been added to until today only certain small businesses and restaurants are exempt. It is reported that 39 states also have laws affecting minimum wages that expand the requirements to intrastate employers or set higher minimums than the federal law. The FLSA is administered by the Wage and Hour Division of the Department of Labor. Its major provisions include the following.

Minimum Wages

In 1981 the minimum wage increased to $3.35 per hour. Minimum wages are designed to decrease welfare costs, which taxpayers must finance, and instead put the cost on the business, which contracted for the labor. The minimum wage also acts as an index since, as the minimum wage is increased, other wages near that hourly rate are also increased. Some economists believe that the minimum wage decreases the number of low-level, entry-type positions because the cost to the employer is too great to establish the position. It is similarly argued that teenagers and trainees should be exempt in order to create more jobs. The counter view is that such changes would be likely to take jobs away from qualified adults. By 1989 there was considerable support in Congress to raise the minimum wage significantly because of the erosion by inflation of the purchasing power of $3.35 over the previous eight years.

Child Labor Prohibitions

The law prohibits most employment of children under age 16 except when employed by a parent or legal guardian and then not in interstate commerce. Between the ages 16 and 18, the law prohibits employment of youths in hazardous industries such as meat packing and lumbering.

Overtime Pay

A covered employee must by law be paid one and one-half times the base wage for hours worked over 40 hours per week. The American Hospital Association was successful in obtaining a modification of this requirement: In the health industry overtime is paid only if the hours worked exceed 80 hours in a two week period. This enables many hospitals to avoid overtime pay by returning the hours (often called compensatory time) during the remainder of the pay period. Overtime also must be paid on any bonus allotment such as a shift differential.

Professional personnel are exempt from the requirements of the overtime law. In an instance of the incongruities of the positions of nursing leadership relative to claims of professionalism, nursing has claimed that staff nurses are not professionals in order that they might obtain payment for overtime services. Nursing should use the FLSA to help straighten out its incongruent language. Associate nurses are technical-level employees and should be entitled to overtime. Professional nurses should be employed under professional job descriptions. In return for giving up claims of overtime pay, professional nurses should be paid a commensurate salary for a defined position.

Equal Pay Act of 1963

This was passed as an amendment to the FLSA and was the first federal antidiscrimination act that applied to women. The Equal Pay Act, which requires equal pay for equal work, applies to all employees covered by the FLSA and, thus, is very broad in coverage. Under the act an employer can establish different wage rates based upon (1) a seniority system, (2) a merit system, (3) a system that measures quantity or quality of production, or (4) any other system not based upon gender. Congress amended the Equal Pay Act in 1972 to cover professional employees at colleges and universities.

Women may have forgotten how recently it was legal to pay men and women differently for the same job. Often a feminine title was assigned to a position as the key to paying less: A janitor was paid more than a janitress while each carried out identical activities. The janitor might have six steps in his pay grade, and the janitress might have only two. An administrative assistant was usually male and earned more than a senior secretary who was female. Union women provided much of the leadership for passing the 1963 legislation. As a result, all job titles have been corrected for sexism, and equalization of pay has been obtained in many fields. Today there are no airline stewardesses; instead both men and women work as flight attendants.

Civil Rights Act of 1964, TITLE VII

This act was passed so soon after the Equal Pay Act that there has been considerable consolidation in the administration of these laws. The Equal Pay Act, the Civil Rights Act of 1964, the Age Discrimination Act of 1974, and the Pregnancy Discrimination Act of 1978 all have been transferred to the Equal Employment Opportunity Commission for administration. Together, these laws prohibit discrimination in hiring, training, compensation, promotion, and termination practices within an organization. Discrimination includes practices based upon an individual's race, color, religion, sex, or national origin. Organizations found guilty have been held responsible for all legal costs and the retroactive pay due the claimant had there been no discrimination.

Under these laws, the employer has the right to establish discriminatory requirements if they are bona fide occupational qualifications. Police departments that eliminated applicants under 5 feet 10 inches successfully eliminated most women applicants, but there were no data to support the belief that tall persons were more successful police officers. The manufacturer of Jockey underwear, however, can defend the decision to employ male models. Theater roles can be sex specific but not race specific unless race is relevant to the plot.

These discrimination laws have been used by almost all health service personnel departments to defend the practice of paying the same to all newly employed staff nurses, with or without an academic degree with or without experience. Since a degree is not required to become a registered nurse, personnel staff have argued that paying more to those with a degree would discriminate in a way that is not a bona fide occupational qualification. Since employers have the right to create descriptions based upon differing levels of education and professional experience, it is not appropriate to write all direct care nursing positions for the same level of competence. This fails to provide the mix of personnel needed for efficient and effective operations and, simultaneously, fails to reward nurses who contribute advanced skills.

Union Influences

The right of workers to bargain collectively with their employer regarding hours, wages, and conditions of work has been established by federal and state laws and has had considerable influence on compensation. Most public sector union activity is controlled by state laws and, because it often involves state or municipal employees, it is not uncommon for these laws to deny the worker the right to the strike. Often there is provision for binding arbitration as an alternative to the strike. The major provisions of state labor laws are quite similar to the federal law. Various groups of federal employees, beginning in 1962, have received the right to bargain collectively through a series of executive orders.

The National Labor Relations act, originally passed in 1935, is a federal law that provides employees of private enterprises the right to organize and to bargain collectively for wages, benefits, and working conditions. The law was established to provide a legal basis for resolving employer-employee disputes. The law assigns the National Labor Relations Board the responsibility (1) to conduct union certification elections and verify the results and (2) to prevent employers and unions from engaging in unfair labor practices.

The Taft-Hartley Amendments (1947) to the NLRA provided that private not-for-profit hospitals were exempt because of their charitable nature and because of the general absence of interstate commerce. In addition, these amendments specified a number of labor practices on the part of unions that would be considered unfair under the law. The Federal Mediation and Conciliation Service was also established as an independent agency to mediate and conciliate labor disputes to avoid strikes.

In 1959, the Landrum-Griffin Amendments provided for extensive reporting and disclosure requirements on the part of labor organizations. The government was interested in protecting the workers against abusive unions and established requirements for union elections and a bill of rights for union members.

In 1974 the Health Amendments were added. These were so named because they brought organizations from the third sector of the economy (private, not-for-profit organizations) under the provisions of the NLRA.

Health service organizations are the largest employers in this group. Congress passed these amendments because members were concerned about the inadequacy of the wages of many categories of hospital workers and the preponderance of female workers who faced wage discrimination. Congressional members also wished to assist labor unions, who needed the legal right to organize the labor-intensive health care industry to offset membership losses in the "smokestack" industries.

Job Content and Measurement

Before a just wage can be attached to the performance of a job, it is necessary to study carefully what the job entails. This is done using objective techniques that permit comparisons with similar or comparable jobs in other occupational families. In this context, a *job* consists of responsibilities and duties sufficiently alike to be covered by one job description. A *position* is the work assigned to one employee. Thus for one job, such as staff nurse, there may be many positions.

Job Analysis

Job analysis is an important part of employment planning and precedes the preparation of job descriptions and specifications. When an organization such as a hospital wishes to study an entire family of jobs (e.g., clerical workers, nurses, or laboratory technicians), the personnel (human resources) department may elect to hire an outside consulting firm to do the analysis. Employees are so personally involved with their own jobs that every recommendation for change is opposed by at least some, if not all, members of the group. It is easier to have any hostility directed at an outside firm whose job analyst leaves the institution when the study is completed. It is also true that job analysis on a broad scale involves special skills that may not be needed permanently in small institutions. Any personnel department, however, would be expected to be able to work with the nursing department to analyze and develop a proposed new position in that department.

In the process of job analysis, information is obtained from employees in the job, immediate supervisors and subordinates, and higher-level supervisors as appropriate. Information is sought by questionnaire, individual and group interviews, and sometimes activity logs maintained by position occupants. Workers may overestimate the importance of their contributions and likewise, a department head can be expected to increase the value of the job because recruitment and employee selection are easier when the attached wage is higher.

Job analysis involves obtaining information about work activities, worker-related activities, equipment and tools used, work performance (standards, error significance), job context (work schedules, physical working conditions, and social context), and personnel requirements of the job (education, experience, and personal attributes). In Appendix A of this chapter is a sample job analysis questionnaire.

Job Design

Following job analysis comes the process of job design or redesign of existing jobs. There are four broad approaches that can be used, each discussed below.

Work Simplification

A larger job may be broken down into subparts, and a new job created around one or more of these subparts. This technique was developed in industry in the early decades of this century and was given wide application by the military in World War I. The advantages are that less well-trained and less costly employees can be utilized with shorter periods of on-the-job training as employees can become skilled more quickly in a narrow range of tasks. Familiar examples to nurses would be the use of nursing assistants, licensed practical nurses, and intravenous or medication nurses.

Job Rotation

A job may be rotated because it is unpleasant or boring. The quick food industry cross-trains employees to function in several work stations. Staff nurses often rotate shifts so that evening and night shifts are shared by all. Sometimes a very unpleasant patient may be rotated through various nurses' assignments. To reduce the problem of indiscriminate floating of nursing personnel, some institutions cross-train one or two nurses who can work equally effectively on two units of a particular service. These selected nurses are then rotated as needed.

Job Enlargement

This third technique is the opposite of job simplification, and the aim is to recombine subparts into a more meaningful whole. By assuming responsibility for a larger unit of the work, it is possible to improve work performance and reduce boredom. The growth of primary nursing is an example of job enlargement. The coordination of patient care can be greatly improved and the work is much more satisfying for nurses who enjoy patient care. Job enlargement is a horizontal growth in task components rather than any increase in the size of work load.

Job Enrichment

As a fourth approach to job design, job enrichment increases responsibility and accountability. It is sometimes referred to as vertical enlargement. In some health service institutions, there has been considerable job enrichment of the traditional position of head nurse by employment of master's-prepared nurses. Decentralization of clinical nursing services has produced enrichment of director of a clinical service positions, including increased financial accountability. Decentralization eliminates the need for positions in the central nursing office as supervisors. Decisions are made where the data exist rather than by referral to higher authority.

Job Description

With precise knowledge of the content and context of the job and with management's plan for the nature of the authority and responsibility of the job occupants, it is possible to prepare a job description. A well-developed job description has several parts or sections (see Appendix B of this chapter). There is a *general description* of two or three sentences followed by a listing of *principal duties and responsibilities*. Such descriptions are useless unless behaviorally based. Behavioral activities and responsibilities can be written if the writer first determines the actual objectives of the job and then states these in behavioral terms. It is important to use verb forms that are strong and imply significant decision making and accountability in order to have appropriate compensation attached to the position. To coordinate and to collaborate are nice ideas, but one is paid to direct, to administer, to initiate, and to determine. Appendix C contains a list of action verbs used in job descriptions.

Another major section of a job description is the *job specifications*. This includes the educational requirements, experience, and competence necessary to do the work. Sometimes qualifications may be presented as minimally acceptable or necessary, with an accompanying list of higher requirements considered desirable. If the employer must appoint someone with minimally acceptable qualifications, it is advantageous to make the appointment for a specified time period and stipulate, in writing, what conditions must be met for the contract to be renewed. The minimally qualified employee is generally paid less as an incentive to become more fully qualified.

There are additional sections of the job description that describe working conditions if these are other than office-type and, finally, reporting relationships. The latter is important if there is more than one line of authority, for example, reporting to a medical care manager as well as to the nursing care manager. In this case, the authority for performance evaluation must lie with the nurse manager because members of the profession do not evaluate members of another profession regarding the professional content of the work. The hospital administrator can evaluate the medical director and the director of nursing relative to their management of their respective departments.

Job Evaluation

Job evaluation is the process by which the relative worth of various jobs in an organization is determined for pay purpose. In small businesses this may be done rather casually using a *ranking* process by which one total job is ranked against another total job. The weakness of the method relates to one's inability to direct attention simultaneously to the various dimensions by which jobs differ. A tree trimmer has hazardous work, but the job may carry minimal responsibility.

Civil service systems often use a *classification system* whereby about 15 to 20 broad-band categories are well-defined, and jobs are analyzed and placed within a category. Thus a staff nurse might be a G–7 and a director of nursing a G–14. Using such a system, one particular position where there is considerable hiring activity may be used as a "benchmark" position. As the benchmark for a particular family of jobs rises or falls in economic worth, the other positions tied to it move in a similar fashion. Historically, such designations have been harmful to nursing since the staff nurse position has been the benchmark, and the college degree is not required. Other nursing positions, then, become pegged to this technical-level benchmark.

Table 5–1   The Factor Evaluation System (FES) Developed by the U.S. Office of Personnel Management to Categorize All Federal Positions According to Broad Job Dimensions.

Knowledge Required by the Position (9)
1. Nature or kind of knowledge and skills needed
2. How these knowledges and skills are used in doing the work

Supervisory Controls (5)
1. How the work is assigned
2. The employee's responsibility for carrying out the work
3. How the work is reviewed

Guidelines (5)
1. The nature of guidelines for performing the work
2. The judgement needed to apply the guidelines or develop new guides

Complexity (6)
1. The nature of the assignment
2. The difficulty in identifying what needs to be done
3. The difficulty and originality involved in performing the work

Scope and Effect (6)
1. The purpose of the work
2. The impact of the work product or service

Personal Contacts (4)

Purpose of Contacts (4)

Physical Demands (3)

Work Environment (3)

Note: Numbers in parentheses refer to the number of degrees that further define or measure the subfactors.

A system that is increasing in popularity because of its great adaptability and reliability is the *point system*. There are generally four to five broad dimensions that contribute information about all jobs and which can be used to legally justify and defend the institution's personnel decisions. Commonly identified dimensions include skill, effort, responsibility, and working conditions. Some systems divide effort into physical and mental effort. Beneath each dimension are three to six factors, and each factor is broken down into five to eight degree levels. Each degree level allots points. Refer to the example of such a model as shown in Appendix D at the end of the chapter. In summary, it can be said that job factors provide a proxy measure of job difficulty and job worth.

Probably the most sophisticated point system has been developed by the U.S. Office of Personnel Management and is called the Factor Evaluation System (FES). The FES was developed after seven years of research involving 7000 jobs in 26 federal agencies. Table 5–1 illustrates the nine dimensions of the 7000 jobs, and the points weighting each dimension of the FES.

It is wise for nurse managers to know and understand the job categorization system used in the employing institution in order to redesign jobs or rewrite job descriptions so that the highest appropriate wage can be obtained. Nurses, too often, take their responsibilities for granted and do not elaborate these sufficiently in job descriptions. They may change dressings on the most repugnant wounds without realizing that society pays persons to do unpleasant tasks. Nurses have been unfairly taught that they knew these unpleasant acts were a part of nursing when they made their career choice. That is true, but it does not mean nurses should not be paid appropriately for difficult and unpleasant tasks. Sometimes it is enlightening to read the claims made on job descriptions in other departments of the institution.

Wage Decisions

The nature of wage decisions is based upon a comparative view of wages from three different perspectives: (1) Wage level is a comparison of wages within one organization versus wages of similar job categories in other organizations; (2) wage structure is a comparison of wages across occupational categories within a single organization; and (3) individual wage determination is a comparison of wages of individuals working with a single job description (Nash & Carroll, 1975). Each of these is described.

Wage Level

Within an organization, management may adopt one of three possible pay strategies relative to pay level. There is a *high pay strategy* in which management believes it will get what it pays for. Paying wages somewhat higher than the average enables organizations to recruit and hold workers who are the best in their fields. These organizations believe that money is saved by being able to recruit the best, by reducing job turnover, and maintaining a satisfied staff. Some hospitals, in favorable market settings, have employed BSN-prepared staff nurses almost exclusively. Then there is a *low pay strategy* where management tries to get the job done with minimal investment in labor. This may be because that is all the organization can pay or it may be an effort to maximize short-range profits while ignoring the long-range costs. The vast majority of organizations adopt a *comparable pay-level strategy* by which management aims to keep even with the competition. An example is the Federal Pay Comparability Act of 1970 whereby Congress established a policy for the civil service to pay position occupants at a rate comparable to wages paid in the private sector.

Variations in pay are attributable to many factors such as:

Organization size—Clearly, large organizations tend to pay higher salaries. This has been documented across many industries and in foreign countries as well.

Proportion of budget utilized in labor costs—Labor-intensive industries such as health care tend to pay less than industries with low labor utilization (e.g., the chemical industry).

Unionization—The presence of unions tends to raise pay levels both through actual collective bargaining and through the mere threat of possible union-organizing activity. Production workers generally earn from 11 to 15 percent higher wages where unionized. This influence is stronger where there are industry-wide single unions (e.g., the United Automobile Workers).

State of the labor market—When the supply of a category of worker is large, the wage level can be expected to be low. In recent years the supply of retail workers has been very large because many women without special job skills have sought employment. Department stores have adopted some of the lowest wage patterns found anywhere. The denial of full-time employment (most employees work 32 hours per week) has enabled the retail industry to greatly reduce its labor costs by eliminating most fringe benefits and overtime pay.

Product market competition—In areas of the country where bed capacity has been overextended and hospitals therefore experience low occupancy, nurses may expect to observe wage deflection or an increase in job specifications. Lesser prepared, direct care givers such as LPNs, who traditionally have worked under close supervision, may have to move to long-term care facilities to find employment.

Status—Many organizations pay above the generally–accepted wage level because management wishes to be perceived as a first-class organization. This would be particularly true in instances where product or service competition has been low and increased product or service costs are easily passed on to the consumer.

Age of organization—New organizations have to establish higher pay levels to recruit the type of personnel needed, probably due to a risk involved in taking these positions. The organization may develop successfully or it may not. Risk is offset by higher salaries and opportunities for more rapid promotion.

Information on wage levels is obtained by salary surveys. Good surveys are made available most often by trade, professional, or occupational groups. To get cooperation, the survey must provide reciprocity (those who provide data will also receive data), anonymity, low cost for the organization, timeliness, and accuracy of data. The data must be obtained from personnel departments. Data from wage recipients tends to be very inaccurate because individuals are not certain of the facts and definition of terms cannot be tightly controlled. Appendix E has a list of important wage surveys useful in the fields of health and education.

Wage Structure

The main goal of the wage structure of an organization is to assure that there will be equivalent compensation for jobs of equal worth and appropriate differentials for jobs that are not of equal worth. Within organizations, jobs are often assigned to major categories that include clerical workers, unskilled and semiskilled workers, skilled craft and trade workers, technicians and paraprofessionals, professionals and administrators. It promotes sex discrimination to put all nursing division employees on one scale. Ward clerks are clerical, nursing assistants are unskilled, LPNs are semiskilled, and associate nurses are technical and paraprofessional. Professional nurses hold advanced clinical and administrative positions. Nursing positions that provide care and plan and administer care are considered a job family.

In Appendix D, there is an edited version of the factor point system model originally prepared by Samaras et al. (1978). Using such a system, an institutional committee composed of representatives from the personnel department, employing department, and institution administration evaluate each job description to determine the total points to be assigned through the job evaluation process. Within a major job family, a point multiplier is developed based upon the highest wage and lowest wage in that group:

Highest Wage/Hour	=	$12.00
Lowest Wage/Hour	=	3.50
(W_D) Wage Difference	=	$ 8.50

Based upon the point value of the highest and lowest job of the category, the points difference and points multiplier can be computed:

1. Highest Average Point Value = 398
   Lowest Average Point Value = 132
   (P^D) Points Difference = 266

2. (P_M) = Points Multiplier = $\dfrac{W_D}{P^D}$

3. $P^M = \dfrac{\$8.50}{266} = .032$

Thus an intermediary job of 220 points would be paid:

220 − 132 = 90 points
90 points × .032 = $2.88
$2.88 + $3.50 = $6.38

It is common practice for executive administration to make final decisions relative to the top and bottom salaries in each major category upon recommendation of the personnel department. Then all other positions can be assigned a wage using the points multiplier for that category.

Individual Wage Determination

The most important wage decisions within an organization are those affecting the pay received by one individual in relation to another when both are performing the same job. Differences that the position occupants do not perceive as justifiable can lead to poor morale. Administrative insecurity relative to individual wage determination is often hidden in institutional secrecy regarding salaries.

There is widespread belief among employees, administrators, and compensation specialists that individual pay should be determined by seniority and quality of performance. Past performance should represent satisfactory performance, but that would assume an appropriate performance evaluation system being in place. Where such an assumption cannot be supported, past performance may represent tolerated performance because the institution would have been unable to hire a replacement. Payment for seniority can lead to payment for obsolescence. Where seniority pay is used to promote retention of staff, it is likely that scheduled periodic bonuses have more influence.

As part of basic pay determination, the vast majority of organizations are making increasing use of salary grades with defined steps. These pay grades are complex to design and difficult to maintain. If such distinctions are not maintained, the result is salary compression and inadequate pay differences between beginning and skilled levels. Henderson (1982, pp. 282–284) has written of some general relationships that should be maintained relative to ranges and increments:

> There should be some overlap between pay grades (5 to 15 percent) but not so much that a promoted worker does not receive an appropriate salary increase.
>
> The midpoint on the salary grade should represent market value, with the lower limit used for probationary employees, the midpoint area for fully accepted employees, and the upper levels for the fully competent.
>
> A pay range of 10 to 20 percent on either side of the midpoint is common, and institutions striving to recognize merit may have ranges as wide as 50 percent. Differences between steps is usually 5.0 to 7.5 percent.
>
> It is common to use narrow pay grades for low-level positions where there is little variation in performance and to use broad pay grades to recognize the great variations in competence found in higher-level positions.
>
> Market survey data are often used to establish the midpoint for a pay grade or job.
>
> Organizations may use multiple pay structures for broad occupational categories (e.g., unskilled, skilled, professional).
>
> Workers who perform below average should not progress beyond the midpoint of the pay range.

External market pressures or a pattern of moving employees up a step in salary for each year of service can create a situation with employees pegged at higher salary levels than their education, experience, or performance would justify. On the other hand, one department in an organization cannot hold the line if other departments are permitted to place their employees on the highest step of each grade.

Wage Adjustments

There are several types of salary actions after initial employment that can influence the pay of the worker. Employees are becoming increasingly so-phisticated and assertive about such matters, and it is important that wages be administered in ways that are perceived as fair by the recipients.

Promotion Adjustment

Sibson (1981, p. 220) has devoted special attention to the importance of pay relationships with subordinates. He has developed five independent criteria dealing with the pay relationships of supervisors and those they supervise, which can be applied as appropriate.

> The supervisor's salary grade should be at least two levels (not steps) higher than the grade of the highest-rated person supervised. In practice, the supervisor is usually three to four salary levels higher.
>
> The supervisor's base salary should be at least 15 percent higher than the straight-time earnings of the highest-paid subordinates.
>
> The supervisor's gross pay (including bonus and any overtime compensation) should be at least 10 percent higher than the gross pay (including overtime) of the highest-paid subordinates.
>
> The gross pay of the supervisor should be at least 25 percent higher than the average gross pay of all subordinates.
>
> The gross pay of the supervisor should be no more than 75 percent higher then the average gross pay of all subordinates.

In many health service institutions, the first-line managers (head nurses) are paid very poorly. Hospitals have found that there is no problem filling these positions. Nurses accept the position, if it is offered, to be free of rotating shifts and weekend assignments. The authority of head nurses suffers irreparably, however, when other nurses on the unit are earning more. It may be that staff nurses collect overtime while head nurse positions are exempt from FLSA regulations. Also, when severe shortages of nurses occur, the reaction is to raise entry-level salaries, which then produces compression of salaries nearest those beginning positions.

Compression can be eased by developing different job descriptions for head nurse positions when the position is filled by someone with an associate degree, a baccalaureate degree, or a master's degree. In fact, the position becomes very different when occupied by persons with different levels of preparation. If job descriptions are developed that are appropriate to management's expectations when different types of nurses are employed, it protects associate nurses from unfair and unreasonable expectations. It also enables the institution to decide what level of nurse it wishes to employ and protects the institution from expending salary monies for a level of worker not employed.

The importance of head nurse positions to the management of care, the complexity and unpredictability of the decision making required, the large numbers of subordinates involved, and the difficulty of supervising on all three shifts—all attest to the need to upgrade the positions and the salaries. Many service settings are redefining these positions and hiring master's-prepared nurses. When the positions are upgraded, the nature of the role changes markedly and so must the salaries.

General Increases

These are changes in the salary of an employee not related to individual performance. Rather, general increases accommodate changes in the rate of inflation, which affect the cost of living, or changes in an occupation's competitive position in the marketplace.

Inflation—Most economists agree that indexing of wages to the rate of inflation as defined by the Consumer Price Index (CPI) is not an appropriate technique. At low income levels, workers may spend all of their earnings on items that relate directly to their cost of living, but, even at these levels, house payments may reflect investment as well as housing. At higher income levels, or in families with multiple income earners, portions of income are for luxuries and investments and, in such cases, indexed payments exaggerate the cost of living. If widely used, indexing promotes inflation.

A typical cost-of-living adjustment in a union contract is a 33-cents-an-hour increase for every 10 points of increase in the CPI, with payment made in a special quarterly check. The Hay Group, a leading compensation consulting firm, has recommended the use of a formula that sets the wage rate increase at 67 percent of the CPI change plus 2.2 percent. This formula, applied over a twenty-year period from 1961 to 1981, appears to provide an accurate estimate without being, itself, inflationary (Bates, 1984).

Market Demand—It also may be necessary to provide general increases to a category of employees in order to remain competitive in the marketplace when recruiting new employees. The practice of merely increasing wages at the entry level tends to create compression between various-ranked jobs for that occupation and is destructive of the compensation model being used. The marketplace demand may require that an institution adjust the salary of a selected position. In the next year's budget, however, broad corrections must be made or serious problems of inequity will develop. It is never acceptable to existing personnel for the organization to hire new people at higher wages than those who are currently employed and who are performing satisfactorily.

In academic settings, it is necessary to adjust faculty salaries both for rank (e.g., instructor, associate professor) and for the discipline. Professors in law, medicine, and engineering are paid more than professors in art, music, and languages. The salary level of the discipline is directly affected by the nature of the competition for those teachers in the outside marketplace. There are few employment opportunities for history professors outside of academia, but clinical nursing faculty experience high demand. Nursing faculty salaries must reflect this outside demand or serious recruitment problems develop, and clinical faculty positions become difficult to fill.

Shift, Holiday, and Weekend Differentials

Institutions that require a second or third shift expect to pay a shift differential (i.e., an increase in the nurse's pay rate above what is earned on the day shift). It is important that differentials be computed as a percentage increase over the individual's base pay rather than a flat amount. Home care agencies are paying weekend differentials of about 50 percent. Hospitals have not commonly paid weekend differentials and instead try to promise staff alternate weekends off or every third weekend off. Holidays are usually computed at time and one-half. None of the differentials is high enough to entice many workers to elect these options.

It is especially important that the differential be high enough to prevent nurses from becoming cheap substitutes to staff the functions of other departments. There should be no activities carried out by nurses on evening and night shifts, holidays, or weekends that those same nurses would not carry out on the day shift unless the affected department is willing to pay the nursing division handsomely for the special service.

Hospital nursing divisions are unlikely to solve their staffing problems until they pay enough on evenings, nights, and weekends to move to an "all volunteer" nursing work force. At the right price, there will be enough nurses who need the money or in fact prefer those working conditions and will elect to work on that shift or day. The military found it could no longer depend upon the draft and developed an all-volunteer armed services. Hospitals must do the same. Some of the cost can be met by paying less to nurses who work on the day shift, Monday through Friday. These salaries can be reduced if no shift rotation is involved.

Performance

The reward of performance is of two general types: longevity (quantity) and excellence (quality). There is agreement that both must be rewarded, but, at that point, agreement seems to vanish. Many excellent compensation models are destroyed by failure of management to maintain appropriate distinctions between these two performance measures.

Longevity

A worker should be rewarded by advancing salary steps for as long as the years of service actually reflect improved performance. For some positions there is also a need to reward the broad judgement that comes with increased knowledge of the history and values of the organization. Annual increases without merit must be avoided for such practices lead to a prohibitively expensive worker.

Sizable bonuses on prescribed anniversary years are used successfully by some organizations. These bonuses can be 5 to 15 percent of the worker's direct pay and are awarded every five years. These awards ($1000 to $3000 for a $20,000-a-year employee) often cost the organization less than hourly rate increases but have a more significant effect on purchasing good will and continued service from the employee. Anniversary bonuses are easy to budget and to administer, and their use protects the organization's compensation model from inappropriate salary advances based on tenure instead of excellence.

Excellence

Failure to reward superior performance is probably the single most important problem in compensation administration. There are many who believe that if excellence cannot be rewarded fairly, such awards will cause more problems in worker morale than they are worth; however, these critics tend to equate fairness with equity. Awards for outstanding performance are not equitable by definition, but they can be fair if criteria for the awards are defined in advance and applied impartially.

Awards for excellence are actually incorporated in a model where the employee is recognized and rewarded by means of a pattern of progression. In the clinical practice of nursing, nurses should progress from associate nurse to professional nurse and clinical nurse specialist. This mechanism provides opportunity to recognize excellence in ways that are rewarding both to the nurses and to the employing institution. In a similar fashion, the nurse faculty member can progress through the academic ranks and each rank is, in itself, a recognition of excellence. Such ranking systems can be used as defined, orderly systems to recognize excellence. To serve this purpose, however, the ranks must reflect sufficient growth to accommodate an entire career for the majority, and the salary distinctions must be significant. In the past, this has not been true of the vast majority of hospital career ladders.

Recognition of excellence in nursing administrative positions should be related to the institution-wide administration reward system. Such programs are most often related to a system of management-by-objectives wherein the administrator earns bonus credits by achieving goals established by the organization. To be successful, these programs must have goals agreed upon jointly by the supervisor and the supervisee, the goals must be stated in ways that are measurable, and the time period for achieving the goals must be made explicit.

Many health professionals are concerned about the true effects of management bonus systems, which are dependent upon cutting costs or saving money. How can society be certain that the savings (and related bonuses) are not made possible by decreases or deterioration in the quality of care? On the other hand, there are no data that indicate that an expensive service is necessarily a better service. If cost reductions are used as a measure of administrative effectiveness, it is necessary to simultaneously collect data relating to standards of care and the quality of services. Economies should only be rewarded if it can be shown that quality has been maintained.

Proposed Salary Model

Description and Rationale

The salary models for nursing as developed in many health service institutions violate important principles upon which salaries should be based. The end result is that nurses' salaries show great compression at the entry levels, and there is little economic reward for the development of advanced skills and competencies. Compensation practices need to be changed to provide individual nurses with sufficient incentives to invest in their own preparation. This investment involves both the direct costs of advanced schooling and the opportunity costs of lost salary while in school.

Table 5–2 portrays a salary model based upon levels of nursing competence defined by two major factors: education and position. Let us bury the myth that in nursing, education doesn't really matter. The only two groups in our society who believe this are those who have neglected to obtain educational preparation and those wishing to control another group. Institutions must stop allotting salary money inappropriately. It is important to nursing, and to the individual nurses involved, for an associate degree graduate to be

---

Table 5–2   Education and Position Factors in Compensation Model

A. Education Factor:
    +30% DNS/PhD
    +20% MSN
       0% BSN (Benchmark Position)
    −20% (RN–AD/Dip)
    −30% (merged Associate Nurse/LPN)
    −40% LPN/LVN

B. Position Factor:
    +200% Corporate VP Nursing–Multiple Units
    +175% VP Nursing–Single Institution
    +130% Director of Nursing
    +100% Director of Nursing Operations
    + 50% Director of Clinical Service, Staff Development, Research, Quality
             Assurance
    + 40% Consultant in Practice, Quality Assurance, Staff Development
             Practitioner
    + 25% Unit Manager, Head Nurse
    + 20% Case Manager
    + 10% Preceptor/Practitioner, Assistant Unit Manager, Charge Nurse, Quality
             Assurance or Infection Control Technician
       0% Clinical Practitioner

able to anticipate a higher salary following investment in baccalaureate education.

In this model, the BSN degree, which has been designated by the American Nurses' Association as the entry level into professional nursing, is used as the benchmark position. It is easily compared with baccalaureate-prepared nurses employed at other institutions and agencies. There are two educational levels above this (MSN and DNS/PhD) and two levels below the benchmark (RN-associate degree/diploma, and LPN). While LPNs have traditionally been paid about 30 percent below the staff nurse position, here it drops to 40 percent because the BSN level is used as the benchmark position.

In this model, the two categories below the BSN level would be protected by the Fair Labor Standards Act, and occupants would be entitled to time and one-half for overtime. Overtime pay would be discontinued for professional-level personnel; these latter workers would be salaried.

Position, the second major factor, means that money is assigned to the position or the activities collected within a job description. Position is not limited to management positions but includes all of the functional areas of nursing: advanced practice, teaching, administration, research, and evaluation. A clinical director prepared at the master's level would work from a different job description than one with a baccalaureate degree because of the different competencies each would bring to the position and the different expectations held for their performance. This model simply operationalizes the phrase, "Salary commensurate with preparation and experience," which is seen so often in advertisements.

Many institutions provide only basic care; there is no advanced clinical practice. Basic care consists of carrying out the physicians' directives plus assisting patients with activities of daily living. If there are no professional nurses planning and providing care, there is no professional care and no advanced clinical practice.

To these two major factors of education and position is added a third, so-called, individual adjustment factor (Table 5–3). This includes (1) performance stages within a position, (2) shift differential for evening, night, or weekend assignments, and (3) bonuses for longevity. The performance stages should not be confused with employment steps where the worker is advanced a step each year almost automatically.

Benner (1984) has defined performance stages as "Novice, Beginner, Competent, Proficient, and Expert." Nurses without previous experience would start at Stage 1 (novice). Movement from Stage 1 to Stage 2 (novice to beginner) can be made by management after the nurse has completed orientation and has demonstrated enough competence to function satisfactorily in the role of a beginner practitioner. Other advancements should be dependent upon a peer review process and, quite appropriately, would require several years to negotiate. It is not expected that all practitioners would reach "expert" stage.

The period as a novice, which occurs only once in each nurse's career,

Table 5–3 Individual Salary Adjustments

A. Performance Stages:

```
       _____ 5% _____
_____ 20% _____
   1          2          3             4          5
Probationary  Beginner  Fully Competent  Proficient  Expert
```

B. Shift Differential:

Afternoons = 25%
Nights = 35%
Weekends = 25%
Days = −10%

C. Bonuses for Longevity:

After 2 years   5% of base salary
      5 years   7%
     10 years 10%
     15 years 15% (and every five years)

protects the institution economically from the high cost incurred in preparing new graduates for staff nurse positions. If the individual practitioner must absorb the cost of being a novice, that nurse will (1) want to demonstrate competence in the role as quickly as possible, and (2), if achievement of that goal is delayed unduly, the nurse will bring pressure against the school of nursing for its inadequate preparation for the expected role.

In this model, shift differentials are shown at 25 percent for evenings and weekends and 35 percent for nights. Along with this goes a 10 percent decrease for the day shift. This assumes that volunteers are taking the unpopular work assignments and the day shift salary can be reduced because an unpopular requirement has been removed. Society is accustomed to paying higher prices for services outside the Monday to Friday daytime hours, and hospital work is no different. Shift differential might have to be increased 5 percent at a time until staffing needs are matched with volunteers. The decrease on days is less than the increase on evenings and nights because of differences in the numbers of nurses needed in the respective areas.

Longevity increases are paid as a bonus. This does not add to the base rate but rewards the permanent employee with sizable sums of money, which tend to hold workers who might otherwise quit on a whim. The use of bonuses avoids annual salary increases that are very costly and buy little for the institution. Since bonuses are a special reward for loyal employees, it is appropriate to limit these to full-time employees.

Table 5–4 Institutional Adjustments

A. Complexity (size as a proxy measure):
  − 10% 150 or fewer beds
   0% 151–400 beds
  + 10% 401 or more beds

B. Regional Labor Costs:
  + or − 0% (Department of Labor data)

C. Cost of Living Adjustments:
  30% above benchmark salary 100% CPI
  Higher salaries 67% CPI

Finally, there are institutional adjustments (Table 5–4). Size is used as a proxy measure for complexity. This is suggested to be -10 percent for hospitals of less than 150 beds, 0 percent for those between 151 and 400 beds, and + 10 percent for those 401 beds and over.

Within the salary levels derived from the education factor, there is incorporated in the benchmark position the regional labor cost differential for a particular section of the country. These regional cost differences generally do not have to be added as a specific factor but rather are already integrated in the model. It is important to recognize that such differences do exist.

A special word about cost-of-living increases. In this model, the increase is equal to the percentage increase in the CPI for those persons earning less than 30 percent above the benchmark position and 67 percent of the CPI for all others. To illustrate, if the salary for the nurse with a BSN degree working as a clinical practitioner is $30,000, the upper limit for full cost-of-living adjustments would be $39,000. Above that figure the increase would be held to 67 percent instead of 100 percent of the CPI.

Model Producing Effects
This model, with variations by thoughtful persons, would be an attempt to reduce the compression at the lower end of the salary scale, which is having a deleterious effect on recruitment into careers in nursing. It would reward loyalty but not obsolescence. It would recognize the central role of education in developing advanced professional practice, education, administration, research, and evaluation skills. It would enable nurses to invest in themselves with some potential for recovering the costs of preparation. Professional nursing salaries for those who obtain advanced preparation are going to have to be competitive with those of other professional fields.

The model is intended to be budget neutral, for the goal is to alter the distribution within nursing. When positions are properly aligned it would then be possible to adjust nursing's pay level relative to other occupations. To increase pay levels within nursing without first correcting the inequities of the present pay structure would result in greatly increased labor costs without appropriate benefits. If the pay structure is revised according to this model, institutions should expect to save money.

Possible Cost Savings

Orientation costs are paid through salary control until productive.

Elimination of across-the-board increases except for cost-of-living adjustments.

Elimination of longevity increases.

Bonus pay reflects one time payments and is not added to base pay.

Elimination of overtime pay for professional nurses.

Reduction of staff development costs by placing more responsiblity on the individual nurse.

Stops the practice of over-paying the under-prepared.

Volunteers for evening, night, and weekend work will reduce the costs associated with excessive turnover.

Reduces the cost of straight day-shift staff nurse employment.

Possible Cost Increase

Evening, night, and weekend differentials would increase.

Payment by educational level would increase some costs, but these are likely offset by those salaries that will hold steady for the under-prepared.

Bonus payments are added but are offset by eliminating annual increases.

Professional nurses would all be on salary,

Examples of The Model's Application

Some illustrations will help to clarify the use of the model. Assume a benchmark salary of $27,000 for a BSN prepared nurse, including the regional labor cost adjustment.

Head Nurse (MSN) in a 600-bed hospital:
Benchmark = \$27,000 plus MSN (20%) = \$32,400 plus
complexity (10%) =
\$35,640 plus position (25%) = \$44,550
versus
Head Nurse (AD) in a 150-bed hospital:
Benchmark = \$27,000 minus (AD)(10%) = \$24,300 minus
complexity (0%) =
\$24,300 plus position (25%) = \$30,375

V.P. of Nursing (MSN) in a 700-bed, single hospital:
Benchmark = \$27,000 plus MSN(20%) = \$32,400 plus
complexity (10%)
\$35,640 plus position (175%) = \$98,010
versus
Director of Nursing (BSN) in a 90-bed single hospital:
Benchmark = \$27,000 plus BSN(0%) = \$27,000 minus
complexity (-10%)
\$24,300 plus position (130%) = \$55,890

Clinical Nurse Specialist (MSN) in a 450-bed hospital:
Benchmark = \$27,000 plus MSN(20%) = \$32,400 plus
complexity (10%)
\$35,640 plus position (40%) = \$49,696
versus
Clinical Practitioner (AD) in the same 450-bed hospital:
Benchmark = \$27,000 plus (AD)(-20%) = \$21,600 plus
complexity (10%)
\$23,760 plus position (0%) = \$23,760 (day shift)
\$32,076 (night shift)

While no model can be adapted in its entirety to every situation, the illustrations from this model do indicate that it is possible to obtain the desired spread of salaries that provide incentive to prepare for advanced positions. The model should be tested within a nursing division to compare the total staff expenditures under varying conditions.

The health care industry needs large numbers of nurses with varying levels of competence and sophistication. The reward systems must be altered to encourage more nurses to become prepared at the baccalaureate and master's levels since these levels reflect the greatest employment need. Hospital care has become much more complex and requires years of practice and education to develop the skills of advanced practitioners. The growth in community-based home care demands nurses who can practice independently with only distant supervision. Job retention can be promoted through opportunities of greater responsibility and financial rewards for advanced levels of performance.

References

Bates, M.W. (1984). Administering salaries in an inflation-prone economy. In M.L. Rock (Ed.), *Handbook of wage and salary administration*. New York: McGraw–Hill.

Benner, P. (1984). *From novice to expert*. Menlo Park, CA: Addison Wesley.

Henderson, R.I. (1982, 1985). *Compensation management: Rewarding performance*. Reston, VA: Reston Publishing.

Nash, A.N., & Carroll, S.J. Jr., (1975). *The management of compensation*. Monterey, CA: Brooks/Cola Publishing.

Rock, M.L. (1984) *Handbook of wage and salary administration*. New York: McGraw–Hill.

Samaras, J.T., Stewart, S.H., & Gerould, M.T., et al. (1978). Wage evaluation methods. *Journal of Nursing Administration, 8*(6), 13–20.

Sibson, R.E. (1981). *Compensation*. New York: American Management Association.

Appendix A

Job Analysis Questionnaire for Health Services Employees

Purpose

This job description quesstionaire is designed to assist you in defining the various elements of your job. Such factual information as you provide concerning the duties, responsibilities, and other requirements of your job will be used in determining its relative value or ranking in comparison with the other jobs in the hospital. You are requested to complete this form because you are most familiar with the details of your work.

Completed job descriptions, based upon the information you provide, will be reviewed with a representative group of employees and all supervisors to insure that all facts that properly apply have been included.

Please be assured that it is the JOB that is analyzed and NOT YOU or your ability to complete the job description questionnaire.

Instructions

Please complete the questionnaire as carefully and thoroughly as possible. State your duties and responsibilities as you understand them rather than confer with others who perform similar work. Any questions you have should be discussed with your supervisor.

In describing the details of your job, tell what you do, starting with the tasks or functions you consider to be the most important. Make sure that the information you provide is sufficiently clear and complete to give the uninformed reader a true picture of the work you do and the skills required.

The following suggestions may be helpful in arranging and setting forth your duties in a simple and effective manner.

1. Think through what you do for a few days and make notes on a separate piece of paper. Divide your job (including special assignments and irregular duties) into separate functions, steps, or tasks. Devote a single, concise, numbered statement to each.
2. Separate the numbered statements according to their importance and frequency of performance (i.e., daily, weekly, monthly, occasionally, etc.).
3. Enter your statements under the appropriate headings on the questionnaire.
4. Emphasize the most important features of your job.

For new positions, use your best estimate when answering questions.

IF MORE SPACE IS NEEDED, USE THE REVERSE OF THE LAST SHEET PROVIDED.

I. *Identification* (Fill out only those parts that are applicable)
   A. Employee name (or name of person completing form): ____

   B. Department or unit: _____

   C. Job title:

      1. Current: _____

      2. Suggested: _____

   D. Years of experience on this job: _____

   E. Years of experience at this facility: _____

   F. Work schedule: _____

      1. Full-time or part-time ____ 3. Regular hours worked: ____

      2. Regular shift: _____ 4. Regular days off: _____

   G. This questionnaire was completed at:

      1. Location: _____

      2. Date: _____ 3. Time: _____

II. *Job Summary* Briefly describe the major purpose or primary function of the job in two or three sentences.

III. *Key Job Duties, Tasks, and Responsibilities* In the table below list the typical duties, tasks, and responsibilities of the job.

A. Number each duty, task or responsibility in order of importance to the job (with 1. being the most important).
B. Try to describe the tasks in such a way that they would be understood by someone not familiar with the job.
   1. Begin each task with an action word such as plan, interview, calculate, schedule, prepare (see Appendix C).
   2. Be sure to include any supervisory duties where applicable.
C. After you have listed all the typical duties, tasks, and responsibilities, indicate the percentage of working time or the number of hours per day or per week usually required for each. Also please include whether duties are performed daily (every day or nearly every day), periodically (weekly or monthly), or occasionally (less frequently than monthly).
D. If additional space is needed, use the comments section at the back of this questionnaire or attach additional pages. Please type or print legibly.

TASK (A)	DESCRIPTION (B)	FREQUENCY (C)

IV. *Extent of Supervision Received*
   A. Indicate the title of the immediate supervisor of *this* job: ___

   B. Circle the number of the statement below that best describes the extent of supervision *received* in doing the job.
      1. Immediate or frequent supervision.
      2. Short assignments, supervised.
      3. Follow standardized procedures with little immediate supervision in normal routine or work.
      4. Follow established procedures generally, refer only unusual cases to supervisor.

    5. Broad assignments, procedure not standardized, usually with little guidance or checking. Rarely refer to supervisor except for matters of policy.

    6. Organize own work, assign and check work, rarely refer specific problems to supervisor.

    7. Under administrative direction, set up own standards of performance, virtual self-supervision.

V. *Supervision Given*

  A. List below the titles of any jobs that this position directly supervises and the number of employees in each title. (If none, skip this section and go to Part VI)

  B. Approximately how many hours per day, or what percentage of time, is devoted to *direct* supervision? _____

  C. Circle the number(s) of the items below that apply to this supervisory job:

1. Determine job requirements.
2. Assign work.
3. Check work.
4. Recommend hire, transfer, or promote.
5. Complete performance evaluations.
6. Recommend salary increases.
7. Train employees.
8. Handle grievances.
9. Discipline employees.
10. Recommend dismissal.

VI. *Promotions*

  A. *From* what jobs are employees normally promoted to this job? _____

_____

  B. *To* what jobs are employees normally promoted from this job? _____

_____

VII. *Planning and Analysis* Does the job require any planning or analysis, such as the gathering and interpretation of data, preparation of reports, or finding solutions to special problems? If so, please give some brief examples.

VIII. *Policy and Methods.* Does the job require you to establish policies, methods, or procedures for the job, or programs connected with the job? If so, please explain and list examples.

IX. *Consequence or Errors* Please indicate the chances for and consequences of errors in this job. Who would catch the error? How soon? How much harm could be done to patients, equipment, the hospital's financial status, and so on?

X. *Confidential Data* To what extent does final responsibility rest on the incumbent of this job for the safeguarding of confidential information, money, materials, reports, and policies? Check off the appropriate column for each confidential element.

Continuous Access	Frequent Access	Occasional Access	Little or No Access	Confidential Element
_____	_____	_____	_____	Patient data
_____	_____	_____	_____	Personnel data
_____	_____	_____	_____	Money
_____	_____	_____	_____	Supplies and equipment
_____	_____	_____	_____	Documents (i.e., forms, contracts, etc., other than patient or personnel data)
_____	_____	_____	_____	Other (specify) ____
_____	_____	_____	_____	_____

XI. *Contact with Others* What kind of contact does this job require, both within and outside of this hospital? Please indicate the frequency and the purpose of contact for the items listed below, if applicable:

Persons Contacted	Purpose (e.g., exchange information, order material, provide services make or obtain commitments)	Frequency (e.g., once per day, twice per week)
Fellow department employees		
Department supervisor or manager		
Other employees		
Other supervisors or managers		
Administration		
Patients		
Visitors		
Salespeople		
Physicians		
Outside contractors		
Other (specify)		

XII. *Education Required*
    A. Formal Education
        1. Indicate below the *minimum* of formal education required to perform this work. (Note: Do not enter the present incumbent's education unless it coincides with your opinion of the minimum requirement.)

      _____ High school   _____ Business school (1–2 yrs.)

      _____ Specialized training   _____ Partial college (2 yrs.)

      _____ **Nursing school (2 yrs.)**   _____ Complete college

_____ Nursing school   _____ College, post graduate
(4 yrs.)

_____ Other technical   _____ Other education
school

(specify) _____   (specify) _____

_____   _____

2. What major course(s) of study should this training include from the sources checked above?

3. Why is the degree of education checked above required as a minimum?

4. Is there a preferred level of education for this job that is higher than the minimum required? If so, what is it, and why is it preferred?

B. Licensing and Professional Affiliations
   1. What licenses or other professional certificates are required by this job as a *minimum*?

   2. To what professional societies or organizations should the employee in this job belong? Why?

XIII. *Experience Required* If someone has the education or training that you stated in answer to the last question, how much experience on this job or a related one would it take before he or she would be able to perform this job adequately?

   A.   Type of job (title): _____

   B.   Type of industry or organization: _____

   C.   Minimum time required: _____

    D.   Why is this experience required?

    E.   Is there a perferred level of experience for this job that is higher than the minimum required? If so, what is it, and why is it preferred?

XIV. *Training Period*   If a new employee has the education and experience previously stated, indicate the *minimum* length of time required to learn this work to the level where the employee can function in a normally independent manner.

    _____ 1 to 2 weeks   _____ 3 to 6 months

    _____ 2 weeks to 1 month   _____ more than 6 months
                                            (specify)

    _____ 1 to 3 months   _____

Why is this training needed? _____

XV. *Machines, Tools, and Equipment*   What machines, tools, or equipment are used or operated on this job, and approximately how much time each day or week is spent using them?

XVI. *Physical and Mental Effort Required*   Check the appropriate frequency for each of the physical and mental demands listed below.

A. Physical Demands

Description	Frequent	Occasional	Rare	Never
1. Finger manipulations (e.g., typing)				
2. Walking				
3. Carrying				
4. Standing				
5. Climbing				

Description	Frequent	Occasional	Rare	Never
6. Reaching				
7. Crawling				
8. Stooping				
9. Kneeling				
10. Lifting light loads (less than 25 lb.)				
11. Lifting heavy loads (more than 25 lb.)				
12. Pushing light loads (less than 50 lb.)				
13. Pushing heavy loads (more than 50 lb.)				
14. Pulling light loads (less than 50 lb.)				
15. Pulling heavy loads (more than 50 lb.)				
16. Visual strain (excessive use of eyes)				
17. Auditory strain (excessive noise)				
18. Other (specify) _____				

B. Mental Demands

Description	Frequent	Occasional	Rare	Never
1. Stress due to time pressure				
2. Stress due to responsibility				
3. Stress due to emergencies				
4. Stress due to interpersonal job demands (working with others)				
5. Work requires intense concentration				

Description	Frequent	Occasional	Rare	Never
6. Work requires use of memory				
7. Work requires abstract reasoning				
8. Work requires vigilance (alert watchfulness)				
9. Work requires decision making				
10. Other (specify) _____				

XVII. *Hazardous or Unpleasant Working Conditions*
   A. Check how often an employee in this job is exposed to each of the following.

Description	Frequent	Occasional	Rare	Never
1. Weather (outdoors)				
2. Excessive heat				
3. Excessive cold				
4. Sudden temperature changes				
5. Excessive humidity				
6. Wet floors				
7. Dust or dirt				
8. Unpleasant odors				
9. Inadequate lighting				
10. Inadequate ventilation				
11. Vibration				
12. Unpleasant noise				
13. Mechanical hazards				
14. Cramped quarters				
15. High places				
16. Exposure to unpleasant sights				
17. Electrical hazards				

Description	Frequent	Occasional	Rare	Never
18. Chemicals				
19. Abrasives				
20. Radiation				
21. Communicable diseases and infections				
22. Other (specify) _____				

B. What are the unusual hours and days that the employee in this job works? (i.e., nights, weekends, holidays)

XVIII. *Comments*   Are there any important aspects concerning this job that have not been covered? Feel free to offer opinions and recommendations.

Appendix B

A Sample Job Description

Position Title

Clinical Nurse Specialist 1

General Description

Provides expertise in patient care to nursing personnel in a clinical service area. Provides direct care to patients with specialized nursing needs. Acts as a consultant, instructor, and resource person for nursing personnel in that service or upon request from personnel of other clinical services.

Principal Duties and Responsibilities

1. Assesses patient in clinical specialty, identifies needs and problems and plans nursing strategies to meet identified needs. Assists other nursing personnel in the identification of patient needs and the planning of short-term and long-term goals for patients.
2. Directs interdisciplinary planning for the provisions of patient care through consultation with nursing and medical staffs and other hospital personnel regarding the needs of patients.
3. Initiates meetings with nursing staff to assist in interpretation of medical regime, psychosocial patient needs, proper operation of equipment, and so forth.
4. Utilizes individual conferences and group rounds to assess quality of care.
5. Plans with the Head Nurse and Director of Clinical Service to resolve problems relative to quality and quantity of care and length of stay.
6. Develops and supervises nursing personnel to improve the quality of their clinical performance.

7. Identifies and assists other nursing personnel to recognize and plan for short-term and long-term needs of patients requiring long-term care.
8. Teaches patients and families in conjunction with and at the request of the primary nurse.
9. Functions as a role model for the nursing staff.

Other Activities

1. Administers IV medications and blood components as indicated.
2. Participates in developing and conducting in-service-related programs for nursing and other hospital personnel.
3. Participates in and is encouraged to initiate clinical nursing research.
4. Provides on-call coverage for weekends and evening shifts as assigned.

Skills and Abilities Required

1. Advanced clinical nursing judgment.
2. Ability to monitor and analyze medical laboratory, x-ray, and physical findings to coordinate nursing care with the medical treatment plan.
3. Interpersonal skills for eliciting medical and psychosocial history, instructing patients and families, and maintaining productive relationships with medical and nursing staff.

Job Specifications

1. Master's degree with a major in nursing.
2. License to practice as registered nurse.
3. Two years related clinical experience.

Reporting Relationships

1. Administrative—Associate Director of the Clinical Service.
2. Medical—Attending Staff Physician for assigned patients.
3. No subordinates.

The above statements are intended to describe the general nature and level of work being performed by nurses assigned this classification. They are not meant to be construed as an exhaustive list of all responsibilities and duties of personnel so assigned.

Appendix C

A Selected List of Action Verbs for Job Descriptions

act	contribute	mediate
activate	control	modify
adapt	counsel	perform
adjust	create	plan
administer	decide	predict
advise	delegate	prepare
advocate	demonstrate	prevent
affirm	design	procure
allot	determine	promote
alter	develop	purchase
amend	devise	rate
analyze	direct	recommend
answer	dispose	rectify
anticipate	endorse	prefer
appoint	engage	reject
appraise	ensure	release
approve	establish	review
arrange	evaluate	revise
ascertain	execute	select
assess	expedite	send
assign	facilitate	sign
assure	formulate	solve
attain	generate	stimulate
authorize	hire	supervise
budget	identify	synthesize
calculate		systematize
chart	implement	test
classify	inform	train
complete	initiate	utilize
compose	lead	verify
compute	institute	
conduct	interpret	
confirm	motivate	
consult	manage	

SOURCE: Henderson, R.I. (1985). *Compensation Management: Rewarding Performance,* pp. 726–741. Reston, VA: Reston Publishing.

Appendix D

A Factor Point System for Job Evaluation

SKILL

1. Education—This factor refers to formal school training or its equivalent, involving a period of organized, structured presentation of knowledge and skills.

		Points
1°	Up to and including twelve years of school. Position requires the ability to read, write, speak, and do minor mathematic calculations competently.	6
2°	Twelve to 12.5 years. Position requires a relatively brief period of special, concentrated study in order to understand and carry out special procedures and techniques.	16
3°	Twelve-and-one-half to fourteen years. Position requires a substantial study period of general information and fundamentals along with much technique and skills.	24
4°	Fourteen to sixteen years. Position requires a long period of preparation in general theory, principles, and methods as well as acquisition of a wide range of differentiated, complex, and specialized skills and techniques.	32

SOURCE: This is an edited version of the model that originally appeared in Samaras, J. T., Stewart, S. H., Gerould, M. T., et al. (1978). Wage Evaluation Methods, *Journal of Nursing Administration, 8*(6), 13–20. Used with permission.

5°   Over sixteen years. Position requires a broad   40
understanding of the theoretical framework and
methodological tools as a basis for interpreting,
assessing and developing appropriate responses
to new and changing situations and
circumstances.

2. Experience—This factor refers to the length of time required in the
working situation to develop and attain the skills and abilities needed to
perform job assignments effectively.

1°   None to six months. Position requires little or   8
no experience since necessary skills and
knowledge are readily attained.

2°   Six months to one year. Position requires   16
familiarity with many tasks and possible
deviations from them.

3°   One to three years. Position requires familiarity   24
with many tasks, their deviations, and
specialized skills and techniques.

4°   Three to six years. Position requires thorough   32
familiarity with tasks as well as competence in a
wide range of situations and circumstances.

5°   More than six years. Position requires a variety   40
of competencies in several types of job
positions and the capacity to deal effectively
with continually changing circumstances and
situations.

3. Initiative and Ingenuity—This factor refers to the ability to synthesize,
compound, transpose, and augment experiences and knowledge in order to develop different, more appropriate standards, procedures, and
methods, and to use them appropriately.

1°   Minimal. Position requires routine procedures,   13
with few details left to the individual's
judgment; instructions and supervision are
detailed.

2°   Little. Position requires only minor variations   26
from routine procedures; only some explanation
and instructions by the supervisor are required
when variations are necessary.

3°   Moderate. Position requires some use of   39
judgment but within well-defined standards and
procedures. Work may be accomplished by
several methods or techniques, and the

individual may be required to select the one
most appropriate for each situation; instructions
from the supervisor are of a general nature.

4°   Much. Position requires basic planning of   52
procedures and methods together with
consideration for related work units and
procedures; accomplishment of assignments
requires drawing upon past parallel experiences
and solutions; instructions from supervisor are
few and of a general nature since exact
procedures and methods are difficult to
prescribe. Individual must be adaptable to new
situations and circumstances, seek out possible
changes, and formulate objectives.

5°   Very much. Position requires continual   65
evaluation and reassessment of precedents,
standards, and procedures, considerable
planning and understanding of a variety of
factors, procedures, and methods together with
understanding of related work units and
procedures. Accomplishment of assignment
involves the development of new procedures,
processes, methods standards, and guidelines
and formulation of short-term and long-term
goals and objectives for the work unit; requires
a high degree of independent action and
imagination; adaptability to new situations and
circumstances.

EFFORT

4. Mental—This factor refers to the amount of thinking required to perform
   job functions. This involves the ability to make judgments based on
   observation and to decide what should be done, by whom, and when.

   1°   Very little. Job is almost totally routine and   5
   involves one's own actions only.

   2°   Thought process involves one's own job and the   10
   actions of at least two others.

   3°   Thought process requires decision making   20
   affecting intradepartmental staff,
   interdepartmental staff, patients, and families.

   4°   Job almost totally thought oriented, involves   30
   decision making, leadership, departmental
   coordination, staff development, control of
   expenditures, and so forth.

      5° Job involves long-range planning, executive   40
leadership, coordination of multiple cost
centers. Job is entirely thought oriented.

5. Physical—This factor refers to the amount of physical exertion involved in the job.

     1° Desk job. Little or no physical exertion.   5
     2° Some light lifting or carrying—involves being   10
on feet four to six hours per day.
     3° Lifting and carrying moderate loads; standing six   15
or more hours per day.
     4° Mostly moderate lifting and carrying; some   20
heavy exertion.
     5° Job is almost totally physical, with considerable   25
lifting and carrying of heavy loads.

6. Observation—This factor refers to observation of patient's vital signs, reactions, and needs, as well as observation of supplies and other operations of the institution.

     1° Some observations of simple patient reactions.   8
     2° Some observation of vital signs and patient   16
reactions.
     3° Involves observations of patient vital signs,   24
physical and interpersonal reactions, and
institutional operations.
     4° Observations of multiple patients and of all   32
institutional operations at the department level.
     5° Observations of multiple department operations   40
and effect on patient welfare.

7. Equipment—This factor refers to the individual's responsibility for, knowledge of, use of, and care of specialized equipment.

     1° Little or no special equipment used in daily   4
performance of job.
     2° Occasional need to use specialized equipment   8
in job performance.
     3° The use of specialized equipment is an integral   12
part of the job, and special training is required.
     4° The use and care of equipment takes 50 percent   16
or more of the employee's time.
     5° Entire job involves the operation of specialized   20
equipment.

8. Patient Contact—This factor measures responsibility for administration of treatment and care to patients.

1°	Rare contact with patients.	4
2°	Occasional contact with patients; little or no effect on treatment or care.	8
3°	Moderate contact with patients; some effect on treatment and care.	12
4°	Great deal of contact with patients; great effect on treatment and care.	24
5°	Limited patient contact; considerable effect on treatment and care policies.	32

9. Safety of Patients and Others—This factor measures responsibilities for the safety of patients and staff and entails such things as enforcement of rules and recognizing and dealing with hazards.

1°	No responsibility other than personal safety.	5
2°	Limited responsibility for safety of patients.	10
3°	Direct responsibility for patient and staff safety with a unit and for enforcement of rules.	15
4°	Direct responsibility for patient and staff safety in more than one unit and for enforcement of safety rules.	20
5°	Overall responsibility for patient and staff safety and for development of safety policies.	25

10. Work of Others—This factor directly measures responsibility for the work of others (i.e., supervisory role).

1°	None or occasional.	5
2°	Responsible for nonprofessional staff only (e.g., LPN).	10
3°	Responsible for professional and nonprofessional staff for eight-hour periods.	15
4°	Administratively responsible for professional or nonprofessional staff or both.	30
5°	Administratively responsible for professional staff working in multiple areas.	45

11. Liability—This factor refers to legal responsibility that may be incurred by actions of staff either directly or indirectly.

| 1° | Slight hazard might be associated with carelessness (e.g., self-inflicted injuries of a minor sort). | 6 |
| 2° | Carelessness or accident can result in patient or employee damage of an embarrassing nature (e.g., losing a patient's personal belongings, locking someone in the bathroom, etc.) | 12 |

3°   Errors in judgment or carelessness can result in
adverse publicity, moderate legal liability, or
moderate patient damage.

4°   Errors in judgment or carelessness can result in   24
adverse publicity, serious legal liability, or
serious patient damage.

5°   Errors in judgment or carelessness can result in   30
a major law suit, adverse publicity, or death or
prolonged disability of patient.

JOB CONDITIONS

12. Mental Stress—This factor refers to the psychological and emotional
burdens and demands of the position due to unpredictable, critical
situations that arise and require immediate response and decisive action
in order to lessen injury and suffering or to prevent death. Restrictions
on freedom and feelings of pressure and strain are real both on-duty and
off-duty.

1°   Very little. Position involves duties and   4
responsibilities that are predictable and
noncritical in nature.

2°   Little. Position requires meeting time schedules   8
and output quotas that are necessary for the
continuity of service operations and patient care.

3°   Moderate. Position requires giving initial care   12
with obligation for such care being relinquished
upon arrival of some other appropriate staff
person.

4°   Much. Position requires immediate accessibility   16
and responsiveness to critical situations, with
obligations for continuing concern and care
throughout periods of duty.

5°   Very much. Position requires accessibility and   20
responsiveness to critical and emergency
situations on a twenty-four-hour basis, with
obligations for continuing concern and care.

13. Physical Stress—This factor refers to the physical surroundings within
which job duties and activities are conducted. Physical stress also involves the degree of unpleasantness and disagreeableness of the work.

1°   Very little. Position involves activities in   4
comfortable surroundings.

2°   Little. Position involves activities in surroundings   8
that are occasionally unpleasant, disagreeable,
and unclean.

3°	Moderate. Position involves activities where sights and odors are often unpleasant, disagreeable, or dirty.	12
4°	Much. Position involves activities where sights, odors, and sounds are frequently very disagreeable, or the working environment is dirty.	16
5°	Very much. Position continuously involves disagreeable activities or dirty working conditions.	20

14. Hazards—This factor refers to exposures to danger of accident and ill health resulting from employee carelessness, operation of equipment, use of dangerous substances, and contact with communicable patient substances. Hazards are unavoidable risks encountered during the normal conduct of duties and activities.

1°	Minimal. Position involves practically no change of injury or ill health due to work activities.	6
2°	Little. Position involves conditions where only minor physical harm could occur in carrying out work activities.	12
3°	Moderate. Position involves chance of major injury or illness resulting from employee carelessness, equipment malfunction, dangerous substances, or exposure to patients with communicable or emotional problems.	18
4°	Much. Position involves chance of permanent, severe injury or disability resulting from employee carelessness, equipment malfunction, or exposure to dangerous substances or seriously ill patients.	24
5°	Very much. Position involves a significant chance of permanent, severe injury or disability resulting from employee carelessness, equipment malfunction, or exposure to dangerous substances or seriously ill patients.	30

16. Hours—Self-explanatory.

1°	Day shift only, Monday to Friday.	4
2°	Day shift only, some weekend and holiday work.	8
3°	Mainly evening shift.	12
4°	Mainly night shift.	20
5°	Rotating, two or three shifts.	24

Appendix E

Wage Surveys Involving Nursing Personnel

Bureau of Labor Statistics Surveys

Areas Wage Surveys—The BLS conducts 180 area wage surveys that included 30 Standard Metropolitan Statistical Areas. These surveys include a wide variety of manufacturing and non-manufacturing positions. Data are reported by mean, median, and interquartile range. These surveys are most useful to nurses because of the data on work schedules, paid holidays, vacations, health insurance, pension plans, shift differentials, sick leave policies, and so forth. Reported in *Monthly Labor Review*.

Industry Wage Surveys—These include about 70 manufacturing and non-manufacturing industries. The survey includes only the non-supervisory workers. Data from the health service industry are limited to about 20 metropolitan areas. Reported in *Monthly Labor Review*.

Business and Professional Magazines

Hospital Administration (Nurses)

Monthly Labor Review—all BLS surveys

US News and World Reports—employee benefits and management compensation

Academe—Academic salaries—published by the American Association of University Professors

American Journal of Nursing—January issue

Nursing Salary Data

Professional and Trade Associations

College and University Personnel Association
11 DuPont Circle, Suite 120
Washington, DC 20036
(administrative positions in Higher Education)

International Foundation of Employee Benefits Plans
P.O. Box 69
Brookfield, WI 53005
(employee benefits)

A. T. Kearney, Inc.
100 Wacker Drive
Chicago, IL 60466
(hospital administrators)

Educational Research Services, Inc.
1800 N. Kent St., #1020
Arlington, VA 22209
(professionals in teaching)

Hospital Compensation Services
115 Watchung Drive
Hawthorne, NJ 07506
(hospital and nursing home employees)

University of Texas
Medical Branch at Galveston
(annual national survey of
hospital and medical School Salaries)

Chapter 6

Employee Benefits

In the preceding chapter, economic aspects of direct compensation were described, that is, payment from employer to employee in exchange for labor services. Employee benefits are the non-cash portion of total compensation, commonly referred to as indirect compensation. Attention is now directed to employee benefits, considering their importance both in terms of costs to employers and as rewards to employees. Employee benefits often are valued at about one-third of wages and salaries and are an important cost of doing business for employers as well as a source of additional benefits received by employees for their labor services. Health insurance is a very important component of employee benefits.

Economic View of Employee Benefits

Before the Great Depression of the 1930s, it was rare for an employer to provide benefits to any but a few white-collar workers. In 1929, the value of such benefits represented only 3.0 percent of the value of all wages and salaries. By 1987, this had grown to 36.2 percent and for some organizations the figure exceeds 50 percent (U.S. Chamber of Commerce, 1988). These benefits can no longer be considered marginal expenses. What used to be

Table 6-1 Growth of Employee Benefits, 1929–1987

Type of payment	1929	1955	1965	1975	1987
		(Percent of wages and salaries)			
1. Legally required	0.8%	3.3%	5.3%	8.4%	11.4%
Old-Age, Survivors, Disability, and Health Insurance (FICA taxes)	0.0	1.4	2.3	4.6	5.9
Unemployment compensation	0.0	0.7	1.0	0.8	1.1
Workers' compensation	0.6	0.5	0.7	1.0	1.4
Government employees retirement	0.2	0.5	1.0	1.7	2.8
Other	0.0	0.2	0.3	0.3	0.2
2. Agreed-upon	0.4	3.6	4.6	7.4	9.9
Pensions	0.2	2.2	2.3	3.6	3.2
Insurance	0.1	1.1	2.0	3.4	5.6
Other	0.1	0.3	0.3	0.4	1.1
3. Rest Periods	1.0	3.0	3.1	3.7	2.7
4. Time not Worked	0.7	5.9	7.3	9.4	11.0
Vacations	0.3	3.0	3.8	4.8	5.7
Holidays	0.3	2.0	2.5	3.2	3.3
Sick leave	0.1	0.8	0.8	1.2	1.4
Other	0.0	0.1	0.2	0.2	0.6
5. Bonuses profit-sharing, etc.	0.1	1.2	1.2	1.1	1.1
Total benefit payments	3.0%	17.0%	21.5%	30.0%	36.2%
			(Billion dollars)		
Wages and Salaries	$50.50	$212.10	$363.70	$814.70	$2,248.30
Total benefit payments	$1.50	$36.10	$78.20	$244.40	$813.90

SOURCE: Reprinted with the permission of the Chamber of Commerce of the United States from *Employee Benefits* © 1988, p.33.

Table 6-2 Employee Benefits as Percent of Payroll, by Region and Industry Groups, 1987

Industry group	Total, all regions	Northeast	East North Central	Southeast	West
Total, all industries	39.0	36.2	44.1	39.2	37.9
Total, all manufacturing	40.3	36.9	55.6	34.1	37.2
Manufacture of:					
Food, beverage, and tobacco	33.7	33.9	40.2	34.0	32.0
Textile products and apparel	28.5	...	37.0	28.5	21.8
Pulp, paper, lumber, and furniture	33.5	31.7	32.6	25.6	40.6
Printing and publishing	33.5	35.0	33.8	28.6	36.4
Chemicals and allied products	33.7	26.7	40.9	31.3	...
Petroleum industry	38.0	...	...	34.4	38.4
Rubber, leather, and plastic products	45.0	38.9	45.6	34.0	...
Stone, clay, and glass products	33.4	34.6	...	...	41.0
Primary metal industries	54.2	57.7	...	44.5	...
Fabricated metal products (excluding machinery and transportation equipment)	42.0	38.5	46.9	36.0	36.8
Machinery (excluding electrical)	34.9	35.3	36.7	27.7	30.6
Electrical machinery, equipment, and supplies	35.2	35.7	31.4	39.7	33.9
Transportation equipment	52.3	36.3	72.5	...	39.3
Instruments and miscellaneous manufacturing					

	All companies				
industries	35.4	37.0	37.4	30.2	34.2
Total, all nonmanufacturing	38.0	34.6	35.3	39.8	38.7
Public utilities (electric, gas, water, telephone, etc.)	41.8	40.1	40.1	40.7	46.2
Department stores	31.5	. . .	31.2	. . .	. . .
Trade (wholesale and other retail)	36.6	. . .	37.8	34.1	35.8
Banks, finance companies, and trust companies	31.5	30.9	29.9	32.1	34.1
Insurance companies	34.4	34.6	34.0	35.0	36.6
Hospitals	33.9	33.4	34.2	31.9	35.8
Miscellaneous nonmanufacturing industries[a]	38.7	31.3	29.6	40.1	35.1
Number of companies	910	176	255	253	226

[a]Includes research, engineering, education, government agencies, construction, etc.

. . . Fewer than three companies reporting.

Northeast—Connecticut, Maine, Massachusetts, New Hampshire, New Jersey, New York, Pennsylvania, Rhode Island, and Vermont.

East North Central—Illinois, Indiana, Michigan, Ohio, and Wisconsin.

Southeast—Alabama, Arkansas, Delaware, District of Columbia, Florida, Georgia, Kentucky, Louisiana, Maryland, Mississippi, North Carolina, Oklahoma, South Carolina, Tennessee, Texas, Virginia, and West Virginia.

West—Alaska, Arizona, California, Colorado, Hawaii, Idaho, Iowa, Kansas, Minnesota, Missouri, Montana, Nebraska, Nevada, New Mexico, North Dakota, Oregon, South Dakota, Utah, Washington, and Wyoming.

SOURCE: Reprinted with the permission of the Chamber of Commerce of the United States from *Employee Benefits* © 1988, p.19.

referred to as fringe benefits because they were rather minor in importance are now referred to as employee benefits.

Table 6–1 breaks down the average costs of employee benefits as a percentage of wages or salaries. These data are based upon all companies, both manufacturing and non-manufacturing. The list is presented in some detail to remind the reader of the wide range of benefits involved, their magnitude in terms of the costs involved, and their growth in importance over time.

There is considerable difference in the benefits paid as percentage of wages and salaries when compared across industries. This is shown in Table 6–2. Manufacturing industries generally provide higher levels of benefits; this is almost certainly associated with a higher proportion of unionized companies in this sector of the economy. Unions have been active there for many more years than in most service industries such as health care. This higher level of benefits may also reflect a greater willingness to strike, if necessary, in those industries. Of the 20 industries listed, hospitals are tied for 13th position in terms of the value of employee benefits as a percent of payroll. This represents important gains since 1980 when hospitals ranked last—20th out of 20 industries in terms of employee benefits (U.S. Chamber of Commerce).

There have been several important economic reasons for the rapid growth in employee benefit packages. The passage of the Social Security Act of 1935 was a federal response to a need for greater security for employees. The Depression produced widespread concern for the unemployed, the disabled, and the elderly. There was acceptance of a belief that every worker was entitled to a security floor (a safety net) and that this responsibility must be shared by the worker and the employer. If this security was not provided by the private sector, the employee could become dependent upon public support.

During World War II, the federal government imposed a widely applied wage freeze as an economic control of anticipated inflation. Labor unions could not negotiate increased wages for their members and instead sought, with considerable success, increased non-cash benefits. This practice produced significant growth in hospital and medical care insurance, in particular.

Escalating federal and state income taxes have also increased the value of non-cash employee benefits. Employer monies used to purchase benefits buy more than an employee could because the purchase is made before taxes while the employee's purchase would be after taxes. There has been great growth in private pensions and tax-sheltered annuities since the early 1970s.

Closely related to the tax saving is the additional advantage that the employer can purchase the benefit at a greatly reduced group rate. For example, savings arise in part because of what economists call economies of scale. The administrative service costs of processing and maintaining a 1000-member group health insurance policy are clearly much lower than those for 1000 individual policies; an obvious example of economies of scale. Another source of savings in the purchase price is likely to be attributable to the fact that employed persons are better risks than the general population as a whole and have fewer claims for most kinds of insurance. Employers have used benefit programs to retain employees. A good employee benefit package can help prevent the loss of valuable, highly productive employees. People tend to accept employment because of the work itself, the work environment, and the salary, but they often *remain* with the organization, at least in part, due to a desirable benefit program. On the other hand, long-term employees who have vested interests in pension plans and other benefits may be difficult to separate from the organization even if they are no longer as productive because of their desire to continue with the firm due to its employee benefits.

Types of Employee Benefits: Security Benefits

Government Required

There are three benefit programs that most employers are required by federal law to make available to their employees: social security, unemployment compensation, and worker's compensation. All are administered by the Social Security Administration (Rejda, 1984). More extensive information about employee benefits can be found in books by the Employee Benefit Research Institute (1987), Henderson (1985), Wolfson and Levin (1985), and Sibson (1981).

Social Security

This legislation established the federal Old-Age, Survivors, Disability and Health Insurance System. It is important to realize that this act provides many potential benefits in addition to the well-known retirement payments. Survivors' benefits, for example, have provided important assistance to spouses and dependent children. In 1983 regulations were altered, and, today, dependents are supported until age 18 and not through college as was the earlier provision. Congress believed the social security support duplicated Department of Education programs already available to college students of low-income families.

The health insurance system provided through social security is better known as Medicare. This will be discussed in considerable detail in Chapter 8, Financing Health Care.

The pension portion of social security was designed to supplement personal savings, private pensions, and part-time employment. Through the years, Congress has expanded the benefits until today it is commonly viewed as a minimal-level retirement program. To maintain the program's solvency, Congress has also increased both the tax rate and the level of the earnings that are taxed. In 1987, the Federal Insurance Contributions Act (FICA) tax was 7.15

percent on the first $43,800 earned by the employee. The FICA tax is matched by the employer so the total in 1987 was 14.3 percent; this increases to 15.3 percent in 1990.

Presently social security's cash benefit programs account for about 4.94 percent of the Gross National Product. At no time during the 25-year forecasting period do social security cash benefit programs account for more than 6.29 percent of the GNP. This is a remarkably stable and modest share of the wealth produced by society. The baby-boom cohort moving through the program will produce only little more than 1% increase (Social Security Administation, 1985).

It is important to remember that social security benefits are tied to the productivity of the working population and not to the ratio of active workers to retired or disabled workers. Social security retirement provisions were not established as an insurance program. If all of the income collected were invested as a private insurance company plan would do, the federal government could purchase much, if not most, of the private industry in the United States. This would be intolerable in a country founded upon free market economic principles. Rather, social security is based, in effect, upon the word of the U.S. Government. The intent is to collect enough money to meet the obligations, and to this end Congress periodically adjusts the FICA tax and the system's benefits to meet this goal.

Unemployment Compensation

This program was established as a part of the Social Security Act of 1935. It is designed to provide a subsistence payment to employees who have lost their jobs. To be eligible for unemployment compensation, the employee must have worked a minimum number of weeks, be without a job without having voluntarily quit, and be willing to look for and accept a suitable position. There are minimum and maximum compensation payments established by each state. A typical computation of unemployment payment is 50 percent of base pay up to 66.7 percent of the average weekly wage for employees in that state. Benefits typically continue for up to 26 weeks or until re-employed, whichever occurs first.

Employers pay federal and state employment insurance tax under the Social Security Act requirements. Employees usually pay nothing. The federal tax is on the first $6000 of earnings at a rate of 3.4 percent, which is divided into 2.7 percent for the state and 0.7 percent for the federal government. The state pays the unemployment compensation and can borrow from the federal fund for unusually high unemployment needs. Thus, the federal tax is really an insurance program to guarantee the solvency of the state-run program.

Organizations with particularly low unemployment histories can earn full credit for the state contribution and thus pay no tax. Essentially, these organizations do not pay the unemployment compensation tax and then function as self-insured. As a result of widespread layoffs in 1984 and 1985, many health service institutions had to pay the unemployment compensation benefits themselves because most had not been paying into their respective state funds.

In the past, many hospitals have avoided unemployment compensation expenditures by encouraging nurses who were not needed to voluntarily take time off. The institution distributes the time off among several nurses, so no one is laid off and no unemployment compensation payments are required. It is also a rather common practice to ask a nurse whose performance is unsatisfactory to voluntarily resign. Again this avoids unemployment compensation payments. Traditionally, nurses have also readily accepted any available RN position, which has also reduced the need for unemployment compensation payments. A nurse employed at a management level or as an instructor does not have to accept a general staff-level position; such a nurse is entitled to unemployment compensation

Worker's Compensation

This is the disability insurance program of social security and is fully paid by the employer. It is designed to compensate the employee for work-related injuries or illness. Workers may receive benefits for permanent or temporary total disability, loss of use of a body member, survivor benefits for fatal injuries, medical and rehabilitation expenses, and disfigurement. While the program is federally required, the provisions are state controlled. Damage due to injury is paid without establishing fault, but illness is covered only if it is work related; states vary greatly in their interpretation of "work related."

Employee health services are generally designed to limit workers' compensation claims rather than to provide an exemplary health service. Employers have a right to protect their liabilities, and it is up to the employees to realize that the service may be limited to that goal.

Employer Offerings

Voluntary employee benefits are most often developed by human resource personnel, reviewed by operations managers, and finally approved by executive level administration and the organization's board. Where workers are unionized, these benefits are a negotiable item. When multiple unions are involved, the unions most often get together in advance to decide which benefit changes will have highest priority. Most organizations require that employee benefits be the same across unions and will not negotiate union-specific packages.

Nurses have received poor employee benefits for many reasons. First of all, the choices for the employing organization have been made by men with little input from women. Men have sought large amounts of life and health insurance for family protection. Nurses, who have had to work rotating shifts in high-crime areas, may have wanted free, well-lighted, patrolled parking facilities. Some nurses have wanted child care services. Most of all, women nurses have not wanted to pay for benefits already provided through their husbands' employment (Cleland, Smith, & McHugh, 1973). Where women were members of top management, and had an opportunity to participate in such decisions, they were most often single women who viewed benefits from a different perspective.

With increasing frequency, companies are developing systems of flexible benefits. The desires of workers are simply too diverse today for one benefit plan to meet the needs of all. Flexible benefit programs are often marketed as "cafeteria" plans. There is a core program of governmentally required benefits and those considered essential to the worker's basic security. Beyond the core package, the employee is permitted to select the remainder. One employee may choose dental insurance, while another selects tuition reimbursement. The option of more money in the pay check has not been available since the Internal Revenue Service ruled in 1984 that the allocation of cash would forfeit the company's tax-exempt status relative to its employee benefit program.

Some of the more common employee benefits are reviewed.

Health Insurance

This is probably the benefit most highly sought by employees and also one of the more expensive. Any of the following components might be included.

Basic medical, hospital, and surgical insurance—This is the oldest and most widespread. Originally coverage included hospitalization for 120 to 365 days (semi-private room), surgeon's fees (80 to 100 percent), and medical diagnostic and treatment services. Insurers providing service benefits pay the service institution (Blue Cross/Blue Shield) and insurance carriers providing indemnity benefits pay the care recipient who is, in turn, responsible for service payment. Indemnity policies rarely provide a sufficient benefit to pay the true cost so health service organizations generally require sizeable cash deposits in advance of service.

Major medical—This is usually superimposed upon a basic policy to take care of physician office expenses and ancillary services not associated with hospitalization but excluding routine health examination. These policies commonly have a deductible (e.g., $250) and a lifetime limit of $250,000.

HMOs and PPOs—Health maintenance organizations and preferred provider organizations are receiving considerable support from employers as a means of controlling health care costs. In general the covered services are very broad, and physician selection is made from an approved, yet extensive, panel. The medical panels and the service organizations are at risk for the hospitalization since the annual fee is capitated.

Psychotherapy—Since the early 1950s, under most major medical policies written by commercial carriers, some out-patient treatment for mental illness has been covered. Generally, there is an initial deductible sum followed by a schedule of co-payments with the insurer paying 50 to 80 percent of out-patient costs with a ceiling for the annual expense. Poor experience records have forced most insurers to limit the number of visits to about 20 per year. By 1980 it was estimated that 50 to 70 percent of the population had some coverage for out-patient mental health services (McGuire, 1981). The lack of agreement on diagnoses and effectiveness of therapy, the presence of five mental health disciplines, plus the industry's insistence on avoiding the long-term costs of psychoanalysis all have combined to make coverage difficult to include without extensive controls on utilization.

Dental—This coverage is becoming more common as families seek assistance with orthodontic services in particular.

Vision and hearing—Like dental services, these services have been much slower to develop mainly because they can be provided by non-physicians. Ophthalmologists prefer to have vision care not covered (eye surgery has always been included) because it helps their natural competitors (optometrists and opticians) more than themselves.

Post-retirement medical—There has been considerable growth in this benefit to protect retired former employees. These policies provide group-rate coverage, either at the employer's or the retiree's expense, for health coverage not provided by Medicare. These costs have been increasing rapidly as the federal government has tightened benefit provisions to control expanding expenditures of the total Medicare program. Where the benefit is provided by the employer, the Financial Accounting Standards Board believes that the future economic liability of such should be accurately portrayed in the organization's current accounting procedures and has made these recommendations. To show this liability on the organization's balance sheet would have a significant negative effect on its profit or bottom line. There has been no legislative action at this time. (Employee Benefit Research Institute, 1988).

Group Life Insurance

Term insurance is commonly available at one or two times the employee's salary. Some policies may be converted to a paid-up policy upon retirement.

Long-term Sickness and Accident–Disability Insurance

This is designed to provide income after other illness and accident benefits have been exhausted.

Private Pensions

Prior to 1974 and passage of the Employee Retirement Income Security Act (ERISA), private pensions in the United States were very unreliable. Many employees were laid off just prior to retirement in order that the company could avoid paying the pension. If a company went bankrupt, the pension would disappear with the organization. Most private pensions were not portable, and the employee had to stay with the same company or forfeit the potential pension.

ERISA does not require that an organization have a pension plan, but, if it does, certain requirements must be met. If requirements are not met, the pension is not fully qualified, and the organization cannot deduct its pension costs for tax purposes. The major provisions follow.

Eligibility

One year of service and 21 years of age have become the most common rules.

Vesting

This means that the employer's contributions can be retained in the employee's pension account upon resignation. The employer is permitted to choose one of three alternatives: (1) 100 percent vesting after 10 years, (2) 25 percent vesting at 5 years up to 100 percent vesting after 15 years, (3) 50 percent vesting when age and service equal 45 (with at least 5 years of service). Employers study carefully their employees' turnover patterns to select the vesting alternative least costly for their organization.

Portability

If vested, and if permitted by employer, the employee's pension assets upon termination of employment can be "rolled over" into an Individual Retirement Account with federal taxes deferred until funds are withdrawn during retirement years. If the employer does not permit withdrawal or rollover of funds, assets are recorded with individual's social security record but remain in the employer's fund and are paid monthly upon retirement.

Contributory or Noncontributory

Contributory plans require the employee to pay a portion (one-half or one-third are common) of the costs. Non-contributory means that the employer assumes full fiscal responsibility.

Defined Benefit or Defined Contribution

Pension plans can be created by either defining the required yearly percentage contribution or by defining the retirement benefit (usually a percentage of the average salary for the five years preceding retirement). If the contribution is defined, the benefits upon retirement will vary. If the benefit is defined, the necessary contributions to assure that benefit will vary.

Integration

Because the employer is also contributing to the employee's social security, the law permits the employer to take credit for this contribution in the pension plan. Integration of plans permit the employer to subtract one-half of the employee's social security monthly benefit from the private monthly pension. The social security payment is unaffected. Many workers do not understand this provision and are startled to find that their private pension is greatly reduced or simply disappears.

Pension Benefit Guaranty Corporation

This is a federal agency funded by employer contributions, which is designed to insure the private pension plans. This corporation was established as a part of ERISA in 1974. The 1980s have seen many corporations filing for bankruptcy under Chapter 11 of the Federal Bankruptcy Act. These corporations have been protected from creditors, allowed to drop their pension plan, to reorganize, and emerge profitable with no further obligation to the retirees. These practices have caused the Pension Benefit Guaranty Corporation in 1987 to be $4,000,000 in debt with many retirees receiving half the pension to which they were entitled originally. Congressional action can be anticipated since the United States Government does not wish to take on obligations that rightly belong to the private sector (Sinclair, 1987).

Public Pensions

Historically, public pensions developed earlier and came about to offset the lower salaries commonly paid employees in the public sector of the economy. Following the Federal Pay Comparability Act of 1970, however, there has been a practice goal in governmental units to pay wages or salaries comparable to those in the private sector. This change in the pattern of direct compensation has not been accompanied by similar changes in public sector pensions. While most governmental pensions are contributory, the benefit levels of public pensions are twice the level of private pensions (Tilove, 1976). Public plans, generally, are not integrated with social security and there are many work categories that permit early retirement with full pension rights after 20 to 30 years of service (e.g., military, police, firemen). Since about 1970, the benefits paid by many public pensions have considerably exceeded the contributions. When pension costs are not properly funded, the differences must be made up by that government's general budget. Rising pension costs are the principal reason certain cities have such serious fiscal problems. Pensions are creating a difficult problem, politically, for elected officials to resolve, but these are serious economic effects that cannot be ignored.

Tuition

Another common benefit is tuition reimbursement. Wise organizations require that tuition be for a program of study (not isolated courses) relevant to the employee's present or potential work responsibilities. To support a nurse in art school does not help the health service agency. Reimbursement should be dependent upon proof of satisfactory completion of the course rather than for proof of registration. Some union representatives believe that where tuition reimbursement is an employee benefit, employees have earned the benefit through their labor and that management has no right to say how the benefit is used. In such instances, the use of the benefit becomes a negotiable matter.

Types of Employee Benefits: Non-work Benefits

Non-work benefits reflect the value of time allowed away from work over and above those days off that are not part of the usual work period each week. Non-work benefits fall into two general classes: days not worked but paid for and days not worked but also not paid for by the employer.

Days Not Worked But Paid
Additional days off with pay have often been sought by union negotiators to gain something their members highly regard when it is impossible to get a wage increase that is equally desired. Some union leaders have admitted that their strategy was to get enough extra paid days that an eventual move to a four-day work week would not be viewed as much more costly. This movement, to add additional paid days, has been markedly slowed during the 1980s. Days not worked are paid to the employee at a daily base rate.

Holidays
There are six classic holidays that nearly every employee receives: New Year's Day, Memorial Day, July 4, Labor Day, Thanksgiving, and Christmas. To these may be added: President's Day, Columbus Day, Presidential Election Day, Veterans Day, Friday after Thanksgiving, Day before Christmas, and Day before New Year's. Employees who must work on holidays are generally given double pay or compensatory time.

Vacations
Time allotted for vacations varies greatly. Vacation time is viewed as a reward for continued service and should be based upon longevity and not upon rank in the organization. The following scale is common:

One week after 6 months of service
Two weeks after 1 to 5 years of service

<u>Three weeks after 5 to 10 years of service</u>
<u>Four weeks after 10 years of service</u>

When institutions have difficulty accommodating large numbers of vacation requests for summer months or holiday periods, cash bonuses may be offered to those selecting other periods. Some organizations refuse or limit vacation requests for certain days or base vacation request approvals on a first-come basis by seniority.

Personal Days

It has been increasingly popular in large organizations to provide 3 to 5 personal days a year. These can be used for any purpose. This avoids the necessity of providing days off for funerals, weddings, house sale closings, family illness and the like. A few organizations are experimenting with personal leave "banks," which combine sick days, personal days, and vacation days, permitting the worker to use days interchangeably and receive payment for unused days. A bank of personal days permits the employee to plan absences with management's full knowledge instead of using "sick days" inappropriately and unannounced. The plan seems to give employees maximum control over their personal time and assists management in better planning.

Jury Duty

It is a citizen's responsibility to serve jury duty when called. Most courts permit a temporary delay but not a permanent exemption. Employers commonly pay the employee regular pay while serving; many require that the court's per diem payment be signed over to the employer to be applied toward this cost.

Severance Pay

When an employee has performed satisfactorily and received commendable performance appraisals but is laid off because of a business downturn or changes in the technology of the work place, severance pay is appropriate. One week of base pay for each year of service is a common rate, but the rules vary greatly. Part-time employees, even when regularly employed, usually do not qualify for severance pay as with certain other benefits depending on the employer.

Nurse administrators are employed by the chief executive officer and can be terminated at will. This does not mean that such persons should be denied economic protection. Executive level positions should not be accepted without a contract or letter of agreement specifying that termination without cause with less than one year of notice will be paid with severance pay of six months (or one year) of salary. This is necessary since it may take 6 months to a year to locate to another comparable position.

Days Not Worked and Not Paid

The main objective is for the employee to be able to retain a position while absent for an extended time period. Organizations may promise a position without assurance that it will be the same position.

Parental Leave

This may be granted to either parent and is for the reason of child-*rearing* responsibilities. Many organizations provide 1-year leaves, without pay, upon request. The second year is much harder to obtain. Maternity leave should be limited to childbearing activity and should be covered by health insurance and sick-leave policies. There is increasing public support for passage of a federal law to assure that parental leaves, without pay, be made available to all workers upon request when there is a new birth, adoption, or divorce with child custody.

Educational Leave

For the employee who wishes to attend school on a full-time basis, employers may provide leaves if the educational program is work related and the employee's preparation is likely to be beneficial to the employer at a later date. Such a leave commits the employee to return to the organization and should not be requested unless that responsibility will be met. Occasionally a particularly valued employee will be given the opportunity to attend school on a paid leave to prepare for a specific position. Here the obligation to return to meet the employment requirement is particularly strong.

Leave of Absence

A relatively small number of organizations permit long-term employees to secure a leave of absence to pursue personal goals or complete additional education. Leaves of 60, 90, or even 180 days may be granted for hardship reasons (e.g., family crisis). Colleges and universities offer faculty members sabbatical leaves after length of service with reduced pay and up to one year in length for research, travel, and scholarly activity to enhance the quality of teaching.

Military Leave

In peacetime, most organizations will not grant military leaves of longer than 30 days. These are designed to accommodate employees serving in the military reserves. Positions are not held for those who enlist in the regular armed forces.

Costing Benefits

Both institutions and unions must be able to use one or more methods for costing benefits. The method to be selected depends, in part, upon the nature of the data needed or the purpose to be fulfilled (Rosenbloom & Hallman, 1981).

Annual Cost for All Employees

This method involves computing the total cost to the organization of each benefit. This is more easily done today with computerized payroll programs. The task becomes quite complex because benefits may vary by age of employee, by job category, by pay rate, by seniority, by experience rating, and by employee choices. The total annual cost methods is most beneficial for projecting budgetary needs.

Cost Per Employee Year

The cost per employee adds still another complexity. The annual cost of all benefits can be totaled and then divided by the number of employees. This can be misleading, however if not all employees participated or used the benefit. For example, a child care service may appear quite inexpensive if the annual cost of the service is divided by all employees; divided by the number of employees who used the service, the child care program may be found to be prohibitively expensive.

If cost-per-employee-per-year data are being communicated to employees to inform them of the value of the organization's benefits program, it is very important that costs be accurately tied to that employee. For example, a life insurance program of term insurance for a 23-year-old female staff nurse is quite different than a contract for a select group of administrative employees that provides extensive amounts of life insurance and where premiums are high enough to make the policy paid up for life upon retirement. It would be inappropriate to spread those costs across all employees.

Percentage of Payroll

This cost method requires that the organization's payroll costs first be determined. Some consider overtime pay as part of payroll, but other organizations consider overtime as a benefit. Once the terms are defined, it is simple to compute benefits as a percentage of total payroll. This figure is most often used for comparisons across institutions or across industry segments.

Cents Per Hour

Here the problem is one of agreeing on the definition of an *hour*. To some it means the number of hours that the organization operated during the past year, to others it means the productive hours of the worker (excluding non-worked hours from total paid hours), and in other organizations it may mean the hours the worker is employed (52 weeks × 40 hours = 2080 hours). Health service institutions are most likely to use the latter definition, but a union needs to make certain before presenting data at the negotiating table regarding cost of a benefit program based upon cents per hour.

Required Data for Costing Benefits

For a union or a personnel committee to properly cost a proposed benefit, it is necessary to have considerable information about members of the bargaining unit or of the department. The data must be provided upon request by a union that is the unit's legal representative. A personnel department would not release the information to an institutional committee but would probably run the analyses and share the findings upon receiving a properly authorized request. The personnel data needed would include the following:

Age	Sex
Base salary	Years of service
Step or grade level	Years in position
Marital status	Number of dependents

Proposals for changes of salaries or benefits that are not properly developed with comparative cost data can only be viewed as wish lists when shown to institutional management.

References

Cleland, V., Smith, J., & Mchugh, N. (1973). Inducements for nursing employment. *Nursing Research, 22*(5), 414–422.

Employee Benefit Research Institute. (1987). *Fundamentals of employee benefit programs* (3rd ed.). Washington, DC: Author.

Henderson, R. I. (1985). *Compensation management: Rewarding performance* (4th ed.). Reston, VA: Reston Publishing.

McGuire, T. G. (1981). *Financing psychotherapy*. Cambridge, MA: Ballinger Publishing.

Rejda, G. E. (1984). *Social insurance and economic security* (2nd ed.). Englewood Cliffs, NJ: Prentice Hall.

Rosenbloom, J. J., & Hallman, G. V. (1981). *Employee benefit planning*. Englewood Cliffs, NJ: Prentice Hall.

Sibson, R. E. (1981). *Compensation*. New York: American Management Association.

Sinclair, M. (1987). Benefits. *Washington Post National Weekly, 4*(42), 20–21.

Social Security Administration. (1985). *Social security trust fund report*. Washington, DC: Department of Health and Human Services.

Tilove, R. (1976). *Public Employees Pension Funds - Twentieth-Century Fund Report.* New York: Columbia University Press.

U.S. Chamber of Commerce. (1988). *Employee benefits*. Washington, DC: Author.

Wolfson, J., & Levin, P. J. (1985). *Managing employee health benefits*. Homewood, IL: Dow Jones-Irwin.

———— (Dec. 1988). Retiree health care: A ticking time bomb. *Healthcare Trends Report 2*(12)6·

Chapter 7

Determinants of Nurses' Salaries

There are several major goals that nursing can pursue to make the field more economically attractive to potential nurses and to those who are currently in the field. Each goal reflects a major problem area, and each has its supporters and detractors. Nationally, or within a state or institution, nursing strategies should be developed, taking into account the political milieu and the likelihood of success. What may be supported and be a successful strategy in one setting, would not work in another. The major goals to consider include:

> Employee productivity enhancement
>
> Removal of sex-based wage discrimination
>
> Improved responsiveness of salaries to market forces
>
> Persuasive collective bargaining

Each of these is reviewed to clarify nursing's options relative to the issue.

Employee Productivity

Employee productivity in nursing is a measure of the efficiency and the effectiveness with which the economic inputs of labor are converted to health care services. Economic measures of employee productivity focus upon the ratio of inputs to outputs within organizational units. Inputs and outputs are measured both in dollars and in workhours; for example, the cost and the hours of nursing care provided per patient day on a specific clinical service of a specific hospital. The cost of care is computed on the basis of the cost of the staff mix used to produce that care. Differences in case mix, physical setting, staffing mix, and support services make it difficult to compare, with any confidence, differences across institutions or even across units unless the measurement of the variables is made standard in some way. Changes in health status (outcomes) occur through the contributions of so many categories of personnel that it is common to measure outputs as patient days, hours of care, numbers of visits or procedures, and patient satisfaction levels.

Measures of productivity are increasingly used by institutional managers and by third-party payers. To merely criticize the methods or to assume that if nurses appear busy then productivity is not a valid concern is not enough. In Chapter 10, some methods of measuring the productivity of the nursing care system are reviewed.

Sibson (1976) has explored employee productivity and its relationship to employee compensation. When worker productivity improves, the gains are rightly passed on to the worker in the form of increased compensation. The gains may represent reduced inputs relative to constant outputs or constant inputs relative to increased outputs. Sibson lists four areas pertaining to the technology of work wherein employee productivity may be increased. These are:

Substitution of equipment for human effort

Improved methods of work

Removal of unproductive practices

Improved management of human resources

Substitution of Equipment for Human Effort

The first area of concern is that of using equipment (economic capital) to replace or substitute for labor. Traditionally, this has been the most consistently effective way to improve productivity. Electric beds have nearly eliminated patient requests to have the bed frame adjusted. Infusion pumps have increased the preciseness and reliability of parenteral infusion and, simultaneously, have saved nurses countless trips to the bedside to monitor fluid flow. The use of disposable equipment has eliminated the need for staff to prepare treatment kits and trays. Computers are taking over massive amounts of paperwork with unlimited potential for greater utilization. In general, equipment developed for the purpose of reducing work effort must be able to reduce relevant labor costs 20 to 25 percent per year to be justified economically; otherwise, the effect of reducing labor time probably is not worth the investment. The use of cost-effectiveness analysis, a fundamental economic tool, is very important in making such decisions.

Technology development relating to new therapies has often increased, rather than decreased, the need for nursing staff. Certainly, it is characteristic in the health field that increased use of diagnostic and treatment technology leads to increased demand for staff. Technical developments are generally not introduced for the purpose of reducing labor costs, but for the purpose of increasing quality of care. Increased technology in these cases does not lead to reduced staffing needs and, therefore, does not lead to increased compensation.

Improved Methods of Work

Examples of applying methodology to nursing include the nursing procedure book, intended to improve worker efficiency by having each nurse on the unit carry out procedures and prepare and replenish equipment and materials in the same fashion; disposable equipment, which reduced the need for repetitiveness in many nursing procedures; and time and motion studies, which could be used to design efficient work stations. If pursued too far, however, methodization techniques can have a poor influence on worker morale.

There have been other marked changes in work design in health care. Decentralization of decision making, primary nursing, the use of intensive care units, substitution of ambulatory care for hospital care—all of these are common examples of improved methods of work.

Removal of Unproductive Practices

There are three major sources of unproductive or restrictive practices in the work setting. One of these is unionization. When unions take the short-term view and protect today's jobs, there is danger of a long-term effect resulting in loss of tomorrow's jobs. It is appropriate for a union to demand protection of an employee with job seniority; it is short sighted to protect a position that may no longer be needed. Unions should not attempt, and management should avoid, specification of work methods in union contracts. Only where health or safety is involved should there be binding specifications regarding how work shall be performed or how much shall be performed.

A second source of nonproductive practices are those deriving from government regulations and requirements. In fairness, it must be acknowledged that new regulations most commonly owe their origins to efforts by individuals or enterprises to evade current regulations in order to reduce costs and increase profitability. For example, a nurse making a home visit may identify a new problem. Multiple steps of paper documentation are necessary if there is to be payment for the additional effort. The paper documentation may be more time consuming than the nursing activity, but without the documentation the government agency cannot be certain the activity was necessary.

The third source of unproductive practices are those initiated by the enterprise itself. Such changes may be initiated to appease the demands of an employee and, thus, the traditional process is permitted to be altered or modified. The practice of allowing physicians to initiate the purchase of personally preferred equipment is a classic example and has resulted in costly excess purchasing and storage requirements. Sometimes a procedural change initiated by one department has unproductive effects on another department. The lack of patient transport services by x-ray departments or specimen pick-ups by laboratories can create wasteful demands on the nurse's time. Also, nurses have been known to carry out clinical procedures in a ritualistic fashion when there is no evidence of effectiveness.

Improved Management of Human Resources

Improved management of nursing's human resources is probably the most important means of improving nurse productivity in health service institutions. Enriching the competence level of the staff mix with larger proportions of licensed professional nurses and associate nurses has been found to increase productivity (Minyard, Wall, & Turner, 1986). Raising the staff competence level can decrease the need for long orientation periods, staff education, and middle-level management—all of which are expensive services to provide. In long-term care facilities, the use of specialists in gerontology and rehabilitation can enable some patients to leave the institution; use of assisting personnel, without adequate professional direction, actually promotes patient dependency. Every setting must have on-going nursing management studies to determine the most cost-effective mix of personnel on each unit. The least costly personnel in terms of hourly rate (economic efficiency) may well be the most expensive when effectiveness is considered (technical efficiency). The absence of support personnel, however, can also waste professional time.

Methods that promote staff stability can increase productivity. It can be professionally wise and economically rewarding for nurses to change positions to seek improved employment. There is considerable job turnover in nursing, however, wherein the nurses do not better their positions but merely change environments. Job-hopping can be decreased with policies that reward experience and provide improved working conditions.

There is almost no difference in the hourly rates of regularly employed full-time and part-time staff level nursing personnel. This, most likely, has come about because of the high demand for part-time nurses to fill partial positions. That demand, in turn, derives from the wide application of variable staffing models based upon patient classification systems. The lack of higher pay rewards for full-time employees has meant nurses who carry on-going unit responsibilities in addition to clinical care are paid no more than part-time nurses who are only responsible for an assignment of patients. Each part-time position must be carefully monitored to determine that it is, in fact, cost effective. Part-time positions can serve both institutional and personal goals by enabling nurses with small children to be employed and maintain their practice competency while simultaneously allowing full-time nurses more weekends off.

In some settings, the hiring of nurses increasingly resembles the hiring of day laborers. Nursing care is not a production line process; staff productivity cannot be maintained with almost daily changes of personnel.

Ultimately, increases in productivity are a justification for increases in compensation that exceed inflation rates. Nursing management and staff, along with nurse educators and researchers, can work together to find ways to make health care more effective and the work of nurses more efficient. To obtain full staff involvement and cooperation, cost savings should be shared through an announced program of detailing both objectives and rewards.

Sex-based Wage Discrimination

Another important determinant of nurses' salaries is sex-based wage discrimination. One economic goal of nurses is that of pay equity or "equal pay for positions of comparable worth." The need for this goal is a result of the problem known as sex-based wage discrimination, the issue is "comparable worth," and the goal is "pay equity" (Mahrenholz, 1987).

The federal Equal Pay Act of 1963 was an amendment to the Fair Labor Standards Act and is administered by the Equal Employment Opportunities Commission. The law requires equal pay for equal work. Through Title VII of the 1964 Civil Rights Act, this requirement was extended to cover acts of sex discrimination. Until recently the federal courts have ruled that equal pay for *comparable* work is not a requirement of the Civil Rights Act of 1964; only equal pay for *equal* work is protected. This is a much stricter standard because equal is interpreted as essentially identical while comparable means similar in terms of difficulty, education required, responsibility, and various other factors.

Pervasiveness of Sex-based Wage Discrimination

Styles has written that,

> *The issue of comparable worth has historical, social, economic, philosophical, moral, religious, political, legal, research, professional, and even psychological aspects. We must marshall our arguments and forces along all these fronts, since—as history has taught us—a value as ingrained in our society as that of depreciation of women's work cannot easily be changed. (Styles, 1985, p. 128)*

For years it has been clearly illegal to pay male nurses more than female nurses when each occupies the same position with equal seniority (comparisons *within* a job classification). The law is less clear when the earnings of registered nurses with baccalaureate degrees are compared with the earnings of physicians' assistants and pharmacists with baccalaureate degrees (comparisons *between* two or more job classifications).

Data from the U.S. Bureau of Labor Statistics indicate that the gap between wages earned by women and by men has fluctuated over the past 30 years with no real change apparent (Table 7–1). These gender differences can be seen also when looking at occupational categories (Table 7–2).

Various theories of wage determination have been used to attempt to account for these differences. One such explanation is the "human capital" investment. Studies based upon this theory examine:

Years of work experience

Amount of vocational training

Years of education

Parents' occupations

Mental ability

Number of hours worked per week

Patterns of discontinuous service

When the effect of these variables is subtracted, the variance in pay that remains is attributed to sex-based wage discrimination.

Another theory relates to labor market characteristics. These include:

Job-required skills, level of responsibility, mental and physical effort

Job family and grade level

Wage level in competitive firms

Degree of unionization, extent of licensing and entry restrictions, level of education and skill

Labor or capital intensive, size, stability

Unemployment rate, productivity rate, inflation rate, trade and government regulations

In these studies, the most significant factor in explaining the sex differences in wages seems to be the extent to which a particular occupation is segregated by sex (Perlman, 1980).

Unfortunately nursing is a classic case of systematic discrimination against predominantly (97 percent) female occupations. Job segregation by sex exists when 70 percent or more of persons employed in a job are of the same sex (Hartman & Treiman, 1984). If the predominant group is female and compensation is low relative to other "comparable" jobs, a claim of pay inequity may

Table 7–1 Earnings of Women in Relation to Those of Men for All Full-time Wage and Salary Earners

Year	Percent	Year	Percent	Year	Percent
1955	63.9	1972	57.9	1982	61.7
1959	61.3	1973	56.6	1983	63.8
1960	60.8	1975	58.0	1984	64.0
1962	59.9	1977	58.9	1985	65.0
1965	60.0	1979	59.6	1986	65.0
1967	57.8	1980	60.2		
1970	59.4	1981	59.2		

SOURCE: U.S. Bureau of the Census, Statistical Abstract of the United States: 1988 (108th ed.) Washington, D.C., 394 (and earlier editions).

Table 7–2 Comparison of 1986 Annual Earnings of Full-time Men and Women in Various Positions or Occupations

Position	Men	Women	Ratio: Women to Men median earnings
Executive, administrative and managerial	$34,962	$21,432	.61
Professional specialty	35,143	23,076	.66
Technicians and related support	27,880	19,236	.69
Sales	26,803	12,956	.48
Administrative support including clerical	22,718	15,509	.68
Precision production, craft and repair	24,281	16,810	.69
Machine operators, assemblers and inspectors	20,551	12,324	.60
Transportation and material moving occupations	21,770	14,310	.66
Handlers, equipment cleaners, helpers and laborers	17,694	12,198	.69
Farming, forestry, fishing	10,748	8,032	.75

SOURCE: U.S. Bureau of the Census, Statistical Abstract of the United States: 1988 (108th ed) Washington, D.C. 1987, p. 395.

be made. To identify comparable jobs, job evaluation tools are used, such as those described in Chapter 5, wherein jobs are compared on the basis of knowledge, skills, responsibility, working conditions, and so forth.

Job evaluation systems can be used to identify employment discrimination or to perpetuate it depending, in large part, upon how the tools are used. Discrimination may be supported by using multiple job evaluation systems within the organization. Where nursing is in a separate system or combined with other female-dominated "health therapist" groups, discrimination is likely present. When the job evaluators are predominantly males, bias in the assignment of job evaluation points is likely to be supported because gender questions are not raised. Finally, even where the evaluation systems show comparability of jobs, the assigned wage may not be comparable.

The arguments against correction of sex-based wage discrimination generally are of two patterns, listed below with their usual counterarguments.

1. There should be no interference with the free market system of supply and demand.
   Counterargument: The market merely incorporates the patterns of discrimination. It cannot correct itself. Society, through legislation, repeatedly uses the law to correct social injustices.
2. Implementation of comparable worth concepts would increase economic cost and instability in industry.
   Counterargument: This is the same argument used against freeing the slaves. The wide range of estimates of costs indicate that the estimates were casually developed. Reliable and more specific data are needed.

The figures below would indicate that to eliminate sex-based discrimination is not as expensive as some would want the public to think (Perlman, 1982).

On a voluntary basis, the State of Minnesota legislated, in 1981, a law to achieve parity of wages in comparable state jobs over a period of 4 years with 1 percent of the state's budget allotted to this goal each year for 4 years.

The City of Colorado Springs corrected its sex-based discrimination in 1 year with a 2 percent increase in the budget.

Ohio's governor requested a 1.5 percent budget increase to correct pay inequities in state positions.

Approaches for Correction

There are numerous approaches that can be taken toward resolution of this issue. Among them are court litigation, legislation, voluntary change, negotiation or arbitration, and public opinion—all of which are discussed here.

Court Litigation

This requires a long process of building case law based upon the 1963 Equal Pay Act and Title VII of the 1964 Civil Rights Act to support the application of these laws to the issue of equal pay for comparable work. The U.S. Supreme Court in *County of Washington* [Oregon] v. *Gunther* (1981), 25 FEP Cases 1521, held that Title VII discrimination complaints are not limited to equal pay for equal work and reaffirmed that intentional sex-based wage discrimination is illegal.

The U.S. Supreme Court also let stand a favorable Appeals Court ruling in *International Union of Electrical Workers v. Westinghouse Corporation* (1980), 23 FEP Cases 588, which found Westinghouse guilty of Title VII violations throughout its sex-segregated work force. This lends support to the courts' willingness to accept discrimination claims when jobs are completely different but are comparable in value.

Federal District Court in 1983 ruled in *AFSCME* v. State of Washington* that there was "overwhelming" evidence that Washington State practices "pervasive, intentional" sex discrimination in violation of Title VII. That case was appealed to the 9th Circuit Court of Appeals, in San Francisco, which ruled in 1985 (38 FEP Cases 1353) that the State of Washington had not violated the law by paying less for jobs held primarily by women. The court said, "Economic reality is that the value of a particular job to an employer is but one factor influencing the rate of compensation for that job." After the appeals court ruling AFSCME and the state reached a settlement that ended the case. Pay raises were scheduled over a 7-year period to 35,000 employees. (Comparable worth, 1985).

In another case in the Federal District court involving Pierce County and Tacoma in the State of Washington, the 9th Circuit Court of Appeals in 1986 upheld Federal District Court's ruling that law enforcement agencies had violated Title VII by paying female "records supervisors" 27 percent less than male "records sergeants." This change in position of a federal appeals court is considered quite significant to women because the court ruled against a claim that the wages were based upon prevailing market rate.

Of special interest to nurses is the suit originally filed in 1983 by the American Nurses' Association (ANA) and Illinois Nurses' Association against the State of Illinois on behalf of individual state employee nurses. The case was dismissed in 1985 by the federal district court in Illinois as being one of "comparable worth" not sex discrimination and as such not covered under the Civil Rights Act of 1964. The ANA appealed the case to the U.S. Court of Appeals in Chicago. That court affirmed that the complaint is one of intentional sex discrimination and, in May 1987, certified the case as a class action suit. A voluntary settlement was approved by the U.S. District Court in Chicago wherein the State of Illinois recognized problems in its pay and job classifica-

---

*American Federation of State, County, and Municipal Employees.

tions for women. Special attention will be directed at increasing employment mobility for women in female-dominated jobs (*The American Nurse,* 1989).

Legislation

National

The federal pay equity bill mandates a study of federal pay and classification systems to promote pay equity within the federal civil service. This bill first passed the U.S. House in 1984. The Senate did not pass the bill but did direct the General Accounting Office to study the feasibility and scope of such a study and report its findings to the Congress. The bill has been re-introduced each term but is unlikely to pass without Administration support.

State and Local

There is some pay equity activity, legislation or executive action, on-going in 46 states. There is more political activity at these levels from unions, women's organizations, and women in government. Many public officials believe the corrections inevitably will have to be made, and to do it on a voluntary basis avoids the costs of court penalties, legal fees, and back pay awards. The State of Washington law was enacted on this basis. Comparable worth regulations have been put into effect in Minnesota, Iowa, New York, California, Florida, District of Columbia, Vermont, Maryland, Wisconsin, and Connecticut and include various groups of public employees. Many cities have passed similar laws.

Voluntary Change

Wing (1984) found pay equity has been accorded employees by only 64 of the nation's 5.1 million private employers, but increasingly personnel managers are promoting it as a good management practice and cost effective. Some companies have started to budget the change in a pro-active manner. The fear of lawsuits and penalties has minimal motivating effect in the private sector because the law is not that clear and private officials do not have to face constituents in an election process.

Negotiation or Arbitration

The efforts of labor unions such as the American Federation of State, County, and Municipal Employees have been very useful in state, city, county, and employment settings where large numbers of pay inequities exist. The traditional blue-collar unions have not been as active since in most instances females are being paid the same as males through corrections following passage of the 1963 Pay Equity Act. Several state nurses' associations are bargaining the issue of comparable worth in setting nursing salaries (Young-kin, 1985).

Public Opinion

The National Committee on Pay Equity, which represents 150 groups including the ANA, National Education Association, and National Organization for Women, has conducted repeated surveys of public opinion. This type of data is important in convincing political candidates that it is safe to support comparable pay issues. The National Committee on Pay Equity provides information to its member organizations on the support or lack of support of the issue by each candidate.

A new and unpredicted source of support for the concept of pay equity is evolving from Bureau of Labor Statistics studies of poverty in the United States. Since many women represent single parent households there may be mounting political pressure to pay women fairly and equitably. The cost to government at all levels for the support of those below the poverty line is too costly for elected officials to ignore the problem.

Responsiveness of Salaries to Market Forces

Work has both positive and negative utility for the nurse as for any other worker. To the extent that the work is interesting, personally satisfying, and financially rewarding, it has positive utility. If a position requires evening hours, is physically exhausting, creates excessive emotional strain, and pays inadequately, it has negative utility. Economic theory assumes the worker rationally balances the choices to maximize the positive and minimize the negative utilities of work.

Price and Income Interaction

One of the special problems of the nursing labor market that is not fully understood is the tension between the desire for employment and the time for family responsibilities for many married female nurses. Initially, salary earnings can have a powerful substitution effect: the working nurse with less free time may purchase more consumer goods "for the family" to substitute for time lost while at work. These items might include family vacations, second cars, or having the kitchen remodeled. The combined salaries of two earners make such purchases less burdensome on the family budget and so this ability to substitute purchases for family time may stimulate increased hours of work.

The desire to work, however, is balanced against a desire not to work or to enjoy increased leisure. At a high enough pay rate, a worker may choose to work fewer hours and to use the income from earnings during extended leisure time. At such times, the dual influences of the price effect (wage rate) and the income effect of an hour of leisure may be equal. Together they may produce a "backward bending" supply curve, unlike the supply curve of traditional labor services. In Figure 7–1, the hours of labor provided decrease at some point as the desire for more income and consumer goods pales in comparison to the worker's desire for more leisure time. This may be

Figure 7-1

Segments of staff nurse labor supply curves.

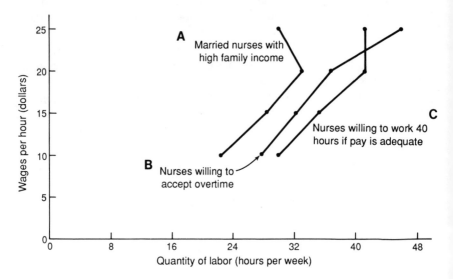

represented by wages above $20 per hour for nurses in Group A. Group B is willing to accept overtime because the pay is very attractive. Group C accepts full-time employment at $20 an hour but at lower rates only works part-time. The nature of family economics is such that, more than likely, the number of nurses in Group C is a great deal larger than Group A. Group B may "burn out" if their employment pattern continues.

Economists have believed that men are subject to a "backward bending" supply of labor curve only with very high incomes and, even then, the prevalence of a required 40-hour work week inhibits most workers' choices between work and leisure. Among men whose income level removes the need to work long hours, other drives (e.g., to control a business or make a public service contribution) may be substituted that support the continuation of employment. As male and female employment patterns, motivations, and earnings become more alike, the differences in observed work patterns should diminish as well.

Mansfield (1982) cites a study by Martin Feldstein who studied the income and leisure substitution phenomenon in physicians in 1970. Feldstein concluded that decreased productivity was due to the rising price of physicians' services and a backward bending of the supply curve for labor. With the increased supply of physicians in the 1980s, many have observed that specialist physicians in private practice have decreased their office hours and increased their fees. Physicians seem to have been able to add leisure hours by decreasing productivity, yet maintain income by increasing fees. Physicians have rather successfully avoided the most common effect of an increased labor supply, namely, decreased earnings.

Among married female nurses the income effect probably operates on total family income, not on the basis of the nurse's income alone. For the nurse, part-time employment is readily available in staff-level positions. Part-time employment may meet a social need to be outside the home and to provide some additional income. Total family income may still be high enough that full-time employment is not as attractive as the additional time with the family. Link and Settle (1981) reported evidence that the labor supply curve for some married staff nurses does bend backward with the income levels associated with more than 2 to 3 days of employment. More research is needed, but, if supported, Link and Settle's conclusion implies that such nurses have to be offered additional non-monetary rewards in order to make full-time nursing employment attractive. Employers may need to direct more attention to significant non-economic rewards while it also may be necessary to make part-time employment less desirable in order to deal with the current nursing shortage.

Employment Collusion to Control Wages

Another potential way to influence nurses' salaries is for individual nurses and state nurses' associations to watch closely for activities reflecting possible collusion by employer trade associations (hospital, home health, or nursing home agencies) designed to control wages. The economic policy of this nation is to allow salaries to move upward or downward on the basis of supply and demand. Superimposed upon this policy are certain laws requiring minimum standards to protect workers. Other control of wages is clearly illegal.

Antitrust is a particularly complex specialty within the practice of law because it is based upon four major antitrust laws, each of which is interpreted, in part, not only on the activities engaged in by organizations but also by the economic effect of those activities. The major federal laws are the Sherman Act, the Clayton Act, the Robinson–Patman Act, and the Federal Trade Commission (FTC) Act. In addition many of the states have their own antitrust laws or "little FTC" acts (Hills, 1978).

The actions of labor unions in negotiating wages for their members are exempt from the antitrust laws and for this reason labor attorneys rarely study antitrust law. Nurses' associations are most likely to employ labor attorneys who are, by nature of their preparation, poor sources of information regarding antitrust law. For this reason among others, nursing has not made appropriate use of the legal potential of antitrust.

Possible illegal practices pertaining to antitrust activity can be ascertained from the following:

Labor costs are a significant element of price of any goods or service and thus are considered part of price control activity subject to antitrust.

The nature of the health service business (for profit or not-for-profit) is not relevant.

Trade associations, learned societies, or professions can be found guilty of antitrust activity. It is not the actor but rather the activity that is the issue.

An unfair method of competition or restraint of trade that has an anti-competitive effect is illegal. Standard of proof is easier under the FTC since the goal is prevention (cease and desist orders). Conspiracy by officers of an association to violate antitrust laws is subject to criminal action with fines and jail terms for conviction.

The most likely antitrust offense relative to nursing relates to Section 5 of the FTC which states, "Unfair methods of competition in or affecting commerce and unfair or deceptive acts or practices in or affecting commerce, are hereby declared unlawful" (Gellhorn, 1981, p. 30). The FTC is given broad power to keep the free enterprise system honest.

The collection of salary data by trade associations for the purpose of controlling wages is unlawful. It is legal to collect salary information if it is collected by a disinterested third party (e.g., an accounting firm). The data cannot be made available in any form identifiable by institution. Use of codes are suspect since institutions can be identified in so many ways and codes can be shared. It is acceptable to report mean, median salaries by broad job categories over a wide geographic area (state, upper midwest region, etc.). Distribution of such data cannot be restricted to member organizations but must be made available to the general public at a reasonable charge. Three examples of hospital collusion reported in the literature are quoted below.

> To test this hypothesis of hospital collusion in the setting of nurses' wages, Donald Yett conducted a survey of the 31 largest hospital associations to determine whether or not they had wage stabilization programs. Fourteen of the 15 hospital associations that responded reported that they did have wage stabilization programs. The one hospital association that did not have one asked how it could start one. Additional evidence of the attempt by hospitals to fix nurses' wages in their area is the following statement that appeared in the Los Angeles Times: "The majority of hospitals fix wages for nurses on recommendations from the Hospital Council of Southern California. The Council's recommendations have always been accepted and are based on recommendations from the management consulting firm of Guffenhagen–Kroager Inc." (Feldstein, 1983, p. 428)

Nancy Perlman, Chairperson of the Board of Directors of the National Committee on Pay Equity, gave testimony before the U.S. House of Representatives, Subcommittee of Civil Service, on September 16, 1982. In describing the nature of biased responses to the marketplace, she reported:

Employers often respond differently to market situations depending on the sex composition of the jobs for which they are setting wages. According to market theory, when there are shortages in occupations the salaries of these occupations should rise. There is a great deal of evidence, however, to suggest that this often does not occur when the occupation is female dominated.

An example of employer collusion in wage setting was uncovered through testimony in the comparable worth case Lemons v. City of Denver *(22 FEP Cases 959). In the City of Denver, gardeners and tree trimmers were paid more than nurses although nurses were in short supply. It turned out that once a year all hospital administrators met to set the salaries of nurses in the Denver metropolitan area. The law of supply and demand was not allowed to function. (Perlman, 1982, p. 13)*

Lois Friss (1987, p. 84) has described an illegal salary survey in Los Angeles that "enabled employers to moderate competition and delay upward pay adjustments, insidiously impeding a free market for nursing services."

When potential legal action under antitrust law is being considered, it is probably best for an association to send a letter of complaint first to the state's attorney general to determine whether state laws are being violated. Action at the state level is cheaper and of greater local interest. If no action is forthcoming from that office, however, action should then be pursued at the central office of the Federal Trade Commission or the appropriate FTC regional field office.

In each instance, all that is required is a letter of complaint outlining the nature of the anticompetitive concern and the nature of the evidence. The nursing association (or a harmed individual) can be the complainant, but the cost and role of plaintiff is borne by the relevant government body.

It should be noted that collusive practices break down when the self-interest of individual institutions is no longer served by the practice. In 1988, the shortage of nurses forced many individual hospitals to award major salary increases with little regard for the practices of neighboring institutions.

Inelasticity of Nurse Supply

During the 1980s there has been increased demand for nurses in health services institutions and agencies. With the demand curve moving to the right to a new level, if the market were functioning properly, a similar movement to the right of the supply curve would be expected over time. This has not happened, however. The collusive practices of many health service councils appeared to have prevented the normal market response. The result has been minimal salary increases that produce only minimal changes in the labor supply. If all hospitals in a region increase their pay levels by a limited amount together (e.g., an agreed upon 3 percent instead of an 8 or 10 percent increase that would be justified by supply and demand), the increase does not produce the market effect that would occur if the institutions freely and independently competed for nurses by "bidding up" their wages. When the

Table 7–3 Salary Ranges of Staff Nurses in Various Cities in 1987

City	Range of start rates	Range of top rates
Boston	19,968 27,040	25,438 43,638
New York City area	24,200 28,808	26,375 32,608
Baltimore	21,362 25,397	24,357 37,107
Miami	19,032 24,122	26,270 35,984
Houston	20,987 22,796	25,084 38,438
Cleveland	22,360 26,416	26,624 39,041
Chicago	18,824 24,752	24,960 42,577
Minneapolis/St. Paul	22,920 24,190	30,659 31,387
Detroit	19,365 26,374	21,632 33,675
Denver	20,800 28,371	28,246 34,403
San Francisco	28,870 34,819	34,861 42,889

SOURCE: Salary Update (1988). *American Journal of Nursing,* 88(1) 114.

increase is planned and implementation is coordinated, the increase avoids competition among employers in the labor market.

In the short run, if pay levels are allowed to increase spontaneously, some nurses who had left the field can be expected to return to nursing employment; part-time nurses can be encouraged to increase their hours of employment. Increased wages encourage institutions to employ support personnel for nurses in order to utilize valuable services more effectively, in turn improving nurses' working conditions and further encouraging additional nurse work hours.

In the long run, increased salaries increase the attractiveness of nursing relative to other fields. Some students already in college would elect to change their majors to nursing. Many others would now initially choose nursing careers who would not have done so. Over time, the number of nurses would increase.

Another important characteristic of nurse supply is the common practice of nurses to spend their entire careers in a local employment market. Institutions believe that nurse supply is restricted geographically, and, therefore competition for nurses by raising wages only increases costs without adding to the local supply of nurses. Institutional loyalty is appropriate, but it should be earned. Examination of 1987 nursing salary data (Table 7–3) shows considerable difference in pay levels in different cities and regions. When one or two institutions do raise their pay levels, there must be a discernible response in the region for other institutions to follow that lead. Increasingly, in families where both spouses have meaningful careers, the decision to move to another city or region is made on the basis of potential effects on total family income and career satisfaction rather than a wife simply moving with her husband and then looking for employment.

In Table 7–4, average nursing salaries by region and by position are shown for 1988. Positions where career professional nurses earn more than $50,000 have grown in great number; some vice presidents of nursing in large medical centers now earn more than $100,000 annually. Where a nurse holds the title of vice president-patient care and holds responsibility for 300,000 patient days, the "midpoint" was placed at $107,300, and the range at $88,000 to $126,000 (Salary Update, 1989, p. 126).

Table 7–4 Average Nursing Salaries by Region and Position in 1988

	Director of nursing	Head nurse	Staff nurse	LPN/LVN
	Average low & high	Average low & high	Average low & high	Average low & high
National	$39,239 $56,141	$28,182 $39,189	$22,485 $31,144	$15,422 $20,828
Northeastern	$40,202 $58,103	$28,157 $38,126	$23,032 $31,313	$16,136 $21,589
Southern	$36,886 $53,833	$26,789 $38,458	$21,011 $30,252	$14,008 $19,535
North Central	$35,773 $50,351	$27,510 $37,886	$22,019 $29,275	$15,189 $20,008
Western	$45,473 $62,975	$30,770 $43,279	$24,041 $34,360	$16,430 $22,322

SOURCE: *Salary update,* (1989). *American Journal of Nursing, 89*(1), 124.

Collective Bargaining

There are national and state labor laws that provide legal means for employees to join together to bargain with employers about hours, wages, and working conditions. Collective bargaining in nursing has not been easy. In 1946, the House of Delegates of the American Nurses' Association adopted the position that state nurses' associations (SNAs) could act as bargaining agents for their member nurses to provide for their economic security.

Nurses and the NLRB

The 1946 ANA decision approving SNA collective bargaining activities probably spurred the American Hospital Association to lobby so diligently and successfully to have not-for-profit hospitals excluded from the jurisdiction of the National Labor Relations Act in the 1947 Taft–Hartley Amendments. From 1947 until 1974, collective bargaining for nurses was essentially limited to a few states with strong public sector labor laws applicable to tax-supported institutions and agencies. In addition, there were a few for-profit hospitals and nursing homes that could be unionized under promulgation of the National Labor Relations Board, but most not-for-profit institutions were exempt until passage of the Health Amendments Act in 1974 (Bryant, 1978).

Through the years there has been a lack of support for collective bargaining by many nurses who viewed the process as unprofessional (Herzog, 1976). Many have been concerned about the appropriateness of a strike in a health care setting. Congress also had this concern and, in the 1974 amendments, included the provision that a strike in a health service institution has to be preceded by 30 days notice to the Federal Mediation and Conciliation Service in order that this third party could try to mediate the differences. Even more importantly, there is a provision in the law that requires 10 days notice to the institution before a strike can be called. Since the average hospital stay is 6-7 days, ten day announcement period permits the vast majority of patients in acute care settings to be discharged before the strike begins and permits management to cease admitting new patients and to transfer to other facilities any remaining patients. Hospital administrators usually send press releases to local newspapers to exert public pressure against the strikers. In truth, a strike against a hospital is an economic issue and is little different from a strike against any other organization. Management is always fearful of losing clients, both physicians and patients.

With increasing frequency, collective bargaining has been accepted by nurses who view the technique as a legal means for enhancing the salaries of nurses and the control of nursing practice. This growing support for professional collectivism has been predicated upon the presence of (1) all-RN bargaining units organized under the SNAs and (2) broadly defined, professionally-based bargaining agenda where units have endeavored to incorporate within the contract such items as the Code for Nurses, Nursing Practice Committees, Professional Performance Committees, and Staff Development Committees (Cleland, 1975, 1978, 1982).

A continuing problem with nursing's collective bargaining programs is the unwillingness of nurses to pay the true cost of the program. Initially programs of collective bargaining were small and it was possible for an SNA to provide the service as part of the general membership programs. It has been possible to show that collective bargaining contracts have a ripple effect that influences the salaries of all nurses and, thus, justify having all members share in the costs. In states where collective bargaining is an active program and large portions of nurses are under contract, it is not possible for the cost to be covered by membership dues alone: Either there is not enough money to do collective bargaining well or other programs of the SNA suffer or both. Most SNAs have not been willing to impose the additional charge of the collective bargaining program with the result that nursing's collective bargaining programs are often weak and understaffed.

Collective Bargaining in the 1980s

There were many changes in the National Labor Relations Board during the Reagan Administration, which have affected application of the law. Rather than apply the law, many Board members have been more interested in weakening its effectiveness. There have been many challenges by hospitals of the all-RN bargaining unit. The concerted delays in rulings and avoidance of decisions relating to charges of unfair labor practices, however, have made organizing activity very difficult. In February 1984, the NLRB had a backlog of 1647 cases, the highest in its 50 year history (Bauknect, 1985).

By July 1987, however, the NLRB had become tired of deciding so many issues on a case-by-case basis. A new rule was developed that there be eight potential bargaining units within an acute care hospital. These are registered nurses, physicians, other professional employees, technical employees, skilled maintenance workers, business office clerical workers, non-professionals and guards employees (Flanagan, 1989).

Where nurses cannot have a bargaining unit composed only of nurses (i.e., school nurses, occupational health nurses, etc.), they are more likely to be represented by a general purpose union. Nurses paying dues to non-nursing unions decrease the likelihood of simultaneously paying dues to a SNA. The use of non-nursing unions representing many fields of practice decreases the likelihood that the union contract can be used as a means to further other nursing practice interests within the institution or agency. Out of necessity work conditions become more narrowly defined. Length of lunch periods may replace a concern for practice committees.

Student nurses have been used to offset the effects of striking nurses. Schools of nursing should not permit students to be used in this manner. Rather, when a strike occurs, students should be reassigned or taken temporarily out of field practice until the practice setting returns to normal conditions (National Student Nurses' Association, 1975).

Flanagan has reported (1983) that 120,000 members of state associations of the American Nurses' Association are represented in collective bargaining. Another 15,000 nurses are represented by the National Union of Hospital Care Employees (District 1199) of Retail, Wholesale, and Department Store Union, AFL–CIO; and about 12,000 by the Service Employees International Union, AFL–CIO. In addition the American Federation of Government Employees, AFL–CIO, represents about 7000; the American Federation of State, County, and Municipal Employees, AFL–CIO, about 6000; and the American Federation of Teachers, AFL–CIO, about 5000 nurses. Together, it is estimated that about 165,000 RNs are covered by union contracts.

Becker, Sloan, and Steinwald (1982) studied union activity in hospitals from 1961 to 1980 and concluded that there was a short spurt of activity after the 1974 amendments and that union victories in elections totalled less than 50 percent throughout the decade. Their data also showed that unions are more successful with public institutions and least successful with private, for-profit organizations. Relative to economic effects, Becker et al. have examined four studies of the impact of collective bargaining on hospital costs and have reported that, typically, unions have a smaller effect on wages for professional nurses and other professionals than for nonprofessional occupations. A model estimate for RNs is about 6 percent; the corresponding figure for non-professionals is about 10 percent. The effect of strikes and other work stoppages have important consequences. In hospitals with unions but no work stoppages, the growth of wages was 3.5 to 4.1 percent. In the presence of work stoppages these figures increased to 9.0 to 10.2 percent (Becker, Sloan, & Steinwald, 1982, p. 11).

Individual staff nurses rarely can negotiate their own employment terms. When there are several hundred nurses in a single job category, there is no individual negotiation. When there are only one or two institutional employers in an area, the nurse merely accepts what is offered. In the absence of a benevolent employer, collective bargaining is probably necessary.

Whether nurses should engage in collective bargaining is not an ideological issue; rather, it is a pragmatic one. How well has the process worked for nursing? How well is it likely to work in the future? Can changes be made to make it more effective? Cleland (1988) has proposed a new model for collective bargaining wherein both the SNA and a union are placed under a common holding company and with an interlocking membership. With such a model, the programs of both the SNA and the union could be more focused, more growth prone, and stronger.

The techniques and processes of productivity enhancement, removal of sex-based wage discrimination, prevention of employer collusion to control salaries, and the development of effective collective bargaining all have advantages and disadvantages relative to the improvement of nurses' salaries.

Improved compensation is necessary in order to recruit and retain the quality and quantity of nurses needed to provide nursing care—an essential human service.

Each of the techniques has one thing in common: It is only effective if nurses are willing to sacrifice some personal freedom for the greater good of the profession as a whole. Each of the processes is dependent upon group action and individual support of the group effort. It is important to make one's voice heard and one's beliefs considered within the organization. If the eventual decision is not to one's liking or it turns out to be a poor one, there will be opportunities for correction. Individual nurses must display the personal discipline expected of members of a profession. A profession can enforce its decisions only when there is sufficient maturity by the rank and file to accept the decisions made by the elected delegates and officers. Too often, individual nurses pick up their marbles and withdraw from the arena of professional play. Individuals, acting alone, are powerless.

References

Bauknect, V.L. (1985). ANA testifies on NLRB backlog. *The American Nurse, 17*(7), 3.

Becker, E.R., Sloan, F.A., & Steinwald, B. (1982). Union activity in hospitals: Past, present and future. *Health Care Financing Review, 3*(4), 1–13.

Bryant, Y. (1978). Labor relations in health care institutions: An analysis of public law 93–360. *Journal of Nursing Administration, 8*(3), 28–39.

Cleland, V. (1975). A professional model for collective bargaining. *American Journal of Nursing, 75,* 288–292.

Cleland, V. (1978). Shared governance in a professional model of collective bargaining. *Journal of Nursing Administration. 8*(5), 39–43.

Cleland, V. (1982). Nurses' economics and the control of nursing practice. In L.H. Aiken (Ed.), *Nursing in the 1980s: Crises, opportunities, challenges* (pp. 383–397). Philadelphia: J.B. Lippincott.

Cleland, V. (1988). A new model for collective bargaining. *Nursing Outlook, 36*(5) 228–230.

Comparable worth (1985). *Fair Employment Practices Manual* (421, pp. 611–620). Washington, DC: Bureau of National Affairs.

Feldstein, P.F. (1983). *Health care economics* (2nd ed.). New York: John Wiley & Sons.

Flanagan, L. (1983). *Collective bargaining and the nursing profession.* Kansas City, MO: American Nurses' Association.

Flanagan, L. (1988). NLRB approves all RN bargaining units. *The American Nurse, 21*(5)4.

Friss, L. (1987). External equity and the free market myth. *Review of Public Personnel Administration, 7*(3), 74–91.

Gellhorn, E. (1981). *Antitrust law and economics.* (2nd ed.) St. Paul, MN: West Publishing.

Hartman, H.I., & Treiman, D.J. (1984). Notes on the National Academy of Sciences study of equal pay for jobs of equal value. In M.L. Rock (Ed.), *Handbook of wage and salary administration.* New York: McGraw–Hill.

Herzog, T.P. (1976). The national labor relations act and the American Nurses' Association: A dilemma of professionalism. *Journal of Nursing Administration, 6*(10), 34–36.

Hills, C.A. (1978). *Antitrust advisor* (2nd ed.). New York: McGraw–Hill.

Link, C.R., & Settle, R.F. (1981). Wage incentives and married professional nurses: A case of back-bending supply? *Economic Inquiry, 19*(1), 144–156.

Mahrenholz, D.M. (1987). Comparable worth: Litigation and legislation. *Nursing Administration Quarterly, 12*(1), 25–31.

Mansfield, E. (1982). *Microeconomics.* New York: W.W. Norton.

Minyard, K., Wall, J., & Turner, B. (1986). RNs may cost less than you think. *Journal of Nursing Administration, 16*(5), 28–34.

National Student Nurses' Association. (1975). *Strike policy.* New York: Author.

Perlman, N. (1982). *Testimony of the National Committee on Pay Equity.* Washington, DC: Subcommittee of Civil Service, House of Representatives.

Perlman, N.D. (1980). *Preliminary memorandum on pay equity.* Washington, DC: Center for Women in Government.

Sibson, R. (1976). *Increasing employee productivity.* New York: American Management Association.

Styles, M.M. (1985). The uphill battle for comparable worth. *Nursing Outlook, 33*(3), 128–132.

Tentative settlement reached in ANA, INA pay equity suit against Illinois. (1989). *The American Nurse, 21*(4), 3.

Wing, R.E. (1984). A current business response to the equal-worth concept. In M.L. Rock (Ed.), *Handbook of wage and salary administration.* New York: McGraw Hill.

Youngkin, E.Q. (1985). Comparable worth: Alternatives to litigation and legislation. *Nursing Economics, 3*(1), 38–43.

Part IV

Financing Health Care, Provider
Payments, and Nursing Costs

Chapter 8

Financing Health Care

Nowhere is the mixed (public and private) economy that has developed in the United States more evident than in the financing of health care. For most individuals, expenses for health care can be divided into four classifications.

1. Direct out-of-pocket costs for personal care, including physician fees, drugs, vitamins, health appliances, and other items not covered by insurance.
2. Insurance premiums paid by the individual or by the individual's employer as a benefit in lieu of other compensation.
3. Local, state, and federal taxes paid by the individual that finance such public expenditures as medicare, medicaid, mental health and public health programs, grants, research, medical education, and allied health education.
4. The health component cost of every product and service, which is included in the purchase price (i.e., when one purchases a car, one part of the cost is employees' health care benefits for all the automobile manufacturers' employees and those of the suppliers and dealers).

Health care financing has evolved from philosophical beliefs about human rights entitlements, income tax codes related to employee benefits deductions, and beliefs that recipients of care won't appreciate, or use sparingly, those things for which they have not directly paid through their own labors.

From all of this has evolved complex systems of health services payment, regulations, and procedures.

The passage of Medicare and Medicaid legislation in 1965 produced significant changes in the financing of health care and greatly increased the market demand for health services. Analysts commonly use that date or the period of phasing in when making market comparisons. The passage of the Social Security Amendments of 1983, which established the Medicare prospective payment system based on diagnosis-related groups, created another such milestone, this time, a competitive market for health services that has stimulated many ongoing changes. When health care expenditures are reviewed, it is necessary to recognize these two major economic alterations.

National Health Care Expenditures

Trends and Influences

All data and exhibits in this section are taken from the annual article on National Health Expenditures developed by the Division of National Cost Estimates of the Health Care Financing Administration and published in its periodical *Health Care Financing Review* (1987).

In Figure 8–1 are pie graphs of the nation's health care dollar. First, let us examine the sources of the money used for payments in the health care system. Direct, out-of-pocket payments account for 25 percent of the monies. The party who receives the service pays the provider directly. These are the first and second parties to the transaction. This means that 75 percent of the payments come through a third party. Since third parties approve the expenditure of 75 percent of the funds, it stands to reason that they have greater influence than the people who directly pay the 25 percent.

Another way of looking at it would be to say that private sources represent 59 percent, and why shouldn't these have the most powerful influence? One reason is that the private sources are not represented by a single body. Business does speak for 31 percent and has a strong influence over the way health insurance policies are written, but the direct pay individuals quietly pay their health service bills and trust the charges to be proper.

Medicare and Medicaid payments together total 27 percent. This is not a particularly large proportion, but remember the government has the power to regulate. Therefore the government has a larger role than may be appropriate. When changes are needed, it is easier to lobby for modifications or additional regulations than to try and get the splintered influences of business and individuals to agree on a change. Government regulations then become the standard for the health industry.

The 3 percent that comes from other private sources generally represents philanthropy. It is a commonly observed fact that the presence of large sums of tax monies tends to drive private philanthropy out of that arena. Gifts are given for research and special projects but not to pay for regular services.

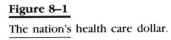

Figure 8-1

The nation's health care dollar.

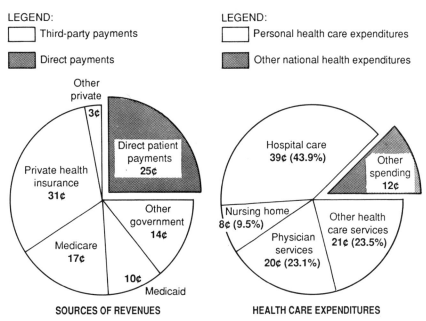

SOURCES OF REVENUES   HEALTH CARE EXPENDITURES

SOURCE: Division of National Cost Estimates. (1987). National health expenditures, 1986-2000. *Health Care Financing Review* 8(4) 3, with permission.

Comparisons with 1974 data (not shown) reveal that all private sources at that time provided 59.5 percent of the monies (now 59 percent); federal government paid 26.2 percent (now 27 percent); state and local governments paid 14.3 percent (now 14 percent). It is interesting to observe that the proportionate shares from private and government sources have changed little since 1974 and are not predicted to change anytime in the near future.

Now let us examine where the money went. The major division shown in Figure 8-1 is between personal health care expenditures and other spending. The latter is money spent on research, construction, administration, and government public policy activity. If we use personal health expenditures as the base (see Table 8-1), which is what is usually used rather than total expenditures, it shows that in 1986 hospitals accounted for 43.9 percent, physician services for 23.1 percent, nursing homes for 9.5 percent, and other personal health care for 23.5 percent.

Now compare these with the 1970 data in Table 8-1. In 1970 hospitals accounted for 42.8 percent, physician services 21.9 percent, nursing homes 7.2 percent, and other personal health care 28.0 percent of total personal

Table 8–1 National Health Expenditures by Type of Expenditure, 1965–2000

Type of expenditure	2000	1995	1990	1987	1986	1985	1984	1980	1970	1965
					Amount in billions					
National health expenditures	$1,529.3	$999.1	$647.3	$496.6	$458.2	$422.6	$391.1	$248.1	$75.0	$41.9
Health services and supplies	1,493.8	972.1	626.5	479.3	442.0	407.2	375.4	236.2	69.6	38.4
Personal health care	1,398.1	900.5	573.5	438.9	404.0	371.3	341.9	219.7	65.4	35.9
Hospital care	621.0	393.6	250.4	192.6	179.6	167.2	156.3	101.6	28.0	14.0
Physician services	319.6	209.0	132.6	101.4	92.0	82.8	75.4	46.8	14.3	8.5
Dentist services	89.6	62.2	41.8	32.4	29.6	27.1	24.6	15.4	4.7	2.8
Other professional services	60.4	38.1	22.9	16.2	14.1	12.4	10.9	5.7	1.6	1.0
Drugs and medical sundries	102.6	65.4	42.1	32.8	30.6	28.7	26.5	18.8	8.0	5.2
Eyeglasses and appliances	24.7	16.7	11.2	8.8	8.2	7.5	7.0	5.1	1.9	1.2
Nursing home care	129.0	84.7	54.5	41.6	38.1	35.0	31.7	20.4	4.7	2.1
Other personal health care	51.2	30.8	18.0	13.1	11.9	10.8	9.4	5.9	2.1	1.1
Program administration and net cost of private health insurance	57.7	44.4	34.6	25.9	24.5	23.6	22.6	9.2	2.8	1.7
Government public health activities	38.0	27.2	18.5	14.4	13.4	12.3	11.0	7.3	1.4	0.8
Research and construction of medical facilities	35.5	26.9	20.7	17.3	16.3	15.4	15.6	11.9	5.4	3.5
Noncommercial research[a]	20.2	15.3	11.5	9.0	8.2	7.4	6.8	5.4	2.0	1.5
Construction	15.3	11.6	9.3	8.3	8.0	8.1	8.9	6.5	3.4	2.0

	|	|	|	|	|	|	|	|	|
	|	|	|	|	|	|	|	|	|

Average annual percent change from previous year shown

National health expenditures	8.9	9.1	9.2	8.4	8.4	8.1	12.0	12.7	12.3
Health services and supplies	9.0	9.2	9.3	8.4	8.5	8.4	12.3	13.0	12.6
Personal health care	9.2	9.4	9.3	8.6	8.8	8.6	11.7	12.9	12.8
Hospital care	9.5	9.5	9.1	7.3	7.4	7.0	11.4	13.8	14.9
Physician services	8.9	9.5	9.3	10.3	11.1	9.8	12.6	12.6	11.1
Dentist services	7.6	8.3	8.9	9.2	9.5	9.9	12.4	12.5	11.1
Other professional services	9.6	10.7	12.4	14.7	13.8	13.5	17.7	13.6	9.1
Drugs and medical sundries	9.4	9.2	8.7	7.4	6.5	8.1	9.1	8.9	9.1
Eyeglasses and appliances	8.2	8.4	8.1	8.1	9.8	7.0	8.3	10.0	10.7
Nursing home care	8.8	9.2	9.4	9.1	9.1	10.1	11.7	15.8	17.8
Other personal health care	10.7	11.4	11.1	9.9	10.2	14.2	12.4	11.1	12.5
Program administration and net cost of private health insurance	5.4	5.2	15.5	2.8	3.8	4.7	25.2	12.5	10.1
Government public health activities	6.9	8.0	13.2	3.8	9.2	11.4	10.8	17.7	11.9
Research and construction of medical facilities	5.7	5.4	9.6	3.1	5.3	-1.2	7.0	8.3	9.0
Noncommercial research[a]	5.7	5.9	12.8	4.8	11.4	8.9	5.6	10.7	5.4
Construction	5.6	4.7	5.9	1.4	-0.2	-9.0	8.0	6.6	11.4

[a] Division of National Cost Estimate. (1987). National health expenditures, 1986–2000. *Health Care Financing Review*, 8(4) 25.

SOURCE: Division of National Cost Estimate. (1987). National health expenditures, 1986–2000. *Health Care Financing Review*, 8(4) 25.

health expenditures in that year. Hospitals, between 1970 and 1987, gained 1.1 percent, which is not surprising given great increases in medical technology and in the intensity of care. Nursing homes' share increased 2.3 percent, which can be explained on the basis of population growth among the elderly and associated larger volume of services to more nursing home residents. The total cost of physician services increased 1.2 percent. Other personal health care obviously lost ground (4.5 percent) at the expense of the other three categories.

In Table 8–1 one of the fastest growing categories is other professional services. A major component of the category is home health care, which is expected to continue showing high growth for the remainder of this century. Physician services also show rapid growth for what is not a new service. "The 1986 expenditures for physician services accounted for 2.2 % of the nation's Gross National Product and was nearly three-fourths the size of the $125.7 billion expenditures for all community hospital inpatient services" (Division of National Cost Estimates, 1987, p. 21). It is this rapid growth of expenditures for physician services that is creating congressional interest in a revised physician fee schedule or some type of prospective payment system for these services.

Table 8–2 exhibits data highlighting the nation's total health care expenditures as a portion of the GNP. At the beginning of the Medicare-Medicaid era the nation was spending 5.9 percent for health services. In 1987 this had grown to 11.2 percent and is projected to reach 15 percent by the year 2000. While the proportion of the total is projected to double between 1965 and 1990, the population will have increased only 26 percent.

There have been sophisticated studies trying to explain the influences of various factors on the growth of health care expenditures. The 1986 data indicate that 11 percent of the increase was due to population growth, 35 percent was due to aging of the population and growth in the intensity of care, and about 32 percent was due to economy-wide inflation affecting all markets. In addition to these factors, 22 percent of the increase was due to medical care price inflation in excess of the general rate of inflation. It is this 22 percent that is most troublesome. It reflects a willingness to pay more than one should pay because the true value of health services is uncertain, because of a high social priority on health care services, because a myriad of services may follow one initial decision to seek assistance, and because of all the other reasons why the health care system does not operate as in the economists' description of an ideal market system.

How Much Should Be Spent?

No one has said, or claims to know, how much *should* be spent for health care. Is 7 percent of the GNP the correct amount? Is 12 percent more appropriate? There is no question but that the American people value health care for themselves. The issue is how much health care are they willing to pay

Table 8–2 Actual and Projected U.S. Population and Health Expenditures as a Percentage of the Gross National Product

Item	2000	1995	1990	1987	1986	1985	1984	1980	1970	1965
					Number in millions					
U.S. population[a]	275.5	267.2	257.8	251.6	249.5	247.2	244.9	235.3	214.9	204.1
					Amount in billions					
Gross national product	$10,164	$7,467	$5,414	$4,433	$4,206	$3,998	$3,765	$2,732	$1,015	$705
				Percent of gross national product						
National health expenditures	15.0	13.4	12.0	11.2	10.9	10.6	10.4	9.1	7.4	5.9

[a]Division of National Cost Estimates. (1987). National health expenditures, 1986–2000. *Health Care Financing Review*, 8(4) 24.

SOURCE: Division of National Cost Estimates. (1987). National health expenditures, 1986–2000. *Health Care Financing Review*, 8(4) 24.

for those who otherwise would not get care. Is health care, like a high school education, a basic social good that all are entitled to have as a public right? Or is the right to health service, like a college education, privately earned? No economist has said that health care services are beyond the capacity of the American economy. Some believe that high employee health care costs, however, are a contributing factor in making it difficult for American businesses to compete in world markets.

In the 1980s, the United States moved away from the concept of health care as an entitlement (Goldsmith, 1984; Murphy, 1986; Quinn, 1984; Reinhardt, 1986). Instead the nation is testing a competitive market-driven model sometimes called a "prudent purchaser" system wherein prices of components of care are negotiated in advance between third party payers and service organization administrators. In addition, there is a tax-based system for selected segments of the population economically unable to purchase insurance. Service contracts are being let to those who will provide the service in the least expensive manner with minimal supervision of quality of care rendered and of actual access to that care (Mundinger, 1985). There are populations currently uncovered by insurance and for whom there is no provision of care. The uninsured would include those temporarily unemployed, or those whose employment provides no health insurance benefit, and the medically uninsurable.

The United States is the only industrially developed nation in the world that does not have a national health insurance system wherein all are insured for some standard level of service. Many believe there is a considerable difference between seeking a cost-effective health care system and controlling expenditures by leaving large groups of people with no health services (Relman & Reinhardt, 1986).

Insurance Terminology

Before reviewing some of the health insurance mechanisms as sources of monies for service payments, it is necessary to review briefly some terms used in the insurance industry (Feldstein, 1983).

Deductibles
A deductible is the sum of money that must be paid by the insured individual for a covered expense before the insurance company starts paying a benefit. Deductibles are intended as a deterrent to the consumer filing a claim. In the health insurance field deductibles are of two types. First is the annual deductible. Each year the consumer may have to pay the first $100 or more per covered member before the insurance company begins payments. Designed to deter usage and hold down annual costs, deductibles are supposedly low enough that the consumer would not hesitate to obtain service if and when it

is really needed. There is concern that Medicare deductibles are a serious tax and significant deterrent to needed care for low-income retirees. In 1989, for example, the first day of hospitalization had a $560 initial deductible fee for Medicare patients. The second type of deductible applies to an individual service such as prescriptions. These are generally created to deter filing of small claims, which cost more to process than the recipient receives. Sometimes, too, these deductibles are used to remind the consumer that the service does, indeed, have a cost and that nothing is free.

Coinsurance

Coinsurance refers to a percentage of all covered costs paid by the consumer, commonly, 10 or 20 percent. This acts as a deterrent to every health service decision. It serves two general purposes: (1) making the consumer a more prudent purchaser, provided the consumer has access to service cost information *before* the service is rendered, and (2) reducing insurance costs to whomever is paying for the insurance. Opponents argue that it deters the poor from obtaining needed services. Insurance policies may require deductibles or coinsurance or both.

Limits or Caps

These are used by insurers to protect against large liabilities. Limits are usually defined by days of service or number of visits covered. These limits have been successful in encouraging service organizations to redefine some types of services. Hospice programs for the terminally ill and 28-day treatment programs for the chemically dependent are examples. The writing of catastrophic or major medical insurance as a separate policy leaves many families unprotected or with astronomical bills. In the latter case, the service organization may be left with an overdue and uncollectible account.

Indemnity or Service Benefits

Indemnity insurance pays the purchaser a cash amount for each day in the hospital or for whatever is covered. The risk to the insurer is well-defined because the rate for the service is specified in advance although the quantity of service is unknown. Service organizations often require a cash down payment when the consumer possesses only an indemnity policy because the policy rarely provides adequate coverage, and payment is sent to the policyholder rather than to the service organization.

A policy that provides a service benefit pays the service institution for a covered service, and the consumer is responsible for any amount charged above that ceiling. A service benefit policy never provides cash payments to the service recipients.

Fee-for-service

Fee-for-service charges and payments based on them have been the traditional, predominant method of payment for health services. Benefits are paid according to the reasonable charges (going rates within an area) of the physician or the institution. It is the provider who professionally determines what services are needed. This method is being used less frequently now because fee-for-service can provide an incentive to supply high volumes of services, adding to health expenditures.

Capitation

The provider receives an annual sum of money per covered individual for which a year of ambulatory and hospital care services for that individual must be provided without additional charges. Under a capitation system, the provider is at financial risk if excessive services are consumed. Therefore, while a capitation system promotes reduced utilization and elimination of unneeded care, there is the potential danger that necessary services may be restricted in order to retain more money (Berenson, 1986). Providers are at risk unless there are large numbers of patients to make the law of averages operative. Providers also must be concerned that patients with high service needs will seek out a capitated health service.

Community-based Rates

These insurance rates are arrived at by taking all of the people in a geographic area as an aggregate and then determining the premium on an actuarial basis, generally by age, sex, and race. A community-based rate may be more or less costly than rates for selected segments of the population as the healthy provide a direct subsidy to the less healthy. Some believe this is quite proper, but business organizations have wanted nothing to do with community-based rates.

Experience-based Rates

The claim experience of the group insured is the basis for the insurance rate. Since the group consists of only employed individuals and their families, it is possible to eliminate much of the utilization experience of the retired, the unemployed, and the physically and mentally unemployable to arrive at a reduced rate more easily marketed to a selected employer.

Administrative Services Only

It has become increasingly popular for large organizations to self-insure for major health costs. These companies set aside a pool of money with which to pay benefit claims. They commonly contract with an insurance company to handle the program and, thus, are called "administrative services only" programs. Such programs cannot be identified by the employee's insurance card. Companies who self-insure generally carry a group insurance policy with a $10,000 to $15,000 deductible to protect the company against catastrophic claims. An advantage to employers is that these plans are not regulated by state insurance departments. This enables them to avoid state taxes on insurance premiums, laws requiring specific services or coverages, and financial reserve requirements of other insurers. In 1987, a survey reported 52 percent of all employers were self-insured for their health benefit programs, and it is estimated that this includes 117 million Americans (Gabel et al., 1988).

Additional advantages to self-insuring companies include retention of interest on insurance reserves and development of aggressive utilization review programs. These latter often lead to in-house prevention programs for employees. Efforts to control smoking in the workplace have expanded as employers become aware of the long-term financial costs of employee smoking.

Private Sector Monies

Self-pay

Self-pay charges are generally of two types. The first covers all health care costs incurred by an individual who has no insurance and, therefore, must assume liability. The second is all health care costs not paid for under insurance, which include deductibles, coinsurance, and noncovered services (e.g., eye glasses, hearing aids, cosmetic surgery, etc.).

Health care services are so unpredictable and so potentially expensive that rarely would even wealthy persons voluntarily leave themselves uninsured, yet by far the largest proportion of self-pay charges fall to those who have no insurance but are legally responsible for their own bills. These are people for whom insurance premiums represent a financial burden, such as the unemployed, the underemployed, and the part-time employed, but whose total resources (not necessarily income) exceed their state's defined poverty lvels and so disqualify them for Medicaid. There are also the medically uninsurable.

The numbers of uninsured has increased significantly since the late 1970s. There were about 26 million uninsured in 1977, which increased to 34 million by 1983 as a result of recession. By 1986 this had risen to 35 to 37 million, depending upon the population base used for estimates (Wilensky, 1988). Since unemployment peaked in 1982, growth in the total uninsured is more closely related to growth in the numbers of American poor and decreased employment insurance coverage of low-income workers and their dependents.

A simple solution is not likely because the uninsured reflect different societal problems. Wilensky has suggested further exploration of some potential policy changes such as (1) national guidelines for Medicaid eligibility so that a state cannot shirk its responsibilities, (2) the use of subsidized insurance pools to share the risk for the medically uninsurable to be covered without any single company alone having to take on that risk, and (3) a mandatory basic health insurance requirement imposed upon employers for all employees on their payroll.

Himmelstein and Woolhandler (1989) have proposed that it is time for the nation to consider a national health insurance program. They assert that too much money is wasted with the multitude of private insurers, with multiple policies, for multiple clusters of employees or other groups. They believe that the money saved on a national health insurance program could provide coverage for today's uninsured.

In the same issue of *The New England Journal of Medicine,* Enthoven and Kronick (1989) propose a universal health insurance program which is incremental in its changes of the existing mosaic of private insurers. Essentially Enthoven has proposed an 8% payroll tax on the first $22,500 of wages paid to non-insured employees including seasonal and temporary workers. Self-employed, early retirees, and others without health insurance would be taxed 8% on their adjusted gross income up to a family income ceiling. These monies would be combined to form a state pool and the state would become the "public sponsor" of group health insurance at a contracted price. There is general consensus developing that the uninsured or inadequately insured have become such a grave problem for the individuals involved, the local and state governments, and the health service providers that significant changes are likely to be made within the next few years.

Employment Related

Blue Cross

The first Blue Cross policy was written in 1929 in Dallas, Texas between Baylor University Hospital and the Houston public school teachers (Clement, 1984). This first policy provided 21 days of hospitalization with a premium of $.50 per month and was developed by the hospital to protect itself against uncollectible accounts. Today, characteristics of Blue Cross organizations include:

1. Plans do not compete with one another.
2. Organizations are nonprofit and nontaxed.
3. Boards of directors must represent doctors, hospitals, and consumers.
4. Plans are supervised by state insurance departments.
5. Blue Cross organizations hold low cash reserves.
6. Plans pay service rather than cash indemnities.
7. Employees are salaried.
8. Sales representatives are not paid on commission.
9. States often require the Blues to offer community-based policies to individuals. (Clement, 1984, p. 478)

Depending, in part, upon the political climate of the state, Blue Cross has moved to a more independent position and no longer exclusively serves the hospital's interests. Blue Cross plans commonly pay the hospital the "lower of costs or charges" in the same manner as the federal government. Blues, because of their nontaxed status, are commonly required to make available community-rated policies for independent subscribers not belonging to an insured group.

Blue Shield

The first Blue Shield plan was developed in 1939 by the California Medical Society. Blue Shield generally covers physicians' fees associated with hospitalization. Since 1978, Blue Cross and Blue Shield have merged nationally for certain advertising, legal, and political activities. At a state level they are often merged for marketing of plans; however, the insurance resources of the plans are kept independent. Depending upon the nature of the service, the physician is paid:

1. The usual and customary fee in the locality in which the physician practices.
2. The indemnity method whereby fixed dollar amounts are paid for care. (Clement, 1984, p. 480)

Commercial Insurance

Plans operated by commercial carriers, providing either benefit or indemnity insurance for hospital and physician care, became a significant factor during World War II when wage freezes forced unions to seek other than cash increases for their employees. Commercial carriers have generally provided coverage less broad than the Blues but at a lower, experience-rated price that is attractive to the employer. They also have become increasingly competitive by being able to market a complete insurance package to the employer, including life, disability, and pension policies.

Managed Health Care

Managed health care encompasses Health Maintenance Organizations, Preferred Provider Organizations, Independent Practice Associations and, most recently, Alternative Delivery Systems. Physician providers along with hospitals and the insurance rating and marketing mechanism—when tied together financially make up a managed health system. In 1987, managed care systems had enrolled over 60 percent of Americans in group insurance plans (Gabel et al., 1988). Each form is described briefly below.

Health Maintenance Organizations

This movement has many historical roots. The United Mine Workers organized an early form in the coal mining regions of Kentucky and West Virginia because the union was dissatisfied with the quality of medical care available to its workers. The United Automobile Workers formed such an organization in Detroit because they were dissatisfied with the cost of health care under fee-for-service mechanisms. The Kaiser–Permanente Organization began because of the absence of health facilities at remote dam building sites.

Health Maintenance Organizations (HMOs) are usually composed of interdependent organizations of which Kaiser–Permanente Medical Care Program is typical. The Kaiser Foundation Health Plan is the insurance marketing organization; the Kaiser Foundation Hospitals and the Permanente Medical Groups provide the services. HMOs have closed panels of physicians but offer considerable freedom of choice to the client within these panels.

HMO development was slow until 1970 because of the lack of support for such organizations by the medical societies who strongly supported fee-for-service payment. The name was assigned during the Nixon Administration in an HMO Act to foster capitation funding as a cost containment strategy. An important provision of this act was the requirement that employers had to offer an HMO alternative to their employees. The initial federal legislation made capital start-up monies available but also required an HMO to offer a comprehensive benefit package in order to be qualified. Mandatory community-rated annual fees, along with open enrollment periods, made developers uneasy about the potential of enrolling large numbers of persons rejected by other carriers because of high service requirements. Such adversely selected enrollees could create high insurer risk. Later amendments have alleviated some of these problems (Wilensky & Rossiter, 1986). In 1981 the federal government ceased investing in HMO development (Moran & Savela, 1986). Davis (1986) reported that at that time about 65 new HMOs were seeking federal approval for payment for Medicare beneficiaries each month. Open competition is the driving force today rather than start-up monies.

Preferred Provider Arrangements

Preferred Provider Organizations (PPO) are a rapidly growing mechanism for providing health services (Gabel & Ermann, 1986). The fee-for-service payment system is left intact with the addition of discounted service charges to the insurer of the PPO. What makes the PPO different than Blue Cross–Blue Shield discounts, which have been commonplace, is the presence of a contractual agreement with cost-effective providers. Contracts are written with hospitals and physicians who, if they do not remain cost effective, are withdrawn from the PPO list. The consumer (employee) receives a lower payroll deduction if health benefits are chosen from the PPO versus a full-charge provider. The PPO may have the consumer advantage of no coinsurance although there may be a small charge for some services. The provider is willing to accept the discounted client of the PPO in exchange for added volume of patients and the promise of faster payments than offered by traditional Medicare and commercial carriers.

The PPOs have advantages because of their flexibility and low start-up costs compared with HMOs, which must finance and develop hospitals and practice settings. If the PPO is organized by physicians and hospitals contracting directly with a business organization, however, there is less economic incentive to control the use of excessive quantities of services. It is common for a community hospital and its physician staff to organize a PPO, selling services to local businesses. In such instances, the goal is marketing, and there is unlikely to be serious control of quality or of service utilization.

Where the PPO is owned by a large insurer and operates in several geographic areas, it maintains a thorough utilization review mechanism (often operated by an independent organization) that enables it to evaluate which providers are, indeed, controlling utilization while at the same time protecting themselves against charges that services are being curtailed inappropriately. Politically, it is very difficult to provide such management reviews within a local setting.

Independent Practice Associations

Most often, but not always, Independent Practice Associations (IPAs) have been organized by Blue Cross–Blue Shield to compete with HMOs. The IPA physician receives a capitated payment and agrees to provide a range of HMO-like services to that client or family. The payment includes risk for hospitalization, and there are shared savings by physician and insurer for reduced hospitalization. There is no third party review of utilization. A physician can simultaneously be a member of a PPO for some clients and a member of an IPA for other clients.

Alternative Delivery Systems

These are so new that most health care providers don't recognize what may become a generic name for the very large, managed health care systems. Patricelli (1986) has outlined what the alternative health system needs to provide to be successful:

1. It must have the resources to be able to market to small and large businesses in a broad geographic area an employee benefit package called the triple option, namely, (1) an HMO (capitation), (2) a PPO (service benefit), and (3) an indemnity option. These options are experience rated and are bundled together for a single program administration that allows the employee maximum choice in physician selection, trade-off between the potential cost of deductibles and benefit payment security, and the relative costs of payroll deduction. Only the large insurance companies have the marketing networks and the ability to produce such insurance packages and, if desired, can sell the package to the business as an administrative services only contract.
2. There must be a hospital chain capable of providing vertically integrated services. This chain can be proprietary or not-for-profit and hospitals may

maintain their individual ownership (e.g., Voluntary Hospitals of America) while agreeing to join together in a joint venture for marketing purposes.
3. It must have contracts with PPOs and HMOs. Physicians also can have choices and can be involved with an alternative delivery system through either a fee-for-service or salaried arrangement.
4. There must be an independent utilization review organization. This is becoming recognized as essential to provide experience data for both the business entity purchasing the insurance and the insurer monitoring its providers. Utilization rates tell the insurer whether the provider is to remain on the preferred list. It is also a requisite quality control device useful in legal disputes. Without independent review, a managed care system has the potential for quality weakness and actuarial risk.

Public Sector Monies

Medicare

Medicare became law in 1965 as Title XVIII of the Social Security Act. Since most employer-provided health insurance was discontinued upon retirement, Medicare was designed to protect the elderly. It is divided into two parts, A and B. Part A pays for hospital care, extended care, and home health care services and is supported by a tax on employment, included in the employee's social security payroll deduction. Social security taxes are regressive in nature; persons with lower income make proportionately higher contributions. This is changing as Federal Insurance Contributions Act (FICA) tax is being assessed on larger portions of workers' earned income each year.

Part B of Medicare pays for physician services inside or outside the hospital and outside medical ancillary services. This is financed as an insurance policy. Senior citizens have the option of purchasing Part B insurance when Part A commences, and the premium is deducted from the recipient's monthly social security payment. In 1988 Part B premiums were increased 38 percent, the major cause being a 22 percent increase in expenditures for physicians' services due to increases in quantity and intensity of services. This was the result of growth in ambulatory services while restraining in-patient care (Gabel et al., 1988).

Through the years, the costs of Medicare have grown in an almost uncontrolled fashion. Critics have described the program as representing a blank check to health care providers. Alleged silent collusion between hospitals and physicians means that neither party interferes with the other's ability to collect the maximum payment believed due. Years of massive data analysis by the federal government has led to some understanding of how the program actually functions. The computer, with its access to physician and hospital practice patterns, is providing the necessary information.

Congress has always been reticent about getting involved in how or how much physicians or hospitals are paid. With limited power to deal with the issue of price, the Health Care Financing Administration has focused upon utilization as the manipulable component of total expenditures (Expenditures = Price × Utilization). To control utilization it has made extensive use of deductibles, coinsurance, and prior approvals to the extent that Medicare recipients have felt forced to purchase more and more private insurance (Medigap policies). In 1985 Medicare paid only $.45 out of every dollar that the aged spent on health care services.

In 1985, the federal government began making capitation payment to HMOs or other Competitive Medical Plans where the organization is at risk for physician services provided under contract or as employees of the service organization (Ginsburg & Hackbarth, 1986; Rice, deLissovoy, Gabel, & Ermann, 1985). These capitation payments for enrollees are 95 percent of the cost of services Medicare would normally provide to beneficiaries in a particular county (Berenson, 1986). This mechanism allows Medicare recipients to shop around for better terms (with fewer deductibles) than the federal Medicare program. Medicare recipients can return to the traditional program on very short notice if they become dissatisfied with their change. These changes in the Medicare regulations allow 29 million Medicare beneficiaries to choose, if they so desire, physician services through other than fee-for-service systems. Here is a powerful, potential market for new and very large systems of care.

Since 40 percent of Medicare beneficiaries make no claims in any particular year, it is possible for an HMO, selective in its client recruitment, to make considerable money. The concern is that elderly persons with high service requirements will self-select HMOs, which then will be unable to provide the services to these high risk (high cost) clients and remain in business. To help prevent economic failure of small HMOs and IPAs, these groups are now limited to accepting no more than 49 percent of total enrollees from Medicare (Rossiter & Langwell, 1988).

The greatest single problem with Medicare is the over emphasis on acute care and the lack of funding for long-term care. The American health system is politically dominated by hospitals and physicians whose major interest is acute care. In 1984, less than 1 percent of the Medicare expenditure was spent for nursing home care (Rice & Estes, 1984; Harrington, Newcomer, & Estes, 1985).

In 1988, with support of the Reagan Administration, the Medicare Catastrophic Protection Act was passed. While senior citizens believe long-term care in nursing homes (average cost about $22,000 a year) is a financial health care catastrophe, the act provides no relief for nursing home costs, which affect 1.5 million residents. The act does provide relief for long periods of hospitalization (up to 365 days) and physician services (annual cap of $1370 on out-of-pocket expenses). By 1991, 60 percent of pharmacy costs will be covered after a $600 deductible. The new act extends coverage from 100 days to 150 days a year in a skilled care facility, but, on the basis of past history, few will qualify. There is no provision for extended home health care, Meals on Wheels, or day care (Rice, 1988).

To pay for these extensions, the Medicare Part B premium will increase each year to $35 per month by 1993. For the first time there will be a surcharge (15 percent) on the income tax of Medicare enrollees, which by 1993 will reach $1050 for an individual with an annual income of $50,000. In the past Medicare has been financed by payroll taxes levied on workers and premiums paid by enrollees. This new method is a special income tax on the elderly.

Medicaid

Medicaid, Title XIX of the Social Security Act, became law at the same time as Medicare and is designed to provide health services for the medically indigent as well as the blind, disabled, and crippled children. The medically indigent generally are defined as those persons who can normally meet their living expenses but have no resources for paying the additional health service costs when they become ill. Medicaid is a complex program funded out of federal and state general funds wherein the amount paid by the federal government to a particular state is dependent upon the range of the services offered as well as the state's per capita income. There is a minimal program of services a state must offer to be a participant in the program.

Medicaid programs provided the economic impetus to empty state hospitals of the chronically mentally ill. Discharging these patients out of state mental health hospitals and into the community and into nursing homes, has shifted a portion of cost to the federal government through the Medicaid program rather than having the state pay the total cost alone (Mechanic, 1985).

Because Medicaid programs are administered by the states who also define the services to be covered, there are great state-by-state differences (Joe, Meltzer, & Yu, 1985). Many states, to save money, have cut payment levels below cost, and there is an increasing problem of willingness to participate on the part of physicians and hospital providers (Iglehart, 1983).

Traditionally, states paid hospitals according to cost-based reimbursement methods and allowed Medicaid recipients access to service of their choice. Old service utilization patterns and the common absence of a personal physician led Medicaid patients to seek service at public institutions and academic medical centers: the most expensive institutions, particularly for primary care services. After the Omnibus Budget Reconciliation Act of 1981 was passed, states were allowed to limit a Medicaid recipient's free choice of provider (Jones & Kilpatrick, 1986).

Various states have been experimenting with new ways to contain costs.

Washington and Arizona have tried programs using a capitated fee and a Primary Care Physician, selected by the Medicaid recipient, to control access to specialty physicians and ancillary services including emergency department utilization. Some states are using a modified DRG system for Medicaid patients when hospitalized. California is well known for its system of competitive bidding to approve hospitals to provide Medicaid (Medi-Cal) services (Johns, 1985).

Military Related

There are two major federal programs that provide health services directly, rather than a mechanism for paying for health services. The Department of Defense maintains a health system that is supported directly from federal budget allocations for each of the military services. The armed services also provide care for military dependents and retirees. For the latter obligations, they maintain an insurance program that enables them to subcontract this care to nonmilitary provides, the Civilian Health and Medical Program for the Uniformed Services (CHAMPUS).

The Veterans Administration (VA) maintains the largest health service system in the United States. Like the military, it is supported directly through the federal budget. The eligibility rules for use of the VA system are poorly defined, and, politically, Congress does not want utilization by veterans restricted to service-related injuries or illnesses. The practice is to not turn away possible recipients of service if the veteran can possibly be accommodated. Aging World War II veterans are producing a greatly increased demand for long-term care services. The increasingly competitive civilian health service environment with more stringent eligibility rules in all programs is, in turn, creating increased demand on the military-related health systems of care.

Schlesinger and Wetle (1986) have presented an interesting proposal to expand the VA services rather than attempt to narrow categorical eligibility as Congress never finds the latter acceptable. These authors would focus on assessment programs leading to targeted service responses and increased integration of care with non-VA health care programs when needs do not justify VA provisions. This could mean, in many settings, that VA hospitals would get out of the acute care business and concentrate on long-term care.

References

Berenson, R.A. (1986). Capitation and conflict of interest. *Health Affairs, 5*(1), 141–146.

Clement, J. (1984). Third party reimbursers. In W.F. Neumann, V.D. Suver, & J. Zelman (Eds.), *Financial management* (2nd ed., pp. 477–487). Owings Mills, MD: Rynd Communications, National Health Publishing.

Davis, C.K. (1986). Health-care reforms: What can we expect? *Nursing Economics, 4,* 10–11.

Division of National Cost Estimates. (1987). National health expenditures, 1986–2000. *Health Care Financing Review, 8*(4), 1–36.

Enthoven, A., & Kronick, R. (1989). A consumer-choice health plan for the 1990s. *New England Journal of Medicine, 320*(1) 29–37 and *320*(2) 94–101.

Feldstein, P.J. (1983). *Health care economics* (2nd ed.). New York: John Wiley and Sons.

Gabel, J., & Ermann, D. (1986). Preferred provider organizations: Performance, problems, and promise. *Health Affairs, 4*(1), 24–40.

Gabel, J., Jajich-Toth, C., deLissovoy, G., et al. (1988). The changing world of health insurance. *Health Affairs, 7*(3), 48–65.

Ginsburg, P.B., & Hackbarth, G.M. (1986). Alternative delivery systems and medicare. *Health Affairs, 5*(1), 6–22.

Goldsmith, J. (1984). Death of a paradigm: The challenge of competition. *Health Affairs, 3*(3), 5–19.

Harrington, C., Newcomer, R.J., & Estes, C.L. (1985). *Long term care and the elderly: Public policy issues.* Beverly Hills, CA: Sage.

Himmelstein, D.U., & Woolhandler, S. (1989). A national health program for the United States. *New England Journal of Medicine, 320*(1) 102–108.

Iglehart, J.K. (1983). Health policy report: Medicaid in transition. *New England Journal of Medicine, 309,* 868–872.

Joe, T.C.W., Meltzer, J., & Yu, P. (1985). Arbitrary access to care: The case for reforming Medicaid eligibility. *Health Affairs, 4*(1), 59–74.

Johns, L. (1985). Selective contracting in California. *Health Affairs, 4*(3), 32–48.

Jones, K.R., & Kilpatrick, K.E. (1986). State strategies for financing indigent care. *Nursing Economics, 4,* 61–65.

Mechanic, D. (1985). Mental health and social policy: Initiatives for the 1980s. *Health Affairs, 4*(1), 75–88.

Moran, D.W., & Savela, T.E. (1986). HMOs, finance, and the hereafter. *Health Affairs, 5*(1), 51–65.

Mundinger, M.O. (1985). Health service funding cuts and declining health of the poor. *New England Journal of Medicine, 313,* 44–47.

Murphy, E.K. (1986). Health care: Right or privilege. *Nursing Economics, 4*(2), 66–68.

Patricelli, R. (1986). Musings of a blind man—reflection on the health care industry. *Health Affairs, 5*(2), 128–134.

Quinn, C.C. (1984). Health care regulation and market forces. *Nursing Economics, 2,* 204–209.

Reinhardt, U.E. (1986). Rationing the health care surplus: An American tragedy. *Nursing Economics, 4,* 101–108.

Relman, A.S., & Reinhardt, U.E. (1986). Debating for-profit health care. *Health Affairs, 5*(2), 5–31.

Rice, D.P. (1988). Medicare catastrophic protection act. *Hospitals, 62*(18) 18.

Rice, D.P., & Estes, C.L. (1984). Health of the elderly: Policy issues and challenges. *Health Affairs, 3*(4), 25–49.

Rice, T., deLissovoy, G., Gabel, J., & Ermann, D. (1985). The state of PPOs: Results from a national survey. *Health Affairs, 4*(4), 25–40.

Rossiter, L.F., & Langwell, K. (1988). Medicare's two systems for paying providers. *Health Affairs, 7*(3), 120–132.

Schlesinger, M., & Wetle, T. (1986). The elder veteran: New directions for change. *Health Affairs,* 5(2), 59–71.

Wilensky, G.R. (1988). Filling the gaps in health insurance. *Health Affairs,* 7(3), 133–149.

Wilensky, G.R., & Rossiter, L.F. (1986). Patient self-selection in HMOs. *Health Affairs,* 5(1), 66–80.

Chapter 9

Provider Payments for Health Care Services

In Chapter 8 an economic view of the sources of monies for financing health care services was presented. Total expenditures for health services, the economic value of health care, public, personal, and employer responsibilities, and the problems of providing for those who cannot or will not adequately provide for their own health care were considered.

In this chapter, the perspective is that of the health service provider. Services rendered must be paid. The services made available by health care facilities are those for which someone is willing to pay. It does not follow that all parties pay the same for a specific service. There are two processes that affect the ultimate payment received by the service provider. The first pertains to the relationship between total financial requirements and allowable costs, and the second involves cost shifting to obtain the full cost of inadequately reimbursed care.

Total Financial Requirements and Cost Shifting

There has been a long struggle regarding allowable costs between third parties who pay for services and service entities who provide the services. The intent of Medicare legislation has been to cover all of the costs associated with health care services of covered beneficiaries. The law expressed Congressional intent but did not include precise accounting and cost allocation rules. Reimbursement procedures have been developed by the Health Care Financing Administration (HCFA), which is responsible for administering and controlling Medicare expenditures. A type of game has evolved between providers concerned with reimbursement of full costs and federal and state agencies and commercial carriers defining allowable costs in an attempt to control total expenditures.

Total Financial Costs

Neumann, Suver, and Zelman (1984) have described the phenomenon of *total financial costs* that the provider may incur. The five major divisions are shown in Table 9–1. Many of these expenses are not reimbursed by nature of the definitions of allowable costs but nevertheless reflect expenses incurred by institutions in the health services business.

Table 9–1   Total Financial Requirement

I.   Cost of doing business

| Direct Patient Care Expenses | Bad Debts | Contractual Allowances |
| Medical Education | Research | Charity Care |

II. Costs of staying in business

| Working Capital | Replacement of Assets | New Technology |

III. Costs of changing business

| Alteration of Existing Service | Providing New Service |

IV. Returns to capital sources

| Interest on Debt | Repayment of Debt (Non-Profit Providers) | Return on Equity (For-Profit Providers) | Return on Community Investment |

V.   Costs of uncertainty

| Legal Decisions | Administrative Decisions | Political Decisions | Contingency Allowances |

Total Financial Requirement = I + II + III + IV + V

SOURCE: Reprinted from Neuman, B. R., Suver, J. D., & Zelman, W. N. *Financial Management: Concepts and Applications for Health Care Providers*, p. 313. Copyright © 1984 by Rynd Communications. Used by permission of National Health Publishing, Owings Mills, MD.

Cost of doing business includes direct patient care expenses, which are generally paid after the patient pays certain deductibles and coinsurance. HCFA is reducing its support of medical education and does not support clinical research in Medicare payments because the government supports these activities through other programs. Studies and surveys for management purposes are allowed. The HCFA has been unwilling to pay a share of the costs of bad debts from other patients on the basis that there was no legislative intent to do this and the federal government has not incurred the obligation. The HCFA does pay service institutions the uncollected billings of Medicare patients. To provide a proportion of charity care is a legal responsibility of the hospital if it has received Hill–Burton monies for construction costs. These construction funds were made available to hospitals defined as providing charitable services and operating as a not-for-profit organization.

Costs of staying in business, changing business, returns to capital sources and costs of uncertainty are generally not reimbursed at all. Service institutions have variously estimated the combined non-reimbursed costs to reflect an additional 15 percent of the reimbursed costs (Neumann, Suver, & Zelman, 1984).

The cost of capital is the greatest problem to service institutions whether this is payment on bonds for building or equipment debt, interest to shareholders as return on equity for proprietary institutions, or voter approval for public bonds financed by taxes for public institutions. Developing sources of capital is viewed by many finance officers as the most crucial issue relating to an institution's survivability. Without the ability to procure capital (which means the ability to pay for it), hospitals cannot purchase new equipment and remodel facilities. Hospitals with out-of-date physical plants and equipment cannot remain competitive in the marketplace.

Cost Shifting

When an institution fails to receive the full cost of providing the service, it is necessary to shift the unmet costs onto other service recipients. Table 9–2 provides an illustration of this process. While the data shown are hypothetical, the actual process can be documented at any institution. It is this cost shifting, from inadequately funded public services to insurance premiums of employees of private businesses, to which business organizations have objected so strongly. The resultant health care insurance premiums for employees are higher than an actuarially-based experience rating for that company would dictate.

Today, companies watch carefully that their insurance premiums closely relate to their own employees' health service utilization and refuse to absorb the costs of other inadequately reimbursed services. It is this close linkage between service utilization and costs that is producing a new health consciousness in many companies. Business managers who see the actual cost of

Table 9–2   The Cost Shifting Process*

100 Patients	Payment method
40% Blue Cross	costs + 10%
30% Medicare	costs
15% Medicaid	90% costs
10% self-pay	charges
5% charity/bad debt	0%

Total Costs	$200,000
Desired Margin	10,000
Total Financial Requirements	$210,000

Fair Share	=	$210,000 ÷ 100	=	$2100 per patient

Cost per Patient	=	$200,000 ÷ 100	=	$2000
Medicaid Cost	=	90% × $2000	=	$1800

Initial Fair Share		=	$2100

The Subsidies

Charity/bad debt	(5% × $2100) ÷ 95%	=	$ 111
	New Fair Share	=	2211
Medicare	($2211 − $2000) × 30% ÷ 65%	=	97
	New Fair Share	=	2308
Medicaid	($2308 − $1800) × 15% ÷ 50%	=	152
	New Fair Share	=	2460
Blue Cross	($2460 − $2200) × 40% ÷ 10%	=	1040
	Charge to Self Pay	=	3500

*Note: Figures have been simplified for easier comprehension of the process.

preventable health problems requiring modification of personal behavior take on a new interest in health promotion programs.

These two financial problems, (1) inability to recover total financial requirements when costs are derived from the operating budget only and (2) non-public insurers refusing to accept cost add-ons from inadequately reimbursed services, explain much of the economic problems of health service institutions and agencies. These two problems directly affect the ability to raise capital.

Estimating Revenues

Closely related to the concepts of total financial requirements and cost shifting is the process of estimating volume and price of services for the revenue portion of the operations or income budget.

A health service entity considers its various sources of income in arriving at an estimate of its total revenues for the year and looks strategically at the years ahead. Hospital days or client visits must be estimated by each type of payer (Medicare, Medicaid, Blue Cross, etc.) to arrive at total revenue. Acute care facilities recruit physicians whose procedures result in high hospital revenues. Transplant surgeons have been particularly sought after. This market has become so exaggerated that Prudential Insurance announced selection of 18 facilities (and surgeons) to do heart, kidney, and liver transplants and lithotripsy procedures in order to control inappropriate expansion. Managed care subscribers must select from these approved facilities. Prudential's fee-for-service clients are not restricted in selection but will have maximum amounts designated for payment (Mullen, 1988).

A home health care agency may provide several types of health service visits, some of which are well reimbursed and others quite poorly. Providing the higher reimbursement services almost exclusively may not be wise if the competition in that field presents too great a challenge. Can quality of the services be improved enough to overcome the competition? Is the attempt worth the risk, or would failure be too costly? Is it wiser to go after a special market niche such as child care?

Some services must be offered even though the activity is inadequately reimbursed. Many acute care facilities view the maternity service as a loss leader. That service, however, is very important in getting young families established with a hospital. It may be worth the initial loss in order to establish a long service relationship with that family.

A contract with a Health Maintenance Organization (HMO), a Preferred Provider Organization (PPO), or a similar entity may require a discounted rate at which the payment no longer meets the full costs. The additional volume, however, may be important in contributing income toward fixed costs (costs which do not vary, within a range, on the basis of the number of clients served). If the discounted price is adequate to pay the variable costs (additional costs incurred for an additional patient's care) and also make a significant contribution to the fixed costs, this may make the contract a useful one for increasing the volume to a financial breakeven point. Nurse managers need to make certain that they actually receive the additional variable costs or it can mean an increased census without additional staff.

The service volume budget is based upon (1) historical trends, (2) community demographics, (3) physician support of the institution, (4) capacity or service changes, and (5) economic and regulatory changes. Increasingly, hospitals are converting their entire census to diagnosis-related groups in order to relate resource utilization to groups of patients and thus create service (product) lines for marketing purposes.

Projecting a financial model of the volume of anticipated activity and the remuneration expected from each service according to the category of payer is an important function of an organization's financial office. In the end, the board of directors or the owners must make the decision of what services to offer and what risks to take. The goals should include both survival and community service.

Conditions of Participation

In order for a health service facility to receive payment for the provision of services, there are participation requirements relating to service programs that have to be met. For detailed information about these conditions, refer to the current *Code of Federal Regulations,* Title 42 Public Health, Chapter IV Health Care Financing Administration. This is published after each session of Congress and is available in public libraries that maintain a government depository. Although Medicare and Medicaid are titles of the Social Security Act, the administration of the payments and related quality standards are the responsibility of the Health Care Financing Administration of the Public Health Service. Federal regulations guide the industry and commercial insurers accept as their own the Medicare standards for conditions of participation, usually requiring nothing more. Conditions of participation involve the major mechanisms of licensure, accreditation, and participation standards relating to specific service program offerings.

Licensure

While the authority to license a facility derives from state law, it was rarely used for health facilities until passage of the National Hospital Survey and Construction Act (Hill–Burton) in 1946. The federal government wanted the states to establish minimum standards for maintenance and performance as a hospital (i.e., to be licensed) in order to qualify for federal construction grants. The states quickly provided such legislation, and today mandatory hospital licensure laws exist in all states. These programs have been expanded to include nursing home and home health care agency licensure. Regulations usually cover the institution's or agency's organization and operation, physical facilities, and personnel staffing with additional requirements for special departments such as pharmacy, clinical laboratories, radiology, and dietary.

Accreditation

For hospitals, accreditation by the Joint Commission on Accreditation of Healthcare Organization (JCAHO) reflects a higher standard than state licensure. Compliance with all state legal regulations, however, is a requirement of JCAHO. State licensure reviews and JCAHO surveys often are scheduled together since the requirements are interdependent. In some states accreditation by the JCAHO can be used in lieu of licensure survey.

When the original Joint Commission on Accreditation of Hospitals (JCAH) was renamed JCAHO in 1987, it was a strategy preparatory to entering the market to accredit HMOs and long-term care facilities. The original organization was established in 1951 with corporate members from the American Medical Association, American College of Surgeons, and the American College of Physicians. The American Dental Association was added as a corporate member in 1979, and a public member was added in 1981. After 30 years of effort, the American Nurses' Association (ANA) is still denied a corporate chair on the Commission. This denial is based on a rationale that all other employee groups would have to be accommodated. The ANA does not accept this rationale and served notice in 1988 that they would use all means, including litigation, to obtain a seat. When nurses have served on the Commission, it has been as representatives of the American Hospital Association rather than the ANA. There is a nurse member on every survey team.

There are four accreditation programs: (1) Hospital Accreditation Program, (2) Accreditation Program/Psychiatric Facilities, (3) Accreditation Program/Long-Term Care, and (4) Accreditation Program/Ambulatory Health Care. These programs became very powerful through the Medicare–Medicaid legislation, which accepted the standards of the JCAHO as meeting the conditions of participation in those programs, that is, the quality assurance standards of the Joint Commission meet the requirements of Medicare–Medicaid. In 1977, the Commission added a Utilization Review standard, discussed below. Another source of power has been the requirement of JCAHO accreditation in order to offer approved medical residencies. To the service institution, accreditation by the JCAHO is an essential requirement for survival.

Although accreditation is not a legal requirement for Medicare participation, approval by either the JCAHO or the American Osteopathic Association is deemed to meet Medicare requirements for hospitals with the exception of three points, which can be attested to in the application for participation. There are no accreditation programs for nursing homes and home care agencies that have the broad recognition of JCAHO approval.

Specific Requirements

Part 482 of Subchapter E of Chapter IV of the *Code of Federal Regulations* provides the specific conditions of participation for hospitals to be certified as a provider of care and thus eligible for reimbursement. The requirements relate to general administration, basic hospital functions (present in all hospitals), discharge planning, optional hospital services, and, finally, requirements for specialty hospitals. These provisions listed in the regulations must be met by any hospital that is not accredited by the JCAHO. With accreditation, the assumption is that these standards have been met.

Utilization Review

Utilization Review (UR) is required by law for all patients whose services are being paid through Medicare–Medicaid. URs are conducted on covered patients receiving services in hospitals, skilled care facilities, nursing homes, home health care agencies, and hospice care. The purpose of UR is to determine the medical necessity of:

1. Admission to the institution or home care service
2. The duration of stays
3. Professional services furnished, including drugs and biologicals

Hospital stays are subject to review only if the stay exceeds the usual days and becomes a statistical outlier. Before an admission or continued stay can be declared as not medically necessary, the UR committee is required to consult with the practitioner responsible for the patient's treatment.

In 1983, with the changes in the Social Security Act that introduced the prospective payment system, the federal government developed legislation combining utilization review and quality control in Peer Review Organizations (PRO). The 54 PROs have considerably more authority than the earlier Professional Standards Review Organizations. They can now deny payment where services are deemed medically unnecessary, furnished in an inappropriate setting, or where substandard care has harmed or threatened the health, safety, or well-being of the patient (42 CFR 466.7).

Registered nurses are commonly employed in UR programs, including preadmission approvals for surgical procedures. It is important to understand that utilization review is a medical requirement and that nurses employed in such programs are assuming responsibility for a medically delegated activity.

Fiscal Intermediaries and Carriers

When all requirements have been met, the HCFA approves the facility or agency as a health service provider and issues a provider number. The institution or agency then is able to submit requests for payment to a fiscal intermediary. Without a provider number no payment is possible.

Fiscal intermediaries were specified in the original Medicare–Medicaid legislation to protect the private insurance industry and reduce federal administrative involvement as the government initiated payment for health services in the private sector. The fiscal intermediary (institutions generally have a choice from at least two) has a contract with the HCFA to receive billings from the service provider and make payments on a cost basis for Medicare Part A covered benefits. Blue Cross and large commercial carriers are common fiscal intermediaries. A minimum of 5 years experience in processing health insurance claims is a general requirement for approval as an intermediary. The HCFA may approve intermediaries for a class of providers, for example, hospital, skilled nursing facility, or home health agency, or they may approve an intermediary for a state or region. In addition to paying claims, the fiscal intermediary is required to provide the HCFA with a great deal of statistical data regarding service utilization and unit costs for use in research underlying policy development or change.

Carriers, like intermediaries, are entities that have contracts with the HCFA to determine and make Medicare payments for Part B benefits payable on a charge basis. Carriers also provide the HCFA with relevant statistical data. The fact that even the fiscal agents for Part A and Part B payments are kept separate seems to reflect congressional intent to maintain clear policy distinctions in the programs.

Methods of Payment

Payment for health services is divided into two major portions: payment to the facility or organization and payment to the professional practitioner. Very different payment methods are used for institutions (derived from actual costs) and physicians (based upon fee-for-service), as discussed below. Remember that in Chapter 1 a distinction was made between work that is controlled administratively and work that is controlled professionally. It is clear that Medicare recognizes the administrative relationship in paying for nurses' services and the professional relationship in paying for physician services.

Institutional Services

Per Diem

The basis for a per diem charge is that it includes all costs for routine services for a 24-hour period. A per diem cost is constructed by taking the total costs for the previous year and dividing that figure by the total number of patient days. For example, where TC = total costs and pd = patient days:

$$\frac{TC}{pd} = \frac{\$30,000,000}{100,000} = \$300$$

The per diem costs for the previous year are then adjusted for the current year. This adjustment includes such factors as changes in reimbursement rules, inflation, and wage rate adjustments. Government agencies or fiscal intermediaries often require justification and approval of changes in the per diem rate. It is not uncommon to have a cap or upper limit on what the per diem rate can be for approved reimbursement of a health service. The upper limit has a tendency to become a standard charge rather quickly. At the end of the fiscal year, the projected figure is converted to an actual per diem, and a fiscal adjustment is made between the institution and the fiscal intermediary.

Facility Charge

This is a common method of charging for patient use of the hospital's specialized facilities under the direction of physicians. Emergency rooms, operating rooms, radiology, laboratories, and clinics develop standard costs that include all costs (labor, materials, equipment, space) except those of physician services. The charge for the facility is assigned on the basis of a visit or procedure or on the basis of the length of time the facility was utilized. Operating room charges are commonly defined by the number of minutes in use. Recovery room costs may be included in developing operating room charges, but recovery room time is more commonly charged at a different rate and for a separate quantity of time.

Per Stay

Medicare's prospective payment system, which involves payment by diagnosis-related groups (DRGs), was implemented in 1983. There are 476 DRGs designed to relate clinically and by the amount of hospital resources utilized in the care of the average patient in the grouping. Payment is based upon a hospital stay rather than per diem. The payment allowed for the DRG is based upon national cost averages. If the hospital can discharge the patient in less time than allowed, 50 percent of the excess revenue can be retained. If the discharge comes after the number of days allowed, the potential loss must be absorbed by the institution.

The DRG cost structure includes inpatient costs for services such as room, board, nursing care, radiology, laboratory services, intensive care if needed, and malpractice insurance. Hospitals receive separate payments for capital costs, direct and indirect cost of medical education (if they train medical residents), bad debts of Medicare patients, and outlier DRG cases if the longer stay or excessive costs are found to be allowable. The goal is to eliminate the wide range of per diem costs and lengths of stay in different hospitals and in different parts of the country that cannot be explained adequately on the basis of case mix. Instead, hospitals are paid a sum approaching the average cost in the nation's hospitals for treating a patient in that DRG category.

Now that the transition period has been completed, the computation of a DRG rate is based upon a 100 percent national rate and becomes somewhat simpler. The rate per case is divided into three subrates for large urban, small urban, and rural hospitals. Each of these three rates is divided into a labor portion and a nonlabor portion. The labor portion is multiplied by the appropriate area wage index for one of the 350 standard metropolitan areas and then combined with the nonlabor portion again. The resultant base rates are then multiplied by the DRG weight to determine the total payment for that patient's stay. The DRG rate is computed:

$$\text{DRG weight} = \frac{\text{Average Costs for Stays in DRG 101}}{\text{Average Costs for All Medical Stays}}$$

DRG payments are adjusted annually by Congress upon recommendations from the Prospective Payment Assessment Commission (ProPac), a national commission established by the act to provide objective review of the rate structures. Children's hospitals, psychiatric hospitals, and rehabilitation hospitals are excluded from the requirements of prospective payment at this time and continue to be reimbursed on the basis of reasonable costs.

Physician Services

Usual, Customary, and Reasonable

The usual, customary, and reasonable (UCR) system by which Medicare and many state Medicaid programs pay physicians came into existence with the establishment of Medicare. Members of Congress did not wish the legislation to involve them in the establishment of physician fees. Fearing that disagreements might mean the legislation would not pass, Congress accepted the vague UCR phrase.

Under UCR, the allowable rate of payment for a covered service is the lowest of the actual billed charge and the values of two fee screens (Langwell & Nelson, 1986). The Level 1 screen or usual fee is the physician's median or modal charge for the service. This is based upon his or her previous year's charges. The Level 2 screen or customary fee is the percentile of the distribution of the Level 1 screen in that geographic area. Medicare permits the use of two Level 2 screens: one for specialists and one for general practitioners. Other insurers use these data differently. Medicare sets its Level 2 screen at the 75th percentile while Blue Shield uses the 90th percentile. Commercial carriers do not maintain separate Level 1 screens for individual physicians and instead pay them at the 90th percentile of the area distribution of usual fees with no differentials for general and specialty practitioners.

The UCR system produced rapid growth in fees. The physician has been prone to raise fees because (1) even if the third party didn't pay, the recipient of service could be billed directly; and (2) even if uncollected, the increased fee raises next year's modal fee (Level 1 screen) for that physician. When the practice is widespread among physicians in the community, it raises the area (Level 2) screen as well.

Beginning in 1984, Medicare developed a participating physician program to help patients identify in advance whether their physician was willing to accept Medicare payment as full payment for the services rendered, that is, will the physician accept assignment. Before this program was introduced, physicians could accept or decline assignment on a case-by-case basis. Physicians who accept assignment submit their claim directly to the Medicare carrier and accept the Medicare approved charges as payment-in-full. Physicians bill the beneficiary for the Part B deductible ($75 annually) and the coinsurance of 20 percent of the approved charges. When the claim is unassigned, the client is responsible also for any difference between actual and approved charges, which is called "balance billing." With the 1984 changes, the physician makes an annual decision of whether to accept assignment on all or none of the Medicare patients. Physicians can no longer opt to take assignment on the poor and decline assignment on their well-to-do patients.

At the same time changes were made in assignment relations, physicians' fees were also frozen for 15 months. Starting in 1986, Medicare began paying a 4 percent differential in favor of participating physicians to further reward their involvement. In March 1987, the national proportion of physicians accepting assignment had grown to 70 percent (Burney & Paradise, 1987).

In examining the effects of the physician fee freeze, Mitchell, Wedig, and Cromwell (1989) conducted a four-state study and found that Medicare beneficiaries were spending 29.5 percent more for physician services (Part B) in 1986 than in 1984. During that same period Medicare payments increased 27.1 percent for all services (Part A). The authors demonstrate convincingly that although the fees were frozen, the physicians increased the volume of services per patient. The authors report spending for physician services increased disproportionately for surgery, radiology and high technology diagnostic tests. Similarly, Schieber and Langenbrunner (1989) of the Office of Research and Demonstrations of HCFA reported that in each of the last 10 years Medicare expenditures for physicians services have increased at average annual rates of 15 percent.

Fee Schedule

A published fee schedule for various professional services represents the maximum amount that the insurer will pay for a given activity. Many states currently use a fee schedule for Medicaid professional payments, which is periodically updated to reflect changes in the cost of medical practice. Fee schedules have a distinct tendency to overvalue surgical procedures and technical tasks and undervalue clinical judgment.

In a study using resource-based relative value units (RBRVU) and the experience of four states in paying Medicare Part B charges, a comparison was made between actual charges and potential charges based upon the resources used to provide the service. This latter was a combination of (1) time to carry out the procedure including preoperative and postoperative care, (2) complexity based upon diagnostic and technical skill required to perform the procedure, (3) opportunity cost associated with length of residency, and (4) physician practice costs associated with that speciality (rent, wages, equipment, insurance). Complexity was derived from self-reports of physicians in that particular specialty. The units derived for each procedure were multiplied by the average cost of a cholecystectomy, chosen because the procedure is common and represents a stable technology. The process was later repeated using lung lobectomy with almost identical results.

Using these RBRVU it was found that Medicare is overpaying 63.4 percent for cataract extraction with lens implant; 53.8 percent for iridectomy for glaucoma; 48.9 percent for lumbar laminectomy and 44.9 percent for total hip replacement (Table 9–3). Simultaneously, Medicare is underpaying 78.3 percent for cystectomy with urinary diversion and 21.9 percent for esophogogastrectomy; however, these are uncommon procedures (Mitchell et al., 1987). Physician fee schedules provide considerable potential for cost savings.

Congress has shown interest in methods to constrain physician fee growth. Congress mandated a large study to develop a relative value scale for a new physician fee schedule based upon resources utilized in that service and created the Physician Payment Review Commission to make recommendations. Hsiao, a Harvard economist, was asked to conduct the Congressional mandated study. Hsiao's study of physician's work, for the Commission, encompassed time, mental effort, judgment, technical skill, physical effort and stress. Assessments were made by practicing physicians. The study showed that the relative value scale differed substantially from the traditional fee schedule. The cognitive and patient management functions used by internists and pediatricians, for example, were rated higher and the highly technical procedures of surgeons were valued less (Hsiao et al., 1988). Armed with Hsiao's scale of RV, it is likely the Physician Payment Review Commission will recommend changes in payment fee schedules for physician services but not until the medical profession has had ample time to study the report and make its own views known.

Managed Care Systems

Under these arrangements, physician groups negotiate for the proportion of their fees that they keep. This varies according to whether the physician group provides its own offices or if these are provided by the system (HMOs or hospital clinics). Which party does the billing and collecting also affects the final service payment. The origins of the payment, however, are based upon a fee schedule and the anticipated frequency of specific procedures in the populations served. It is usual for a portion of the capitated sum to be withheld from the physician group until the end of the year. If service utilization has been well-controlled, there will be surplus funds to distribute to that medical group. If service has not been "managed" well, there will be no end-of-year distribution.

Table 9–3 Comparisons of Current Medicare Charges and Potential Payments Under a Resource-Based Relative Value Scale (RBRVS)

Procedure	Medicare reasonable charge[a]	RBRVS value[b]	Resource-based payment[c]	Percent change
General surgery				
Cholecystectomy (index procedure)	$ 704	2.01	$ 704	0.0%
Diagnostic colonoscopy	278	0.73	256	−7.9
Inguinal hernia repair	465	0.98	343	−26.2
Tracheostomy	288	0.83	291	+1.0
Modified radical mastectomy	876	2.56	897	+2.4
Esophogogastrectomy	1,727	6.01	2,105	+21.9
General surgery/Obstetrics-Gynecology				
Total abdominal hysterectomy	825	1.88	658	−20.2
Obstetrics-Gynecology				
Diagnostic dilation and curettage	222	0.48	168	−24.3
Laparoscopy	362	0.63	221	−39.0
Urology				
Diagnostic cystourethroscopy	87	0.25	88	+1.1
Transurethral resection of medium bladder tumor	600	1.04	364	−39.3
Ureterolithotomy	923	2.09	732	−20.7
Total cystectomy with urinary diversion	1,695	8.63	3,023	+78.3
Transurethral resection of the prostate	1,013	1.85	648	−36.0
Suprapubic prostatectomy	1,086	2.05	718	−33.9
Orthopedic surgery				
Total hip replacement	2,040	3.21	1,124	−44.9
Decompression of carpal tunnel	440	0.72	252	−42.7
Reduction of wrist fracture	277	0.79	277	0.0
Femoral fracture with open treatment and internal fixation	1,105	2.75	963	−12.9
Lumbar laminectomy	1,400	2.04	715	−48.9
Thoracic surgery				
Permanent pacemaker insertion	854	1.49	522	−38.9
Lung Lobectomy	1,428	4.16	1,457	+2.0
Insertion of intra-aortic balloon pump	433	1.02	357	−17.6
Mitral valve replacement	2,702	6.52	2,284	−15.5
Coronary artery bypass graft, three arteries	3,666	7.05	2,469	−32.7
Ophthalmology				
Peripheral iridectomy for glaucoma	561	0.74	259	−53.8
Laser photocoagulation for retinopathy	499	0.79	277	−44.5
Lens extraction, intracapsular	987	1.37	480	−51.4
Extraction with intraocular lens insertion (one-stage procedure)	1,444	1.51[d]	529	−63.4
Intraocular lens insertion only	939	1.36	476	−49.3
Scleral buckling for retinal detachment	1,403	2.43	851	−39.3

[a]Average charges calculated from 1984 Part B claims in Alabama, Connecticut, Washington, and Wisconsin.

[b]Obtained from Hsiao et al., 1985.

[c]Estimates based on formula: $704 times (RBRVS/2.01).

[d]Estimate derived by authors, extrapolating from the RBRVS value for lens extraction alone.

SOURCE: Mitchell, J. B., Stason, W. B., & Calore, K. A., et al. (1987). Are some surgical procedures overpaid? *Health Affairs*, 6(2), p. 124.

Hospital-based Physicians

In the case of radiologists, anesthesiologists, and pathologists (RAPs), the hospital is their place of practice, and they essentially serve other physicians. The physician directors of these departments are often paid a percentage of the net or a smaller percentage of the gross income of the department. There has been considerable concern about the rate of growth of the incomes of these physicians who bill patients for professional services often provided by hospital employees.

The HCFA has wanted to limit RAP physicians to professional fees when a direct professional service is provided and an administrative payment for supervising the service involved. Efforts to fold these fees into the DRG payment met with considerable resistance from hospital administrators who did not wish to stand between these physicians and their fees from the HCFA.

Under the DRG system, the facility-related charges are included in the DRG payment. The DRG payment mechanism has eliminated a hospital's ability to gain financially from additional diagnostic procedures being performed on Medicare patients. At the same time, many hospitals experience economic pressure from physician practice groups that have established their own laboratories, imaging centers, and surgi-centers.

Overview

The mechanisms for payment for professional services are being studied more today than in any time since 1965 (Wilensky & Rossiter, 1986). Fee-for-service is strongly motivating and tends to have a very positive effect on productivity, but there is no control for overservice and unnecessary procedures. Fee-per-stay has shown merit in hospitalized care and Medicare may, in the future, develop a physician's fee to coincide with those DRGs. There are many questions, however, relating to the division of the fee among different physician groups serving the hospitalized patient. Capitation is an efficient mechanism for controlling the cost of processing claims and aggregates the risks well. Capitation systems protect the patient from overservice but make it difficult for the patient to change providers. It also fails to protect the client from the potential of underservice.

Organized Nursing Services

Reimbursement for nursing services has always been available under Medicare and Medicaid policies. The issue of particular relevance to nursing has been the lack of direct and identifiable reimbursement for services by nurses (La Bar & McKibbin, 1986). Nursing care is not recognized as a professional service and instead is part of the routine services, which also include room, meals, and housekeeping. Payment for nursing care must be approved by an institution or be under the direction of a physician in the case of home care or nursing home care.

Hospital Care

See the preceding section in this chapter on Institutional Services.

Nursing Home Care

The significant payers for nursing home care are Medicaid and self-pay individuals. Medicare has such stringent regulations that less than 1 percent of nursing home care has been paid by that program (Harrington, Newcomer and Estes, 1985). Medicare pays for skilled nursing care only when such services can potentially lead to rehabilitation and follow hospitalization. Medicare pays for no intermediate care or custodial, domiciliary care.

There are three categories of service available through nursing homes: skilled nursing, intermediate care and intermediate care for the mentally retarded.

Medicaid

Each state determines its own policies relative to payment for services. Some pay a per diem rate dependent upon the type of licensure of the facility (skilled care facility or intermediate care facility), and other states determine a per diem rate dependent upon the level of nursing care need of the patient with multiple categories in each classification.

There is considerable variation in what is an allowable cost as defined by the states. Ancillary services covered might include physical and occupational therapy, nonprescription drugs, prescription drugs, medical supplies, and durable medical equipment. A major problem for individual facilities is the determination of a disallowed charge after the service has been rendered. This often can be traced back to inadequate documentation in the record that the service was needed or imprecise language that failed to use the "proper word" necessary for an allowable cost.

Swan and Harrington (1985) have summarized the great array of payment mechanisms in nursing home care as follows:

Retrospective Method—Payment is made after services are rendered based upon the expenses incurred.

Prospective Method—Reimbursement rates are set in advance based upon some formula of past expenses.

Facility Specific Method—Reimbursement is set for each facility and is based upon either a retrospective or prospective model.

Class-based Method—Rates are set for groups of similar facilities grouped by size, location, or ownership.

Self-pay

The competitive market determines the per diem rates that nursing homes charge their self-pay patients. Many patients start out as self-pay and "spend down" to the financial resource level necessary to qualify for Medicaid payment. Nursing homes who refuse new Medicaid patients may require a family guarantee of so many months of self-pay reimbursement before they will agree to accept Medicaid reimbursement.

Whatever the source of the monies, the per diem charges in nursing homes have been based upon low wages to poorly prepared nursing assistants and a few nurses. Nationally, nursing homes average only one RN for 17.5 patients. Salaries for RNs in nursing homes are substantially below those in hospitals. In nursing homes, 10 percent of RNs earn less than $15,600 and only 17 percent earn above $26,000 per year (Mezey and Scanlon, 1988).

The American Nurses' Association continues to lobby to have the per diem rates increased to enable nursing homes to pay salaries comparable to what nurses earn in acute care settings and to make it possible for nursing homes to employ some nurse practitioners prepared in gerontologic nursing. For the present, society has not shown the willingness to pay the cost of quality service. Powerful allies are evolving among senior citizen lobbies that may change the potential for quality care.

Home Health Care

Medicare

Eligibility for Medicare payment for home health services includes those entitled to Medicare (over 65 years of age and paid up members of Social Security or Railroad Retirement systems) or eligible on the basis of being disabled for at least 24 months or having end-stage renal disease. This coverage includes spouses and in the case of end-stage renal disease, dependents also. The patient must be homebound, in need of medically necessary, skilled nursing care on an intermittent basis, and have a treatment plan established by a physician (Stuart-Siddall, 1986).

The actual payment allowed is restricted to the lesser of the reasonable cost of the service or the customary charges. Reasonable cost is defined as including the direct and indirect costs of the service. As it was possible for an agency to inflate the indirect costs, the HCFA established caps on the cost per visit for each discipline for different parts of the country. Starting in 1985 the caps were replaced by a new methodology wherein the limits were set at 120 percent of the mean labor-related and nonlabor components of the per visit cost. The figure was lowered to 115 percent in 1986 and 112 percent in 1987. This method effectively limits expansion of indirect costs. It also leaves agencies very vulnerable to failing to obtain the total financial requirements necessary for survival in what has become a very competitive business (Gelder and Burnstein, 1986).

In 1986 the Secretary of Health and Human Services submitted a report to Congress on alternative methods of reimbursement for home health care services. Analysis of cost growth in home health care services showed a significant part attributable to Congressional expansion of the program in 1972 to include the disabled and those with end-stage renal disease. Also, in 1980, certification requirements were eased to permit proprietary agencies which produced an almost doubling of agencies (1980—2,924; 1985—5,965). The case load per agency has almost doubled (168—327) during that same five year period which is probably due to earlier discharges of sicker patients from hospitals. However, none of these factors can account for the great variation in costs between agencies which HCFA is inclined to believe relates to great variations in efficiency. Cost reimbursement fosters the survival of inefficient providers. HCFA is exploring alternatives such as prospective payment in combination with, or separate from, competitive bidding. Until more research has been completed, HCFA will continue to employ administrative measures to assure consistency in billing and coverage criteria (Alternative Methods of Reimbursement, 1988).

Medicaid

Every state is required to have a Medicaid state plan and receives 50 percent in matching federal assistance to service those people who meet the medical care and income requirements. The programs vary greatly from state to state, but home health care is one service each state is required to provide, including nursing care, home health aid, supplies, and equipment. The state has the option to provide physical, speech, and occupational therapy. Agencies must be Medicare certified in order to qualify for Medicaid reimbursement. Medicaid does not have homebound requirements nor must nursing care be of a skilled nature.

In 1981, a program of community-based and home-based care waivers were made available as a state option. This program permits federal matching monies for payment for services not normally covered but which permit a patient to be kept out of an institution. The care must cost less than institutionalization. Under this program patients with very complex needs have been discharged from hospitals and skilled care facilities back into their homes. This program has significantly changed the nature of home care and created a great demand in home care for nurses with advanced technical skills.

Independent Nursing Practice

Individual nurses with special skills often market their services as consultants or as practitioners. Many find that creating limited partnerships, or business or professional corporations makes it easier for them to negotiate contractual arrangements with other health service organizations or physician groups.

Insurance Carriers

Some direct reimbursement for nurse practitioners, nurse anesthetists, and nurse midwives is possible through selected private carriers. Client coverage depends upon specific conditions defined in the policy. Coverage should be verified in writing with each carrier and for each policy type. Most carriers pay if the service is a covered benefit and can be legally provided within the scope of practice of the practitioner's license. Nurses have also found that developing two-way referrals with supportive physicians can lead to combined billing for joint services; however, for nurse practitioners to have their services billed as medical services is inappropriate. Since the nurse is paid less, the physician collects extra fees for the practitioner's efforts. This denies the client or the third party paying the physician's charges the economic advantage when the service has been rendered by a less costly provider.

Direct Client Billing

Nurses should not forget that many would-be clients have the means to pay directly for nursing care. For example, many persons would purchase evaluative visits to a family member in a nursing home to ascertain whether the care is appropriate and satisfactory. The mobility of the American family has meant that many elderly reside in areas with no relatives nearby. The public is not accustomed to paying directly for such services and needs assistance in learning how to make such purchases. In a study by Aydelotte, Hardy, and Hope (1988) of 364 nurses in private practice, almost 92 percent reported that they receive direct client payments.

Contract Services

Nurses can develop contracts to provide specific services independently for subgroups being served by an HMO, PPO, or similar. State health departments also are awarding contracts to nursing organizations for services needed by special clients. These groups are less concerned about professional boundaries and are most interested in the cost of the service and who can legally and safely provide that service. Case management is a special need of selected high service requirement patients. Nurses are especially well-equipped to evaluate care of patients undergoing expensive rehabilitation services or those needing long-term institutional care or hospice services.

Service contracting is a matter of defining a required service for a group of clients that is difficult to provide with existing staff. Alternately one can identify within a hospital or agency a service that it could be preferable to subcontract than have to staff and supervise. For example, it may be possible to contract to provide the nursing care for the psychiatric service, the emergency service, or the operating room service of a community hospital. There are growing opportunities for nurses with entrepreneurial interests. A non-nursing reference helpful to nurses considering contracting services is that of Rehfuss (1989).

Conclusions

Payment systems for services by health practitioners and service organizations will continue to be dominated by the federal government. Because the consumer has little basis for estimating the value of a particular service, payment will be based on estimates of the costs of resources utilized in providing the services. This has been done with DRGs for hospital payment and most likely will be done with relative value scales for physician fee schedules.

Nurses should be especially cognizant that when the money flows directly to an agency or institution, the demand for their services increases. Nurses are used as a cost effective substitute for more expensive services in hospitals and HMOs. When the money flows directly to physicians for payment for services, it is in nursing's interests to see these services unbundled and with separate fee schedules. For example, if post-surgical follow-up were unbundled, nurses could provide much of that service cheaper and better than surgeons. Unbundling the service, enables the third party to bargain for a cheaper rate which brings about the reassignment.

References

Alternative methods of reimbursement: A health and human services study. (1988). *Caring, 7*(2), 32–35.

Aydelotte, M.K., Hardy, M.A., & Hope, K.L. (1988). *Nurses in private practice.* Kansas City, MO: American Nurses' Foundation.

Burney, I., & Paradise, J. (1987). Trends in Medicare physician participation and assignment. *Health Affairs, 6*(2), 107–120.

Estes, C.L., & Lee, P.R. (1985). Social, political and economic background of long term care policy. In C. Harrington, R.J. Newcomer, & C.L. Estes (Eds.), *Long term care of the elderly: Public policy issues.* Beverly Hills, CA: Sage.

Gelder, S.W., & Burnstein, J. (1986). Home health care in the era of hospital prospective payment. *Pride Institute Journal of Long-term Home Health Care, 5*(1), 3–11.

Hsiao, W.C., Braun, P., Yntema, D.& Becker, E.R. (1988, Sept.). Results and policy implications of the resource-based relative value study. *The New England Journal of Medicine, 319*(13), 881–888.

LaBar, C., & McKibbin, R.C. (1986). *New organizational models and financial arrangements for nursing services.* Kansas City, MO: American Nurses' Association.

Langwell, K.M., & Nelson, L.M. (1986). Physician payment systems: A review of history, alternatives and evidence. *Medical Care Review, 43*(1), 5–58.

Mezey, M.D., & Scanlon, W. (1988). Registered nurses in nursing homes. In Secretary's Commission on Nursing. *Support studies and background information* (vol. II). Washington, D.C.: Department of Health and Human Services.

Mitchell, J.B., Stason, W.B., & Calore, K.A., et al. (1987). Are some surgical procedures overpaid? *Health Affairs, 6*(2), 121–131.

Mitchell, J., Wedig, G., & Cromwell, J. (1989). The Medicare physician fee freeze. *Health Affairs, 8*(1), 21–33.

Mullen, P. (1988). Prudential selects 18 facilities to be centers. *Health Week, 2*(16), 3.

Neumann, B.R., Suver, J.D., & Zelman, W.N. (1984). *Financial management: Concepts and applications for health care providers* (pp. 311–314). Owings Mills, MD: Rynd Communications.

Rehfuss, J.A. (1989). *Contracting out in government.* San Francisco, CA: Jossey-Bass.

Schieber, G.J., & Langenbrummer, J.C. (1989). Physician payment research efforts at HCFA. *Health Affairs, 8*(1), 214–218.

Stuart-Siddall, S. (Ed.). (1986). *Home health care nursing.* Rockville, MD: Aspen.

Swan, J.H., & Harrington, C. (1985). Medical nursing home reimbursement policies. In C. Harrington, R.J. Newcomer, & C.L. Estes (Eds.), *Long term care of the elderly* (pp. 125–151). Beverly Hills, CA: Sage.

Wilensky, G.R., & Rossiter, L.F. (1986). Alternative units of payment for physician services: An overview of the issues. *Medical Care Review, 43*(1), 133–156.

Chapter 10

Costs, Standards, and Quality of Care

Economics is sometimes viewed as if it involves decisions regarding only the least cost, or the cheapest way of obtaining an objective. But recall that economics is really a science of choice—choice among competing alternatives. In terms of nursing, this has much to do with the quality of care rendered on behalf of clients. Previously, the distinction has been made between needs, wants, and demand. How does all of this relate to quality?

Cost-benefit Decisions

Quality is, necessarily, both a subjective and objective term in health care and in other areas of economic activity. What may be *best* may not be affordable. What is *correct* in terms of treatment or care protocols may not be known with certainty. Professional nurses, therefore, constantly make judgments about the nature, level, and duration of nursing interventions on behalf of patients. From an economic perspective, how should those decisions be made?

Marginal Costs

The concept of margin was introduced in Chapter 2. It is applicable to nursing situations as follows: both *marginal benefits* and *marginal costs* (in terms of time and effort or expense or both) can be identified. For any given patient care situation, nursing care interventions involve both benefits and costs. Benefits to the patient and sometimes to the family or the community; costs to the organization providing nursing service, to the third party responsible for payment and to the individual for out-of-pocket expense. What is the appropriate relationship between marginal benefits and costs?

In general terms, the answer is provided in Figure 10–1. As the graph illustrates, there is a point at which value of the marginal benefits of increased care or effort or treatment, no longer exceed their associated costs. For purposes of illustration, let us take a public health example. Approximately ⅓ or 60 million adults smoke. Suppose the United States were to undertake more intensive anti-smoking efforts. Should the goal be to totally eliminate smoking? Economic analysis would suggest that the answer is *no*. Why? As illustrated, the costs of encouraging all people who smoke to cease doing so would far outweigh the social benefits associated with smoking cessation (i.e., fewer work loss days, reduced mortality rates attributable to smoking, etc.).

Figure 10–1

Marginal costs and benefits related to improvements in quality of care.

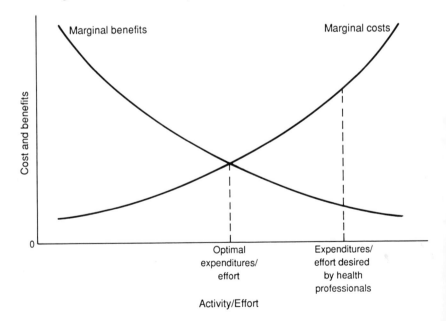

It is the tendency of health professionals, including nurses, to assume that appropriate efforts to curtail smoking should extend beyond the point at which marginal costs and marginal benefits are equal. Why? It is apparent that additional health benefits do occur. Suppose, however, this anti-smoking campaign has reached the point that the only smokers left are over 80, confined to nursing homes, and subject to other debilitating if not fatal conditions—it should be obvious that major expenditures to induce these people to stop smoking are not economically sound investments.

How about the actual experience of a staff nurse working in a hospital? Time is limited during every work period. Some things are done, others that might be done go uncompleted. This decision-making process involves an assessment of the marginal costs (including opportunity costs) and marginal benefits of providing various services to individual patients. It is common sense to do that which is most essential or important at the time. Not everything desirable to do can be done. The economic concept involved is to choose to do those things that have the most impact, value, and significance.

Some nurses, when time is scarce, choose to do those things for which there are medical orders. In countless situations, selected medical orders (no longer or perhaps never relevant) may have the least impact, value, or significance to the patient. Decisions are then being based on administrative expediency instead of clinical judgment.

Quality of Care

With the movement in 1983 to prospective payment and a competitive health care system, the issue of quality of care has taken on new importance. When hospitals are paid a lump sum for a patient's care, how can consumers be certain that potential therapies were not needed versus not provided in order to save money or enhance profitability of the provider? Might care be denied or rationed in order that third parties can avoid paying for services that have low cost-benefit ratios? How, and by whom, are these decisions to be made? Quality-of-care assessments were mandated in the prospective payment legislation because of the danger of improper withholding of service and premature discharge from care facilities.

Quality of care is generally defined by criteria and standards relating to the evaluation of structure, process, and outcomes of care. Standards relating to structure include educational qualifications of staff and accreditation of institutions. Assessments of the care provided have focused upon appropriate professional decision making and utilization of resources.

The science of measuring outcomes of care is in its infancy and is currently focused upon mortality rates, incidence rates of complications, and some measures of client satisfaction and accessibility to service. Increasingly, measures of the satisfaction of patients and their representatives are seen as relevant outcomes.

The most fundamental question to be addressed by the federal government is the effectiveness of care. Are there scientific data available about the effectiveness of the treatment obtained under controlled conditions, such as a double-blind study where neither the patient nor the examining physician knows which treatment the patient received? There is considerable evidence that treatment modalities can become popular without enough evidence that they are more effective than no treatment or a less expensive treatment.

Eddy and Billings (1988) have written convincingly about the quality of medical evidence on which clinical decisions are made. In a review of the literature relating percutaneous transluminal angioplasty (PTA) and a comparison of PTA with an alternative treatment, bypass surgery, these authors have written

> *The only possible conclusion is that, given the available evidence, there is no way to determine with any degree of accuracy the relative merits of the two approaches. How then do practitioners decide which procedure to use when patients enter their offices? . . . We can only surmise that the procedure chosen might depend on which specialist dominates the decision. A nonsurgeon is likely to choose PTA; a surgeon, bypass surgery. (p 22)*

The authors show how widespread is the problem of accurate clinical knowledge

> *The following are clues that the problems might be widespread. (1) The Congressional Office of Technology Assessment has estimated that only 10-20 percent of practices are supported by randomized controlled trials. (2) A review of the statistical methods in published articles concluded that "approximately half the articles that used statistical methods used them incorrectly". (3) A group of published papers about the effectiveness of magnetic resonance imaging (MRI) were scored for quality of design and reporting; on a scale of 1 to 100, the average score was 13. In short, a major problem to the first task of a quality assurance program is that for some practices we simply do not have the direct evidence needed to determine the outcomes of the practice. (p 23)*

One is left to wonder how much high technology should be financed by third parties before there is independent documentation relating to the effectiveness. Families want everything possible to be done but decisions of choice with no economic implications bearing upon that decision are merely statements of wants.

There is increasing concurrence that differences among institutions and among physician providers in quality, cost, and availability of services should be made public. How else can clients make rational decisions? There is broad disagreement, however, about how this should be done. There is particular concern that institutions and physicians who treat more complex cases cannot be properly protected from inappropriate comparisons. The Health Care Financing Administration is conducting research that constructs multivariate models for predicting a hospital-specific mortality rate to be compared with the actual rate.

Many insurers already have this kind of data about the quality of the services received by their members. An experiment is being conducted in Pennsylvania to determine if quality measures derived from common instruments can be standardized for an area and then, with cost-quality data made available to employers, promote "Buy Right" instead of "Buy Cheap" health insurance enrollments with preferred providers (Iglehart, 1988). Quality of nursing care is included as one part of composite quality measures of the health service institutions where nurses are employed.

Regulation of Nursing

The evaluation of structure criteria relevant to nursing focuses upon credentialing standards that include criteria for education, accreditation, licensure, and certification. As nursing is a broad, inclusive occupation with many categories of personnel, it is necessary to define the legal and professional bases for these groupings.

There is always concern by health economists and health policy analysts that professional licensure decreases access to defined fields of employment, increases the cost of the protected service, and that the process of licensure is almost always effectively controlled by members of the group being licensed (Feldstein, 1983). It is also true that licensed workers, as defined units of production, save employers large expenditures through selective recruitment and greatly reduced on-the-job training and supervision costs. There are no cost-benefit or cost-effectiveness studies that have attempted to compare these alternatives. Certainly, in nursing, the public has not paid a high price for the safety and improved quality that licensure provides.

All terms and definitions used in this section are taken from the final report of the 1979 American Nurses' Association (ANA) *Study of Credentialing in Nursing*. That report begins with the basic premise that:

> *credentialing exists primarily to benefit and protect the public. In addition, . . . credentialing also benefits those who are credentialed. The legitimate interests of the involved occupation of institution and of the general public should be reflected in each credentialing mechanism. Accountability should be an essential component of any credentialing process . . . a system of checks and balances within the credentialing system should assure equitable treatment of all parties involved. Periodic assessments with the potential for sanction are essential components of an effective credentialing mechanism. Objective standards and criteria and persons competent in their use, are essential to the credentialing process. (American Nurses' Association, 1979, pp. 43–46)*

These, then, are some of the underlying principles that must exist to protect the general public and the individual consumer as well as the individual who is credentialed.

Educational Degrees

An academic degree is a title awarded to an individual who has successfully taken an officially recognized predetermined series of steps in a particular branch of learning. The designation of the degree signifies the level of education and indicates an arts or science area. The professional degree is similar but the designation differs in indicating the specific professional field of study. (American Nurses' Association, 1979, p. 69)

The degree attests to a level of knowledge at some point in time, but it cannot be used alone to demonstrate continued competence.

Since the American Nurses' Association position paper on nursing education in 1965, it has been clear that the BSN was the profession's preferred route of entry into nursing. The BSN degree is followed by the master's (MSN) degree with a major in nursing and the doctorate (PhD or DNS) for those wishing research preparation, increasingly a requirement for a career in academic nursing. These three degrees are the standards of professional nursing education.

The 1986 publication of the American Association of Colleges of Nursing titled *Essentials of College and University Education for Professional Nursing* delineates the essential knowledge, practice, and values for the education of the professional nurse. This monograph clearly enunciates upper division (junior and senior years of college) expectations of a college education.

Associate degrees earned in community colleges are the standard for preparation in technical nursing. Increasingly, programs originally intended for the preparation of licensed practical nurses are being merged into associate programs. There is no public or professional reason for maintaining both programs for there is not enough difference in 12 months versus 18 months of preparation. To merge the two categories takes LPN program graduates out of the cul-de-sac of blocked opportunities for advancement.

It logically follows that every type of program cannot be available in every community. Students of nursing may have to travel to appropriate colleges or universities as do students in other professional fields. The fundamental educational pattern in nursing generalizes to 2–4–6–8 years or 4–6–8 years of higher education as follows:

Associate Degree — Technical Nursing (AD or ADN)

Bachelor Degree — Professional Nursing (BSN, BS, BN)

Master's Degree — Advanced Specialization (MSN, MS, MN)

Doctoral Degree — Research Competence (PhD, DNS)

Individuals will continue to make choices regarding their own preparation and, for many, it will mean development of different levels of competency at different periods of their life.

Licensure and Registration

> Licensure *is a process by which an agency of state government grants permission to individuals accountable for the practice of that profession and prohibits all others from legally doing so. It permits use of a particular title. Its purpose is to protect the public by ensuring a minimum level of professional competence. Established standards and methods of evaluation are used to determine eligibility for initial licensure and for periodic renewal. Effective means are employed for taking action against licensees for acts of professional misconduct, incompetence, and/or negligence. (American Nurses' Association, 1979, pp. 64–65)*

> Registration *is a process by which qualified individuals are listed on an official roster maintained by a governmental or non-governmental agency. It enables such persons to use a particular title and attests to employing agencies and individuals that minimum qualifications have been met and maintained. (American Nurses' Association, 1979, p. 66)*

These terms are not used properly in nursing. Early legal efforts in the United States generally consisted of state registries of graduates of approved schools of nursing and thus the name *registered nurse*. In the late 1940s and 1950s, state registration laws were expanded to include *licensed practical nurses*. These terms have been written into licensure laws of all 50 states and into countless federal and state health system regulations.

The ANA's House of Delegates in 1985 voted to retain the title registered nurse for the professional nurse holding a baccalaureate degree with a major in nursing. The title associate nurse was accepted for persons who practice technical nursing. Such persons should enter practice holding an associate degree in nursing. The House of Delegates reaffirmed that these degrees should be awarded by state-chartered institutions of higher learning, repudiating once more the preparation offered by hospital-based diploma schools of nursing (Selby, 1985). The title associate nurse is congruent with that passed by the International Council of Nurses (McCarty, 1985).

Over time, on a state-by-state basis, it is proposed that the title registered nurse be restricted to professional nurses who have earned their baccalaureate degrees with a major in nursing and who can assume responsibility for the full scope of nursing practice. In most states, persons already licensed as registered nurses, more than likely, would be permitted to retain that title as long as they maintain active registration. To legally continue licensure status in this manner (grandfathering) is generally recognized as professionally humane and politically necessary in order to get the support of legislators who do not wish to offend, or economically harm, constituents.

Some individual states may choose not to license any LPNs into a new technical nursing category or might choose to license only LPNs who provide special evidence of competency in the category. States electing not to grandfather all LPNs into an associate nurse category would probably continue to renew LPN licenses while not licensing new LPNs.

Certification

> Certification *is a process by which a non-governmental agency or association certifies that an individual licensed to practice a profession has met certain predetermined standards specified by that profession for specialty practice. Its purpose is to assure various publics that an individual has mastered a body of knowledge and acquired skills in a particular specialty. American Nurses' Association, 1979, p. 88)*

Through a program of documented experience, education, and written examinations, certification is awarded in a field of practice. Certification is particularly needed to recognize competence in areas of advanced specialization at the master's level. Gradually, the practice divisions of the ANA are raising the criteria for their respective certification processes. The term registered nurse clinical specialist (RNCS) is used to recognize competence in a specialty area included in a master's program in nursing. When an academic degree is not required, registered nurse certified (RNC) is the designation. Certification also requires updating every 5 years, designed to assure a competence currency requirement (Fickeissen, 1985).

Some certification programs exist outside of the ANA. These include nurse midwives (American College of Nurse Midwives), nurse anesthetists (Council on Certification of Nurse Anesthetists) and operating room nurses (Association of Operating Room Nurses). In addition there are certification programs that represent practice limited to a specific field of nursing rather than advanced preparation in that field. These programs might be compared to a physician who limits his or her practice to adult medicine but who has not had the advanced preparation required of physicians who are Board certified in Internal Medicine.

Margretta Styles, serving as a Distinguished Scholar of the American Nurses Foundation, was asked to study specialization and what constitutes a speciality in nursing. She has proposed that an approved speciality should provide evidence of the following:

1. The speciality defines itself as nursing and subscribes to the overall purpose and functions of nursing.
2. The specialty subscribes to the overall education, practice, and ethical standards of the profession.
3. There is both demand and need for the services of the specialty.
4. The specialty is national in its geographic scope.
5. The specialty is clearly defined in relationship to and differentiated from other specialties.
6. The specialty is sufficiently complex and advanced that it is beyond the qualifications for general practice.
7. Practice standards have been developed for the specialty.
8. The specialty knowledge base is well developed and is concerned with phenomena and problems within the discipline and practice of nursing.

9. Mechanisms exist for supporting, reviewing, and disseminating research.
10. Advanced education programs, leading to a certificate or graduate degree in nursing, prepare specialists in the field. A process exists for peer review of such programs to ensure that the standards of the Board are met.
11. The area of specialization includes a substantial number of practitioners who devote most of their practice to the specialty.
12. Practitioners of the specialty are licensed as registered nurses.
13. A peer review certification program exists to evaluate candidates to ensure initial and continued competence in the specialty.
14. Practitioners are organized and represented within a specialty association or branch of a parent organization. (Styles, 1989, pp. 57–58)

Accreditation

> Accreditation *is the process by which a voluntary, non-governmental agency or organization appraises and grants accredited status to institutions and/or programs or services which meet predetermined structure, process, and outcome criteria. Its purposes are to evaluate the performance of a service or educational program and to provide to various publics information upon which to base decisions about the utilization of the institutions, programs, services, and/or graduates. Periodic assessment is an integral part of the accreditation process in order to ensure continual acceptable performance. Accreditation is conducted by agencies which have been recognized or approved by an organized peer group of agencies as having integrity and consistency in their practices. (American Nurses' Association, 1979, p. 70)*

With the establishment of the National League for Nursing (NLN) in 1952 came the accreditation program for schools of nursing. This has been a very successful program of the NLN and has had a significant effect in upgrading the quality of education in baccalaureate and higher degree programs.

Many institutions have not sought accreditation for associate degree programs. The explanation has been that accreditation is expensive to the school and that recruitment of students is local and not affected by accreditation status. It is also true that programs which do not seek accreditation do not have external reviewers (1) asking questions about curricular decisions or (2) seeking documentation regarding the quantity and quality of nursing faculty and students.

In 1980 to 1981, 97 percent of graduations were from baccalaureate programs accredited by the NLN but only 65 percent of graduations were from associate programs accredited by the NLN (National League for Nursing, 1984). Nurse educators developing their own careers are advised to gain teaching experience in accredited institutions so as not to limit their mobility.

NLN accreditation of nursing services programs has had a very different history. Hospitals have been unwilling to have their nursing departments accredited separately from the hospital itself. There are legitimate concerns about duplication of effort and increased costs. The NLN has been recognized by the federal government for the accreditation of freestanding home care agencies. In the case of home care agencies owned and operated by hospitals, these are accredited as part of the hospital.

Nursing Practice Standards

The education, licensure, certification, and accreditation standards provide the major criteria for evaluating the structure of nursing. The nursing practice standards, as well as the Nurse Practice Acts which legally define the practice of nursing in a particular state, provide the criteria for evaluating the process of nursing.

Scope of Practice

In 1987, the House of Delegates of the American Nurses' Association approved a new statement of the scope of nursing practice clearly delineating that there is a single scope of clinical nursing practice. Within that scope there are differences between the professional and technical practice of nursing related to the knowledge base of the practitioner, role of the practitioner, and the nature of the practice environment. ANA's *The Scope of Nursing Practice* (1987) makes clear that technical nurses practice in settings in which nursing is controlled through mechanisms such as organized nursing services, professional staff structures, and professional nursing standards, policies, procedures, and protocols. The practice of professional nurses is limited only by the depth and breadth to which the profession has evolved.

Nurses in individual states will attempt to incorporate model language into their own nurse practice act when the act is next opened for revision. Revision of the state's practice act is a political process, and it is not always possible to revise the act as nursing leaders might desire. The revision of a state's practice act may follow by years the profession's revised definition of its scope of practice.

In the meantime, the profession's definitions are important because in court cases those definitions can be used to demonstrate a professional standard having broad support even though it does not have the force of law in a particular state. The profession's definition of what is, and what is not, nursing practice is the single most important standard.

The New York State Statute is probably the strongest in the United States in that it defines a profession independent of medicine. That law states:

> *The practice of the profession of nursing as a registered professional nurse is defined as diagnosing and treating human responses to actual and potential health problems through such services as case finding, health teaching, health counseling and provision of care supportive to or restorative of life and well*

being, and executing medical regimes prescribed by a licensed or otherwise authorized physician or dentist. A nursing regime shall be consistent with and shall not vary any existing medical regime. (N.Y. Education Law in Henry, 1987, 6–7.)

It is the responsibility of service institutions to not expect employed nurses to engage in practices that are in violation of the law. In the past nurse administrators may have found it necessary to resign in protest over an institutionally demanded illegality. Any individual nurse questioning a practice as being in violation of the nurse practice act of that state should consult the state nurses' association. If the law is not being violated, the nurse's employment might be jeopardized unnecessarily in a public display of conflict. If the law is being violated, it is very important that all of the nurses— nurse managers and nursing staff—take united action, which can only be done with the assistance of the professional association.

An example of a difficult situation may be when an institution asks a nurse to train a subordinate to take over a nursing function when there are insufficient numbers of nurses available to carry out that activity. Delegation of functions coinciding with advancing technology is common, and whether it is or is not in violation of the practice act may be a complex matter (LaBar, 1986). It is important not to ignore the new practice but, instead, obtain expert opinion. If the nurse practice act is not supported by practicing nurses, some institutions may employ cheaper substitutes and expect the existing nurses to train them. The public must be protected when economic motivations drive the decision making without regard for the quality and safety of nursing care.

Code for Nurses

The *Code for Nurses* (last revised in 1985) has been developed by the American Nurses' Association and represents the standard of behavior for professional nurses. Courts readily utilize professional codes in determining the "community standard" of behavior applicable to that profession's practitioners. It is important that individual nurses understand the code and realize that its application as a community standard for registered nurses is an important protection to client welfare.

Practice Standards

In 1973 the American Nurses' Association published the *Standards of Nursing Practice*, which is a generic definition of how nursing should be practiced based upon the use of the nursing process. Various nursing practice divisions of the ANA have developed standards for specific areas of practice. Certainly every nurse has an obligation to uphold the standards of professional practice of the clinical area in which employed. Professional practice standards developed or revised between 1976 and 1986 include the following:

Standards of Community Health Nursing Practice

Standards of College Health Nursing Practice

Standards of Home Health Nursing Practice

Standards of Nursing Practice in Correctional Facilities

Standards of School Nursing Practice

Standards of Gerontological Nursing Practice

Standards of Maternal–Child Health Nursing Practice

Standards of Rehabilitation Nursing Practice

Standards of Perioperative Nursing Practice

Standards of Cardiovascular Nursing Practice

Standards of Psychiatric–Mental Health Nursing Practice

Standards of Child and Adolescent Psychiatric and Mental Health Nursing Practice

Standards of Practice for the Perinatal Nurse Specialist

Standards of Pediatric Oncology Nursing Practice

Standards of Neurological and Neurosurgical Nursing Practice

Standards of Urologic Nursing Practice

Standards of Practice for the Primary Health Care Nurse Practitioner

Standards of Organized Nursing Services

In addition to standards of practice, there are professionally defined standards for the organization of nursing services. These were updated by the ANA in 1988 and at that time were made applicable to all health service settings. The standards are repeated here but the reader is strongly encouraged to see them in more complete form with the criteria for each standard also listed.

1. Organized nursing services have a philosophy and structure that ensure the delivery of effective nursing care.
2. Organized nursing services are administered by qualified and competent nurse administrators.
3. The nurse executive determines and administers the fiscal resources of organized nursing services. The nurse executive has an interactive role in the determination of the organization's fiscal resource requirements and their acquisition, allocation, and utilization.
4. Within organized nursing services, the nursing process is used as the framework for providing nursing care to recipients.
5. An environment is created within organized nursing services that en-

hances nursing practice and facilitates the delivery of care by all nursing staff.
6. Organized nursing services have a quality assurance program.
7. Organized nursing services have policies to guide ethical decision making based on the code for nurses.
8. Within organized nursing services, research in nursing, health, and nursing systems are facilitated; research findings are disseminated; and support is provided for integration of these findings into the delivery of nursing care and nursing administration.
9. Organized nursing services provide policies and practices that address equality and continuity of nursing services and recognize cultural, economic, and social differences among recipients served by the health care organization. (American Nurses' Association, 1988, pp. 3–8)

Every nurse should maintain a personal collection of (1) *The Scope of Nursing Practice*, (2) *Nursing: A Social Policy Statement* (which defines the practice of nursing), (3) *Nursing Standards* (for his or her particular field of nursing), (4) *Standards for Organized Nursing Services*, and (5) *Code for Nurses with Interpretive Statements*. These publications are available from the American Nurses' Association and are the official positions about nursing as made by the professional association. These statements can be used over and over again to promote the professionalization of nursing practice in work settings.

Quality Assurance

Most quality assurance activities as observed today originated in the 1970s and became a formal program requirement in 1979 when the Joint Commission on Hospital Accreditation, for the first time, included a quality assurance (QA) standard in its accreditation requirements. The new QA requirements included two fundamental components: an institution has to develop (1) an effective problem-solving process that identifies and resolves important problems in patient care and (2) a comprehensive program that integrates or coordinates all quality-related activities.

QA activities after 1979 became focused upon resolving problems that may pose dangers to clients. There is considerably less emphasis on specific numerical requirements, such as performing so many chart audits in a period of time, that were a common early goal. Today the goal is to identify problems and correct them, collecting as much data as are needed for that purpose. At this time QA programs involve every department of the institution. There is also considerable linkage between QA and continuing education to correct or modify staff performance that may be a cause of the QA-identified problem (Affeldt & Walczak, 1984).

In many institutions, programs in "risk management" or avoidance and correction of problems that could lead to institutional liability are combined with QA. Risk management programs not aligned with QA tend to emphasize the avoidance of lawsuits rather than the correction of problems.

Quality Assurance programs are often directed and staffed by nurses because they have the technical knowledge, interpersonal and management skills, understand the activities of other departments, and have better knowledge of the institution as a whole. A report in *Hospitals* (Insurance, 1987) indicated that registered nurses have primary responsibility for QA in 52 to 56 percent of hospitals.

Integration of Costs, Standards, and Quality of Care

The Joint Commission on Accreditation of Healthcare Organizations, in its fourth nursing service standard, calls for a "sufficient number of qualified registered nurses on duty at all times to give patients the nursing care that requires the judgment and specialized skills of a registered nurse" (1988, p. 137) The Commission also specifies that the number of registered nurses and ancillary nursing personnel needed can be determined only by evaluating the patient care requirements and the staff expertise. In this standard, nursing is given a threefold mandate to: (1) evaluate the patients' nursing care requirements (2) utilize appropriate levels of nursing personnel and (3) integrate these factors to provide a staff of sufficient numbers and competence for quality care.

In addition, within organized nursing services, it is important to be able to relate the costs of care inputs to the value of care outputs. Are the activities prescribed by nurses effective and, if that is true, are these services rendered in an efficient manner? Progress is being made in defining and measuring some pieces of the puzzle. It is important to realize that other professions, not just nursing, have failed to define in an objective manner the value of their services. Nursing's problems merely reflect the state of productivity research in the field of human services (Davis & Levine, 1986).

Care Requirements

Most care measures have derived from medical science (measures of clinical state or stage for routine care and critical care), management science (measures of resources utilized such as for DRGs or skilled care facilities), or nursing science (measures of patient need for nursing as in St. Luke's Hospital–Phoenix classification scale, Medicus Systems, GRASP Systems, etc.). Early studies of patients' needs for nursing care were instrumental in the development of critical care units to provide high quantities of care for patients with high levels of need.

Using time studies and other work measurement tools, institutions have developed instruments to measure the nursing care requirements of patients. Since 1979 hospitals, as an accreditation requirement, must regularly make such assessments. Some instruments categorize patients into prototypes in relation to their care requirements, such as self-care, assisted care, moderate care, and critical care; other instruments involve checking of procedures or tasks (Giovannetti, 1979). Time allotted for each patient is then summed to create a time estimate for nursing care on that unit (Lewis & Carini, 1984; Jackson & Resnick, 1982).

Prescott and Phillips have developed a Patient Intensity of Nursing Index, which is an improved classification concept as it measures both the amount and the complexity of care needed. This is obviously a better measure of resource consumption. The complexity measure contains two items: "one that focuses on knowledge, skill and experience associated with the procedures and treatments needed by the patients and another that focuses on the complexity of decision making measured in terms of the nursing process and the level of personnel appropriate for the patient's care" (Prescott & Phillips, 1988, p. 20). The examination of 19 Patient Classification Systems demonstrated the great range in hours assigned to patients by level of care.

While some type of patient classification device is in use in all accredited institutions, there is considerable variation in the reliability and validity of these instruments. Many institutions infrequently, or never, repeat the reliability and validity studies necessary to assure that the instrument is measuring in a consistent manner that which it purports to measure. This is not done in spite of extensive turnover in nursing staff using the instrument (Alward, 1983; Giovannetti & Mayer, 1984; Kasper, 1986).

Staffing Mix

The system of credentialing nurses for different competency levels can be cost effective for service institutions if personnel are utilized appropriately and not necessarily all levels employed in a single institution or on a single care unit. If this cannot be assured, the public is at risk of receiving inept and incompetent care and, for the institution, the cost of supervising and training personnel who are inappropriately assigned offsets any potential savings. To equate RN personnel, from an inexperienced associate graduate to a master's-prepared clinical nurse specialist, in a staffing ratio of "RNs: LPNs: Other Personnel" is inadequate.

Cleland has developed indices that make possible the quantification of nursing practice levels and nursing care requirements, the relating of the two into a composite score, and finally into a staffing evaluation model (Cleland, Marz, & Killeen, 1985).

Competency Full-time Equivalents Score

This registered nurse categorization system is based upon three factors: level of nursing education, job-relevant experience, and nursing management and peer evaluation of job performance. To require RN3s and RN4s to have ANA certification is a useful way to document competence. RN3s should be expected to have certification as a generalist and RN4s would be expected to have Advanced Certification in their respective fields of practice.

Relative to the compensation model in Chapter 5, the assumption here is that each of these four levels of registered nurses is functioning as clinical practitioners, which is their position factor. Compensation also would be influenced by education and performance stage.

The four RN employment levels are described below (Cleland, Marz, & Killeen, 1985).

Registered Nurse 1 (RN1)

This is an associate degree or diploma graduate with less than one year of experience, a baccalaureate graduate receiving orientation, or a nurse without recent applicable experience in nursing practice. RN1s function under the direction of a more experienced nurse. (A registered nurse who floats temporarily on another unit is classified as an RN1 in relation to the level of care that can be assumed during that assignment, but pay level is not altered since the move was management's choice. If floating is a regular occurrence within 2 to 3 units of the same clinical service, no adjustments are required.)

Registered Nurse 2 (RN2)

This is an associate degree or diploma graduate who has had at least one year of applicable experience within the last five years and has completed orientation or a baccalaureate graduate who has completed orientation. Essential responsibilities consist of planning and organizing patient care congruent with the medical therapy plan (basic care).

Registered Nurse 3 (RN3)

This is a graduate of an accredited baccalaureate nursing program who has had one year of clinical experience and demonstrates ability to practice professional nursing in a clinical area. This nurse has responsibility and authority for planning, providing, and evaluating care for a specific group of patients and is expected to have understanding and skill in the use of teaching and learning theories, exercise group leadership, and can evaluate the work performance of others. An RN3 is able to engage in effective group teaching and can carry out a home assessment, by telephone or in person, of a discharged patient.

Registered Nurse 4 (RN4)

This is a graduate of a master's degree program with a major in nursing who has had at least three years of applicable experience within the last five years. This nurse is able to utilize a comprehensive understanding of mental health concepts, community nursing, family dynamics, teaching–learning theories, and management of care in addition to demonstrated competency in a specialty area of clinical practice. The RN4 may have a component of time assigned to a functional area such as administration, teaching, or quality assurance as well as direct care contributions (advanced practice).

The Competency Full-Time Equivalent Score (COFTES) combines the practice level data with the number of full-time equivalents to provide a measure reflective of both the quality and quantity of the staff. The Competency FTE Score (pronounced COF'tes) is computed

$$\text{COFTES} = (S_{RN4} \times 4.0) + (S_{RN3} \times 3.0) + (S_{RN2} \times 2.0) + (S_{RN1} \times 1.0)$$
$$= (S_{LPN} \times 0.5)$$

where S is the number of staff hours provided by the respective levels of nursing personnel. Staff hours are multiplied by a constant reflecting the competency weighting assigned to each category.

Nursing Care Classification Score

The purpose of this index is to combine patient care classification data, which reflect distinctions in patients' nursing care requirements and census data. The Nursing Care Classification Score (pronounced NICKS) is computed

$$\text{NCCS} = (P_1 \times H_1) + (P_2 \times H_2) + (P_3 \times H_3) + (P_4 \times H_4)$$

where P is the number of patients and H is the hours of care used as a standard in an institution for the respective categories of patients. The sum of $P_1 + P_2 + P_3 + P_4 = $ the unit census. The NCCS represents the total direct hours of nursing care needed on the unit and can be computed using any valid and reliable classificatory instrument.

Tetradic Score

Since the Nursing Care Classification Score relates the number of patients to their nursing care requirements and the Competency Full-Time Equivalents Score relates the number of full-time equivalent staff members to their competency level, it is useful to divide the COFTES by the NCCS to create a single score to relate the four measures:

$$\text{TS} = \frac{\text{COFTES}}{\text{NCCS}}$$

It is identified as a nursing unit's Tetradic Score (TS) because this score synthesizes the four measures of the *quantity* and *quality* of *patients'* nursing care requirements with the *quantity* and *quality* of the *nursing staff*. The TS by itself has no standard and thus cannot be evaluated. It is used in the Staffing Evaluation Model, which provides a standard.

Staffing Evaluation Model

In this model (Cleland, Marz, & Killeen, 1985), nursing administration determines staffing requirements for each nursing unit. The patients' nursing requirements are quantified through a patient care classification instrument, and the nursing staff hours are determined by relating hours of care to levels of competency of nursing personnel.

The steps in the use of the staffing evaluation model are:

1. Determine the average Nursing Care Classification Score (hours) for the unit.
2. Develop a staffing model for the unit based upon nursing hours required.
   Stage 1—Determine minimal core staff
   Stage 2—Distribute variable staff hours
   Stage 3—Transpose staff hours to budget requirements
3. Compute competency points for model staffing.
4. $\dfrac{\text{Model COFTES}}{\text{Model NCCS}} = \text{Model Tetradic Score}$

   $\dfrac{\text{Actual COFTES}}{\text{Actual NCCS}} = \text{Actual Tetradic Score}$

   $\dfrac{\text{Actual TS}}{\text{Model TS}} = \text{Staffing Ratio} \times 100 = \begin{array}{l}\text{Staffing Evaluation Score (SES)} \\ \text{or percentage of staffing model}\end{array}$

The Model Tetradic Score is based upon the staffing level approved by management at the time of budget preparation and becomes the standard for that unit. Other units in the setting would have a different standard based upon their staffing needs relative to their planned census and all the other factors that enter into a staffing plan. Actual Tetradic Score can be determined for a day, a week, or any other time period. When the Actual Tetradic Score is divided by the Model Tetradic Score and multiplied by 100, the resultant percentage if above 100 percent would indicate a higher staffing level than planned and if below 100 percent a lower level than intended. This score provides an evaluation of the mix of quantity and quality of patient care requirements relative to the quantity and quality of staff present. External reviewers can examine both the adequacy of the model plan and the adequacy of achievement.

Costing of Care

Once the hours of direct care needed for a particular patient census are known, it is relatively easy to add the indirect hours (nursing hours not used directly in patient care) and determine total staffing needs and budget requirements for that unit. All indirect costs will be fixed costs, that is, will not vary with normal census fluctuations. It is common to include some of the direct hours of the staffing requirement as a fixed cost. This assumes that as long as the unit is operating, some level of direct care hours are needed. Where nursing divisions put baccalaureate-prepared nurses on salary, those services are considered a fixed cost. The remainder are variable costs, that is, costs that vary according to the census.

Direct hours as an accounting concept and direct hours as a nursing concept, meaning in the presence of the patient, should not be confused. The latter is not relevant for costing purposes.

Some institutions are using patient classification instruments, which record the variable demand for nursing care, as a device for implementing a system of variable patient billing for nursing care (Higgerson & Van Slyck, 1982; Mitchell, Miller, Welches & Walker, 1984). It is possible to develop actual hourly costs for nursing care on a particular unit and then multiply that cost rate by the number of hours of care for a particular patient. The nursing care cost for an individual patient will vary then according to his or her own nursing care requirements as identified by the staff. The traditional per diem charge for routine services is divided, and the patient is billed separately for the hotel-type costs and for nursing care. Nursing care is computed as direct care costs for that patient plus a per diem share of all indirect costs. For costing purposes, it is better to use institution-wide average salary costs for various categories of workers so that all nursing care costs are developed on the same cost basis.

Commercial insurers have responded well to variable billing but Medicare DRG payments are not affected. Costing data developed by institutions accurately enough to permit variable billing are also very useful for budgeting, pricing of services, and in negotiating discounts for selected purchasers. To engage in variable billing of the nursing care provided brings an opportunity for a new level of professional accountability. When consumers are made knowledgeable about the services for which they are charged, they ask questions and seek explanations. Such questions, in turn, increase nursing's leverage within the institution (Walker, 1983; Riley & Shaefers, 1983; Minyard, Wall & Turner, 1986; Conference on Costing Hospital Nursing Services, 1987).

Cost by Quality Levels

Ehrat (1987) has published a paper relating quality assurance results to nursing labor hour and, thus, to costs. There has been a great increase in concern about quality with the prospective payment system because of the inherent potential danger to provide less care in order to save money. Ehrat, in demonstrating how the cost-quality data can be related, is careful to avoid any suggestion of defining acceptable levels of quality effectiveness, efficiency, or cost. Rather, these are techniques that can be used to quantify what are inherently qualitative characteristics—the nature of nursing care received.

Table 10–1 is taken from Ehrat. This particular unit has defined 20 quality assurance criteria. Some of these criteria are common to all nursing units in

Table 10-1 Nursing Unit Quality Care Criteria

Month _____

Criteria	Column 1 Weight	Column 2 Points per compliance	×	Column 3 # in compliance (1-10)	=	Column 4 Total score
1. Prescribed treatments are administered to the patients as ordered (record review).	8% (80 pts.)	8	×	10	=	80
2. Medications are administered correctly to the patients ±30 minutes of ordered times (record/physician order review).	8% (80 pts.)	8	×	6	=	48
3. Patient responses to analgesic medication are evidenced in the patient record.	7% (70 pts.)	7	×	8	=	56
4. Care plans are individualized to the patients including teaching needs.	8% (80 pts.)	8	×	10	=	80
. . . .	. . . . .	. . . .		. . . .		. . . . . .
. . . .						. . . . . .
. . . .						. . . . . .
20. Narcotics and controlled substances records are properly signed.	2% (20 pts.)	2	×	9	=	m 18
Total	100% (1000 pts.)					839

SOURCE: Ehrat, K., (1987). Cost-quality balance. *Journal of Nursing Administration, 17*(5), 8. Reprinted with permission of J. B. Lippincott, Philadelphia, PA.

the hospital while some are specific to the unit. The criteria are assigned weights according to staff beliefs about relative importance. Through a process of random sampling, each criterion is examined ten times during the month (or week). Column 3 shows the number of times the criterion was found to be in compliance. The compliance level times the weight produces a subscore for that criterion. These are all added to create a nursing unit quality care score. The raw quality care score can be divided by the maximum possible score to produce a percentage of quality effectiveness.

$$\frac{839 \text{ raw quality score}}{1000 \text{ maximum raw quality score}} = .839 \text{ Quality effectiveness}$$

Then to obtain some measure of efficiency, Ehrat suggests using the patient days of service provided divided by the worked hours.

$$\frac{870 \text{ patient days (output)}}{2560 \text{ worked hours (input)}} = .340 \text{ patient days per worked hour}$$

This means for every worked hour, the nursing unit produced .340 patient days. Patient days could be multiplied by the average acuity level of those patients and convert output to the number of patient acuity days.

Returning to Ehrat's example, one can multiply the quality effectiveness (.839) times the number of patient days to obtain the number of quality days.

$$\text{Measure of Quality Output} \times \text{Patient Days} = \text{Quality Days}$$
$$.839 \times 870 = 730 \text{ Quality Days}$$

$$\frac{730 \text{ Quality Days}}{2560 \text{ Worked Hours}} = .285 \text{ Quality Days per Worked Hour}$$

Ehrat demonstrates a series of techniques that make it possible for nurses on a unit to actually track their unit's quality efficiency. Since the same nurses would probably select the quality assurance standards for their unit, this can become a useful mechanism for staff teamwork as well as providing meaningful data. Quality audits should be performed on a random basis by nurses from other units.

Using quite a different model, Deines (1985) has shown how varying hours of care can be related to the standards of care on the unit (Table 10–2). Deines' work is particularly meaningful when staffing is not at an appropriate level for any reason. This helps the staff to determine in *advance* of the situation what care can be provided and what activities left undone. On the basis of available staffing, the nurses provide optimum care, good care, fair care, or safe care. This is a useful method to assist the nursing staff to reduce services when staff have not been made available. It provides a way to document the effect of inadequate staffing. At the same time it permits clinical judgment to be used to best protect patients' welfare.

Table 10–2 Levels of Care Based Upon Various Hours Per Patient Day

Quality assurance			Optimum level HPPD Req. 4.62		Good level HPPD Req. 3.83		Fair level HPPD Req. 2.84		Safe level HPPD Req. 2.58	
Care required	# of pts. requiring this care	Av. time required each task	Frequency	Total time required (minutes)	Frequency	Total time required (minutes)	Frequency	Total time required (minutes)	Frequency	Total time required (minutes)
HYGIENE										
Bath & Bed	65%/25.25 35%/15.75	6 min 18 min	qd &prn	175.5 min 283.5 469 min	qod & prn	229.5	2 × wk & prn	131.1	weekly	65.5 min
Back Care	90%/40.5	3 min	qd & prn	121.5 min	qod & prn	60.75	2 × wk	34.7	weekly & prn	17.0
Mouth Care	10%/4.5	3 min	qid & prn	54 min	tid	40.5	bid	27	qd	13.5
Shampoo	2%/.9	8 min	qod	4 min	2 × wk	2.28	weekly	1.14	prn	.6
Nail Care	35%/15.75	3 min	qod	23.62	2 × wk	6.75	weekly	3.37	qd	1.68
Peri Care	90%/40.5	3 min	qid	486 min	tid	364.5	bid	243	qd	121.5
Comb Hair	35%/15.75	2 min	bid	63 min	qd	31.5	prn	15	prn	15
EXERCISE Ambulation										
1. OOB Walking	15%/6.75	8 min	as ordered (av. qid)	216 min	tid	162	bid	108	qd	54
2. Chair	45%/20.25	4 min	as ordered (av. qid)	324	tid	243	bia	162	qd	81

3. Dangle	10%/4.5	3 min	as ordered (av. qid)	54 min	tid	40.5	bid	27	qd	13.5
4. BRP	45%/20.25	6 min	pt. req. (av. q4h)	729	qid	486	when poss.	121.5	bed pan urinal	81
Bedrest 1. ROM	5%/2.25	6 min	as ordered (av.q4h)	81 min	q shift	40.5	bid	27	qd	13.5
2. Position (turn)	5%/2.25	3 min	q1h (days, eve) q2h	135 min	q3h	54	q4h	40.5	q shift & prn	20.25
T.C & DB	14%/6.3	1 min	q1h (days, eve), q2h nites	126 min	q3h	50.4	q4h	37.8	q shift & prn	25.2
SAFETY 1. Side rails	35%/15.75	1 min	up, prn	15.75	up, prn	15.75	up, prn	15.75	up	8 min
2. Restraints	5%/2.25	5 min	on c̄ q2h removal & reapplication	135 min	q4h	67.5	q8h	33.75	qd	11.25
3. Isolation	Av. 1 pt	2 min	q2h (days, eve), q4h nites	20 min	q3h	16	q4h	12	q6h	8 min
4. Position of surrounding needs (phone, call, light, waste basket, etc.)	all pts.	1 min	maintained	405 min	maintained	405 min	maintained	405 min ⟶		

(continued)

Table 10—2 (Continued)

Quality assurance			Optimum level HPPD Req. 4.62		Good level HPPD Req. 3.83		Fair level HPPD Req. 2.84		Safe level HPPD Req. 2.58	
Care required	# of pts. requiring this care	Av. time required each task	Frequency	Total time required (minutes)	Frequency	Total time required (minutes)	Frequency	Total time required (minutes)	Frequency	Total time required (minutes)
SAFETY (*continued*)										
5. Effective Housekeeping	100%/45	2 min	maintained	810 min —————————————————————————————————————→						
PHYSICAL ASSESSMENT										
1. Observation (subjective)	100%/45	10 min per shift per pt	q1h prn	1350 —————————————————————————————————————→						
2. Planning Nursing Care Plan	20%/9	30 min	initiated on admission	270	within same shift	20/10 270	before end of following shift	20/20 360	within 24 hours	20/20 360
	1005/45	5 min	update q shift & prn	675 ————————————————→			update q 24 hrs	225	update prn	110

SOURCE: Deines, E. (1985). Coping with PPS and DRGs. *Nursing Management, 16*(10), 43. Reproduced with permission by *Nursing Management*.

It becomes apparent that progress is being made in relating standards, staffing, costs, and quality of care. With only a short history, there have been significant accomplishments that sharpen the conceptualization and improve the measurement of the subparts. Eventually an integrated model will be developed using outcome measures of nursing care.

References

Affeldt, J.E., & Walczak, R.M. (1984). The role of JCHA in assuring quality care. In J.J. Pena, A.N. Rosen, & D.W. Light (Eds), *Hospitals quality assurance*. Rockville, MD: Aspen.

Alward, R.R. (1983). Patient classification systems: The ideal vs reality. *Journal of Nursing Administration, 13*(2), 14–17.

American Association of Colleges of Nursing (1986). *Essentials of college and university education for professional nursing*. Washington, DC: Author.

American Nurses' Association. (1973). *Standards of nursing practice*. Kansas City, MO: Author.

American Nurses' Association. (1979). *The study of credentialing in nursing*. Kansas City, MO: Author.

American Nurses' Association. (1985). *Code for nurses with interpretive statements*. Kansas City, MO: Author.

American Nurses' Association. (1987). *The scope of nursing practice*. Kansas City, MO: Author.

American Nurses' Association. (1988). *Standards for organized nursing services*. Kansas City, MO: Author.

Cleland, V., Marz, M.S., & Killeen, M.B. (1985). A nurse staffing evaluation model. *Michigan Hospitals, 21*(2), 13–17.

Davis, A.R. & Levine, E. (1986). *The national conference on nursing productivity: Report of the conference*. Washington, DC: Georgetown University Hospital Nursing Department.

Deines, E. (1985). Coping with PPS and DRGs: The levels of care approach. *Nursing Management, 16*(10), 43–52.

Division of Nursing. (1987). *Costing hospital nursing services: Report of conference*. Washington, DC: Department of Health and Human Services, HRP-090702.

Eddy, D.M. & Billings, J. (1988). The quality of medical evidence: Implications for quality of care. *Health Affairs, 7*(1) 19–32.

Ehrat, K.S. (1987). The cost-quality balance. *Journal of Nursing Administration, 17*(5), 6–13.

Feldstein, P. (1983). *Health care economics*. New York: John Wiley.

Fickeissen, J.L. (1985). Getting certified. *American Journal of Nursing, 85*. 265–269.

Giovannetti, P. (1979). Understanding patient classification systems. *Journal of Nursing Administration, 9*(2), 4–9.

Giovannetti, P. & Mayer, G.G. (1984). Building confidence in patient classification systems. *Nursing Management, 15*(8), 31–34.

Henry, K.H. (Ed.) (1987). *Nursing administration and law manual*. Rockville, MD: Aspen.

Higgerson, N.J. & Van Slyck, A. (1982). Variable billing for services: New fiscal direction for nursing. *Journal of Nursing Administration, 12*(6), 20–27.

Iglehart, J.K. (1988). Competition and the pursuit of quality: A conversation with Walter McClure. *Health Affairs, 7*(1), 79–90.

Insurance and liability. (1987). *Hospitals, 61*(18), 34.

Jackson, B.S. & Resnick, J. (1982). Comparing classification systems. *Nursing Management, 13*(11), 13–19.

Joint Commission on Accreditation of Healthcare Organizations. (1988). *Accreditation manual for hospitals, 1987*. Chicago: Author.

Kasper, D. (1986). The credibility of patient classification instruments. In F.A. Shaffer (Ed.) *Patients and purse strings: Patient classification and cost management.* (pp 23–32). New York: National League for Nursing.

LeBar, C. (1986). *Enforcement of the nursing practice act*. Kansas City, MO: American Nurses' Association.

Lewis, E.N. & Carini, P.V. (1984). *Nursing staffing and patient classification*. Rockville, MD: Aspen.

McCarty, P.I. (1985). ICN adopts Styles report on regulation. *The American Nurse, 17*(7), 3.

Minyard, K., Wall, J., & Turner, R. (1986). RNs may cost less than you think. *Journal of Nursing Administration, 16*(5), 28–34.

Mitchell, M., Miller, J., & Welches, L., & Walker, D. (1984). Determining the cost of direct care by DRGs. *Nursing Management, 15*(4), 29–32.

National League for Nursing. (1984). *Nursing data book 1983–84*. New York: Author.

Prescott, P.H. & Phillips, C.V. (1988). Gauging nursing intensity to bring costs to light. *Nursing and Health Care, 9*(1), 17–21.

Riley, W. & Shaefers, V. (1983). Costing nursing services. *Nursing Management, 14*(12), 40–43.

Selby, T.L. (1985). House votes associate as second title. *The American Nurse, 17*(8), 1.

Styles, M.M. (1989). *On specialization in nursing: Toward a new empowerment*. Kansas City, MO: American Nurses' Association.

Walker, D. (1983). The cost of nursing care in hospitals. *Journal of Nursing Administration, 13*(3), 13–18.

Part V

An Overall View of the
Economics of Health Care
and Nursing

Chapter 11

Government Programs and Policies for Health Care and Their Relation to Nursing

Richard C. McKibbin

Government activity profoundly influences the nation's economy. As a major component of the nation's economy, health care is also greatly influenced by government activity. The United States government has more influence over health care than it does in many other areas of the nation's economy because of the special characteristics of health care, such as special needs to protect the public and to provide at least minimal health services to all people. The purpose of this chapter is to examine government programs and policies for health care and to consider their relation to nursing.

How Government Influences the Health Care Economy

All three levels of government—federal, state, and local—have an influence on the nation's health care delivery system. Examples of each are familiar. Traditionally, local governments have operated public health clinics and agencies as well as hospitals. The county hospital still provides a focal point for acute care for many people, particularly the poor or medically indigent (a category that includes those classified as poor plus those non-poor who do not have enough of their own resources or insurance to pay for their health care needs). Most state governments operate state-owned and state-financed mental hospitals. In addition, some states regulate health care services and providers through mechanisms such as certificate-of-need laws, which re-quire prior approval for major equipment purchases or construction projects. The states also regulate health care through the licensure of nursing homes and other extended care facilities, and through the licensure of health professionals including registered nurses. Since 1965, states have assumed an additional major role in the payment for health care services for the poor and medically indigent through the state-financed portion of Medicaid.

The federal government, in addition to paying a share of the Medicaid program's costs, provides funding for Medicare, the largest government health program. The federal government is also involved in health care in a myriad of other ways. It owns and operates hospitals and clinics that are part of the Veterans Administration, the Defense Department's health system, and the Indian Health Services. It has established and annually spends billions of dollars on and employs tens of thousands of people at the nearly 20 National Institutes of health, the U.S. Public Health Service, and the Centers for Disease Control. These agencies play a critical role in health care research and innovation, such as in current efforts to develop more effective treatments for AIDS. The federal government also oversees a health program·for military personnel and their dependents, the Civilian Health and Medical Program for the Uniformed Services (CHAMPUS).

Apart from these rather direct and fairly obvious roles, the federal government influences health care in other ways. Certain legal and regulatory influences of government on health care are rather subtle. For example, the tax laws permit (for those taxpayers who itemize deductions) the deduction on a federal return of medical expenses. In recent years, however, the threshold level of expenditure before health expenses become deductible has been raised from 2 percent to 5 percent of adjusted gross income. How would this affect the health sector? To a minor extent, no doubt, but some individuals, now knowing that their health expenses would not be large enough to deduct, would try to utilize those services more sparingly, reducing overall health spending in the nation. Thus, this government tax law change, a policy designed primarily to increase tax revenues, also has the effect of reducing health expenditures from the level they would have reached in the absence of the change.

Another example of the subtle influence of government on health care may be illustrative. To encourage private companies to research, develop, and distribute new drugs, drug manufacturers may patent new drug formulations. The patent gives the inventing company the exclusive right to sell and profit from the new drug for a period of years. The rationale for offering patent protection is that, without it, no drug maker would have any incentive to invest in research and development because any or all other drug manufacturers could also freely produce a newly invented drug formulation. Thus, the patent provides a period of exclusive production, potentially high profits, and an incentive to develop new formulations of drugs. It is ironic that the protection offered by patents has led to the discovery of new and effective formularies for some less-common and even rare illnesses, but the potential revenues from the sale of these drugs do not justify, economically, the manufacturer bringing supplies of these drugs to the marketplace. This is a curious situation. The federal government's encouragement of research (through patents) has succeeded to such an extent that the federal government itself must, if these "orphan" drugs are to be made available, step in and subsidize their production and sale. One government policy affecting health care can lead to the creation of another.

Another government influence on the health sector is through educational assistance. For example, funds have been available for students in medical, nursing, and other health professions schools. Loans and grants help with the costs of a medical or nursing education and encourage more students to pursue such careers than would otherwise be the case. The current shortage of nurses, plus a major impending surplus of physicians, may suggest changes in how government funds are directed to these programs. Fewer dollars for educational support should flow to medical schools, and more should be allocated to nursing schools.

The foregoing are but a few examples of the ways in which government, at all levels, influences health care. The general types of influences that government exerts on the health care delivery system are now summarized.

Direct Ownership, Provision, or Control of Health Services

As has been seen, the government may directly own or provide or otherwise fully control the nature of, access to, and quality of health services. In the United States, direct ownership or provision of health services is much less a factor in the health care delivery system than is true in most major developed nations. These other countries utilize a system of national health care, whereby the government owns or operates hospitals and clinics and employs health care professionals and other workers. In the United States this direct, governmentally-controlled component of the health care system is limited to certain areas: the Veterans Administration system, the Department of Defense health care installations, and the Indian Health Services where the federal government has special obligations and responsibilities.

Major debate has occurred for many years as to what extent central control by government of health services is desirable, necessary, or appropriate. A national health insurance system was debated in the U.S. Congress for many years but never adopted. Even this measure would not have conveyed ownership or direct provision of health services into government hands. Instead, it would have provided for the payment, for all Americans, for covered health services received in the private sector. Of course such a system would have been coupled with extensive regulations and other controls.

Should government own, provide, and control health services delivery? The answer is ultimately a philosophical one. Empirically, to an economist, the answer is in part a function of other factors, such as: Do people have uniform access to care? Does discrimination by age, race, or sex limit people's right to health? Does the health system treat people with equal problems equally? Are there substantial barriers, financial or otherwise, that limit the appropriate utilization of health services?

Even if a health care system is found to be defective in terms of such criteria, failing to provide equal access and quality to all, it may not warrant direct ownership, provision, or control of health services delivery. Indirect means may accomplish similar ends.

Legal and Regulatory Influences and Control of Health Services

The second major category or type of influence over health care which government exerts is through legal and regulatory mechanisms. In the earlier example involving a drug company, the patent served as a legal mechanism to bestow the exclusive right of manufacture to the inventor for a period of years. Other incentives to spend more—or less—for health can be found in the tax code and are also examples of government legal influences on health care. Many legal and regulatory influences on health care are even more basic. It is government that controls who can establish a business—and what it can do. Can it be for-profit or not-for-profit? Can health professionals establish a professional corporation in which to practice, thus limiting their individual financial liability? There are the laws regarding tort and limitations for malpractice awards. The government decides what body establishes, licenses, and regulates health professionals and what group, if any, assures the continuing competence of health professionals. How much, and what type of training, if any, must aides, orderlies, attendants, and similar workers have? Must nursing homes have at least one RN on duty each shift? In order to receive payment from government health programs, facilities generally must be approved. What shall approval consist of? Should government itself judge the structural, process, and outcome components of care, or leave this to another agent, such as the Joint Commission on the Accreditation of Healthcare Organizations?

The legal and regulatory influences of government on health care could continue for many pages, even volumes. Medicare's regulations, if assembled in one location, would tally to perhaps 10,000 pages. A 1987 Health Care Financing Administration publication, attempting to examine care quality using mortality data for Medicare recipients who died in or soon after a hospitalization, exceeds 6000 pages in length. Health care workers complain that, in some instances, a significant portion of their work has been prescribed by the legal and regulatory environment in which they practice rather than by the dictates of professionalism and quality care. It is difficult to overestimate the extent to which legal and regulatory matters influence the health care delivery system. Indeed, it seems apparent that government can effectively control the health care system even without direct ownership of health facilities or without directly providing health services through government auspices.

Fiscal Influences on Health Services

Fiscal influences on health care represent the effects on the direction and control of health care that result from the fact that government is the largest payer for health care services. The use of fiscal influences in government programs and policies is widespread; indeed, they are often taken for granted. In combination with legal and regulatory influences, however, these ways in which the nation's government affects health care are part of the social fabric of the nation. Some view this as "safety net" while others perceive the lack of such a net, yet it would be oversimplifying to assert that this governmentally-influenced social fabric for health care only affects the poor, needy, or homeless.

The fiscal influences of government on health care will continue to increase if for no other reason than the government will continue to pay more, both in absolute and relative terms for health care. For example, the proportion of the gross national product (the value of all goods and services produced in the country in a year) devoted to health is expected to rise from 10.9 percent in 1986 to 15.0 percent in the year 2000 (Division of National Cost Estimates, 1987, p. 24). Health expenditures, from 1986 levels to those in 2000, will more than triple, reaching *1½ trillion dollars annually*. With the immense annual expenditures our government will make for health services, it would be naive to believe that the government will have anything less than major, if not controlling, influences over health care programs and policies for the nation. These, in turn, will have important effects on nurses.

The three basic types of government policies and programs influencing health care have been considered. Their potential future influence, as a central component or keystone of the nation's health delivery system, has also been projected. It is therefore appropriate to turn now to specific examples of government programs and policies for health care to show their economic effects on health care and their relation to nursing.

Medicare: Policy and Relation to Nursing

The central federal government program for health is Medicare. Enacted in 1965, Medicare is surrounded by a myriad of policies profoundly affecting health care delivery in the United States and nursing care as well. Medicare warrants careful attention as it is the largest federal health program.

Medicare, the nation's health protection program for the aged, was designed to deal with a long-term legislative concern: the lack of adequate hospital insurance among the elderly. Since Medicare program expenditures come exclusively from federal funds, program control, development, and evolution have been more focused and uniform than has been possible with Medicaid, the nation's health program for the poor, which is jointly funded with the states.

Program Expansion

Expenditure growth under Medicare has been dramatic. In 1968, the program's expenditures represented 2.6 percent of the Federal budget; in fiscal 1988, that percentage has risen to 7.5 percent of the budget. By 1993, 10.6 percent of all federal spending is expected to be devoted to Medicare (Wessel, 1988). In dollar terms, spending growth is even more dramatic: $1 billion was spent in 1966, Medicare's first year of operations; $18.4 billion a decade later and $76 billion in 1986.

Policy revisions have had major impact on Medicare and on segments of the nation's populations. In 1973, coverage was extended to persons suffering from end stage renal disease as it was to certain categories of disabled individuals. Certain changes have also been made in Part B, the physician services and outpatient services component of Medicare. Efforts to change Medicare fiscal and reimbursement policies have, however, been much more dramatic than changes in the population or services covered by Medicare.

Efforts to Contain Costs

Cost containment efforts for Medicare began as early as the 1972 amendments to the Social Security Act. These amendments authorized the government to determine reasonable per diem cost limits and to withhold payments for hospitals deemed to have incurred unreasonable expenses. Professional Standards Review Organizations were established by the same legislation, with a goal of reducing unnecessary hospital days.

Hospitals, like other major components of the economy, had already felt cost control pressures beginning in August 1971, when President Nixon imposed mandatory wage and price controls on American industry to combat inflation. These controls continued, in modified form, through 1974. During this time, health care was also affected by government-stimulated growth (through grants, loans, and other provisions) of health maintenance organizations (HMOs), at least in part with the intent of reducing the demand for and expense of hospital stays. In 1974, a national network of Health System Agencies for state-wide planning was introduced to determine whether new health care equipment purchases or construction projects should be permitted. The goal was to control the development of excess capacity. Excess capacity in health care increases the price of procedures and total expenditures because the basic or fixed costs of providing a service, which are constant, must be divided among fewer patients. President Carter attempted, without success, to persuade Congress to implement mandatory cost controls for hospitals in the late 1970s. Instead, the hospital industry attempted to police itself; the results of this voluntary activity in controlling costs were not very successful.

Over time, these various efforts produced little in the way of control over Medicare expenditure growth. Why? Economists recognized the crux of the dilemma in the area of rapidly increasing Medicare costs as follows: Medicare costs for the government represent the *prices* of services rendered multiplied by the *quantities* of those services (prices × quantities = total expenditure). First, there has been no direct attempt to control prices because of fear that physicians would cease to participate in the Medicare program. This has been true under both Republican and Democratic administrations. The Health Service Agencies were charged by law with being concerned about improving quality and access as well as costs and often made decisions that increased costs; HMOs enrolled only a small segment of the population and virtually no Medicare beneficiaries; the other cost containment policies of the 1970s were similarly ineffective. Second, government policies were unable to control utilization, or quantities, in the equation. Certificate-of-need legislation attempted to address capacity and, indirectly, utilization but did this ineffectively.

If the government did succeed in controlling prices on a few procedures, utilization could still rise, raising total expenses as much as before. If physician office visit fees were capped at $25, the government could find itself unable to control how often patients were asked to return for subsequent visits or what additional laboratory tests might be ordered and charged. Thus, a physician participating in Medicare who might otherwise charge $35 per office visit but was paid $25 by Medicare could capture the difference through more frequent patient visits or through additional tests in the physician's own laboratory.

The entire Medicare program was experiencing year after year of expenditure increases at double-digit rates in the mid and late 1970s and early 1980s. This, plus growing overall federal budget deficits, finally led to dramatic health policy action that has affected all of health care including the nursing profession and individual nurses.

Prospective Payment and DRGs

In March 1983, amendments to the Social Security Act authorized the Medicare program to begin paying for the hospital care of Medicare beneficiaries based on diagnosis-related groups (DRGs) at rates determined prospectively (in advance). The system was implemented beginning in October 1983. The Prospective Payment System (PPS) based on DRGs has had profound effects on health care, on the level of acuity of hospitalized patients, on how much revenue is collected by hospitals from Medicare, and on nurses' workloads and expectations for nurses in the workplace.

These consequences flow from powerful incentives in the PPS payment methodology. Based on a patient's DRG, a hospital receives a fixed, predetermined payment from Medicare. If costs are reduced by having the patient stay fewer days or having fewer tests or procedures, the hospital can keep the money saved. The incentives are clear: reduce lengths of stay and minimize testing and procedures in the treatment of Medicare patients. Actual lengths of stay for those age 65 and older have fallen an average of 2 days since the introduction of PPS.

Many unanswered questions surround the implementation of the prospective payment system. One such is the extent to which the average intensity of care or severity of illness varies within DRGs among different hospitals. Significant variations among hospitals may exist in this regard as discussed below. These have not entered into determination of hospital payment levels from Medicare, thus, raising significant questions about the equity of PPS and how it affects key hospital employees such as nurses.

Potential Problems with DRGs

No two persons suffer from, nor recover from, an episode of illness in an identical fashion. Likewise, people differ in their response rate to treatment regimes so that for any health condition, such as those described by DRGs, the prognoses for the patients will differ, as will their lengths of stay while hospitalized. Their utilization of hospital resources and their dependence on hospital staff vary also. Thus the actual costs of providing care for individuals in a DRG differ, but the payment for each case is fixed under Medicare's PPS.

Variability in length of stay, resource use, and cost within DRGs is not problematic so long as no systematic biases exist among hospitals with respect to these measures of hospital activity. DRG relative costs weights, the basis for determining payment rates under PPS, reflect average values for length of stay, resource use, and costs over large numbers of Medicare patients. Considerable differences exist with respect to these variables within DRGs, however, so that the possibility of systematic biases among hospitals warrants examination.

For example, consider a relatively common Medicare DRG: chronic obstructive pulmonary disease (COPD), with a national average length of stay of 7.4 days. This is one of the DRGs studied in the DRGs and Nursing Care Project (McKibbin et al., 1985). Patients in hospitals under study were hospitalized for as few as one and as many as 24 days for this condition. COPD is a non-surgical, relative-intensive disorder in terms of nursing care requirements. Measures of nursing care for patients in this DRG are thus significant indicators of overall hospital resources devoted to COPD treatment. As measured by a standard patient acuity and nursing care requirements tool, 25 percent of COPD patients requiring the greatest amount of nursing resources were found to utilize five times as much nursing care as the lowest quartile of patients. Clearly, if one hospital could admit primarily those patients requiring only short stays and relatively modest daily levels of nursing resources, such as three, four, and five-day COPD patients, it would be advantageous for it to do so.

Major differences in these measures of hospital activity and costs are found in many, if not most, DRGs. That awareness of the normal ranges could result in biases among hospitals under the Medicare payment plan is, therefore, a justifiable concern. Such biases were not taken into account when the PPS was developed. The 1988 DRG price adjustments, using different rates for large urban, small urban, and rural hospitals, are designed to correct, in part, possible hospital selection bias.

Nursing Care, DRGs, and Medicare's PPS

Major portions of the variations in hospital resource use and cost that arise from differences in patients' severities of illness are attributable to nursing activities. Few methodologies, however, separately or explicitly consider nursing time or nursing costs as a variable for measuring the intensity of hospital care. Robert Fetter, an originator of DRGs, was one of the authors of a recent study indicating that nursing time algorithms may be needed to develop

> distinct subgroups of existing DRGs, subgroups which could not be defined on the basis of routine or ancillary costs alone. In our view, research to introduce nursing weights into existing DRGs is the next logical step in DRG refinement. (Smits, Fetter, and McMahon, 1984, p. 76)

John Thompson, another key individual in the development of DRGs recognizes that,

> At this stage in the development of DRGs, there is an imperfect record of the value and amount of nursing resources used by the individual patient during a single hospital stay. This occurs because the utilization of routine nursing services, unlike those of ancillary services, cannot be derived from the patient's bill. (Thompson, 1984, p. 47)

Increased patient acuity and earlier discharges have resulted in a significant increase in the workload per registered nurse. Nurses who work in settings where allocated registered nurse positions cannot be filled are forced to change the way they provide care. They are required to take on an accelerated pace of activities in an effort to "stay on top of everything." One alteration in their work style often leads to another; as their workload increases they must set new priorities for the nursing care they give. When nurses have an unrealistic workload, the margin for error increases. Patients may not be monitored as frequently or as thoroughly. This means that gradual

changes signaling the onset of more serious problems may not be immediately recognized. Crisis situations occur that might have been prevented.
Psychosocial care, teaching, emotional support, and counseling are often
omitted.

In addition, when vacancies exist, hospitals often mandate that nurses work
extra hours (i.e., double shifts and assigned days off duty). Nurses in one
Louisville, Kentucky, hospital, for example, reportedly have worked as many
as five double shifts a week (American Nurses' Association, 1988). This
exploitation of limited human resources has prompted many nurses to
express concern regarding patients' welfare and the quality of care being
delivered.

The great growth of variable staffing coincides with economic pressures of
the PPS, instituted first by Medicare and followed later by state Medicaid
programs and managed care systems. In turn, variable staffing has promoted
the use of part-time nurses and nurses being sent home, without pay, if
census fluctuated downward. In the short-term this is cost efficient. In the
long-term, it is highly disruptive to nursing and can adversely affect the
profession's desirability. Reports on television about overworked nurses do
not make nursing attractive to teenagers or to those considering a career
change. With variable staffing there are no recovery days, no catch-up days, no
days when there is time to say and to do the nice thing with or for a colleague.
Nurses may become emotionally and physically depleted and turn to part-
time employment or seek other health related careers.

When coping with institutional expectations by reducing their hours,
nurses then demand higher wages to maintain their incomes. This creates
increased demand for nurses, with both higher costs in hourly wages and loss
of productivity per nurse. Health care becomes more expensive and less of it
is available. This situation is neither efficient nor cost effective.

Overall, Medicare's PPS based on DRGs is a fundamental change in a major
government policy for health care. Its effects are far reaching, including
possible dramatic and potentially damaging effects on nursing workloads and
the quality of patient care. As should be evident from the Medicare example,
government programs and policies for health care have a pervasive influence
on health care delivery in the United States.

Regulation and Competition

This section considers competition as an alternative to regulation in health
care. These concepts are central to a major public policy debate occurring in
the nation regarding how government's role in health care should be oriented and how specific government programs and policies should be designed to influence the nation's health care delivery system. At least since the
end of World War II, the United States has relied primarily on regulation to

control health care. Despite regulation, health expenditures have continued to increase at rates much greater than inflation. This plus more conservative political orientation in the nation during the Reagan presidency, has led to an increased interest in competitive means to control health care expenditures.

The Issue of Competition Versus Regulation in Health Care

In recent years, as health care costs have escalated and the political climate has shifted, competition and deregulation have become key concepts. A genuine shift in emphasis and approach toward health care appears to be developing. Government has backed away from advocacy of national health insurance while employers are actively seeking ways to reduce the cost of health coverage for their employees. Continued increases in health costs are interpreted by many as the failure of the regulatory approach and add further interest in competition. A large body of literature on competition in health care is emerging. Legislative initiatives to promote such competition have been introduced in Congress each year since 1980. Proposals suggest the introduction of competitive elements into the health delivery system with reductions of the federal government's role in and financial commitments to health services.

In effect, these recent efforts intend to test the hypothesis that greater reliance on market forces by consumers, employers, insurance carriers, institutional providers, and health professionals will promote greater efficiency in health care delivery, reduce utilization rates, and ultimately control health care costs. If more pro-competitive approaches are adopted, they may ultimately lead to fundamental changes. These changes would affect the organization of health services, utilization rates for various health services, access to health services among subgroups of the population, consumer involvement in health care decisions, and the government's role and responsibility for health services.

A fundamental principle behind competition is the belief, espoused more than 200 years ago by Adam Smith (the founder of economics as a science), that individual consumers making decisions in their own economic self-interest in an open marketplace will solve collective societal problems more effectively than can government. Following this reasoning, supporters of the competitive model turn to the free market for solutions to health care inflation and other problems in the health services sector of the economy.

On the one hand, competition, in a general sense, refers simply to a rivalry. In the simplest business context, it is the effort of two or more parties acting independently to secure the business of a third party by offering more favorable terms of sale. On the other hand, to economists, it can mean price competition in the marketplace that becomes the organizational and theoretical base for many nation's economic systems. In the free market political philosophy, competition involves economic units (consumers and producers) freely and independently making those decisions that affect their exchanges of goods, services, physical and financial resources, and labor efforts. In the process, these units determine the prices and quantities of all the goods, services, assets, and productive resources produced and distributed throughout the economy.

In addition, competition requires the following:

> Buyer's financial responsibility for the consequences of one's actions
>
> Full and complete knowledge on the part of the buyer concerning the product and its price
>
> Large numbers of buyers and sellers so that there is a broad range of choices
>
> Freedom for buyers or sellers to enter or leave the marketplace in response to financial considerations
>
> Limited size of buyers or sellers relative to the market to prevent their actions from influencing market prices

Few actual markets and no entire national economy are truly competitive in all these senses. Health care delivery is clearly not competitive in these regards.

Implications of Competition for Health Care

By the introduction of competition into the health care industry, consumers, rather than government, would theoretically determine what health services they want, how much they are willing to pay for those services, and how much health insurance they wish to have. It is assumed that providers, as a result, would develop innovative and cost-effective ways of delivering care to meet the demands of consumers rather than regulators.

With the multiple and confusing uses of the term competition—and because true competition is not widespread in health care—the term "pro-competition" might be preferable. Pro-competition would refer to an approach for providing incentives for consumers, providers, employers, and insurers (economic units) to act more like they would if competition actually existed. This could also be called simulated competition or regulated competition.

In the most general sense, pro-competition can be achieved best through the use of behavioral incentives. These can encourage desired behaviors (e.g., tax reductions or the introduction of subsidy payments), or negative behaviors (e.g., higher taxes, fees, penalties, or legal prohibitions). Whatever the form, pro-competitive approaches attempt to alter behavior by providing *incentives*. Regulatory approaches, on the other hand, attempt to alter behavior through *prohibitions*. In the most simplistic terms of all, the choice between competition and regulation is a choice between "the carrot and the stick."

From another perspective, pro-competitive approaches can be divided into two general types: proposals for small changes within the existing health care delivery system, or "micro" strategies; and proposals involving fundamental change that alters the health care delivery system itself, or "macro" strategies.

Common Elements in the Pro-competitive Approach

The following three elements exist, in varying degrees, in pro-competitive concepts for health care.

Tax laws would be changed to encourage the choice of less costly employee health insurance programs. Thus, employers who offer health benefits would be required to make available alternative benefit packages, operating under a designated limit on the amount of contributions an employer would be permitted to make that could be treated as untaxed income for the employee. Employers would be required to contribute equal amounts for all employees. If an employee chooses a plan that is less expensive than the employer contribution, some rebate would be due the employee based on the amount by which the chosen benefit package is less than the maximum contribution made by the employer. Thereby, employers would be prohibited from contributing more than a specified amount for tax-free health benefits, and employees would have a financial incentive to choose less costly plans. Certain minimum benefits, of course, would have to be provided in all plans.

All persons would be provided with catastrophic expense provisions providing that any out-of-pocket expenses in excess of a certain (high) dollar amount would be covered by an insurance plan or the government, thus protecting all persons from expensive, financially devastating health care bills.

Some form of cost sharing, through deductible and coinsurance, would be included in plans for both the employed and Medicare or Medicaid beneficiaries in an attempt to foster an awareness of the real costs of health care.

There are, however, practical difficulties inherent in the pro-competitive approach. The mere complexity of these proposals is one such difficulty. These proposals also involve untried concepts in the health care arena and major changes in existing organizational and financing mechanisms. There are concerns over whether or not consumers really want major changes in the current system for financing health care. For example, health maintenance organizations (HMOs) appear to encounter consumer resistance in many areas, limiting their ability to attract enrollees. Providers, as well, tend toward the status quo. Licensure requirements and their attendant limitations on the scope of professional activity within each health profession category may also prove to be a formidable barrier to innovative, pro-competitive approaches. For example, the limitations may prevent new cost-effective programs that use less expensive personnel to perform tasks where the qualifications are not clearly or directly related to the quality of service.

Political Support and Opposition

There are numerous political barriers to the acceptance of pro-competitive health care approaches. Proposals that would change the status quo are likely to bring forth strong political responses from certain provider organizations and some consumer organizations. As a practical matter, the more a pro-competitive strategy depends on major legislative or policy initiatives, the longer it would probably take to implement.

It does appear that support for pro-competitive efforts and legislation comes largely from the following groups:

Those who feel that individuals should bear more of the cost for their own health care services and that this will reduce utilization

Those who believe that competition among providers will reduce the likelihood of more regulation or cost controls on them

Those who hope that pro-competitive approaches will reduce the federal deficit

Those who oppose national health insurance and thus anticipate that the attention on pro-competition will delay or divert such interest

Those who support HMOs

Opposition to pro-competitive health care approaches is evident among the following groups:

Teaching hospitals and financially-strapped inner city hospitals

Private health insurers

Consumer groups, which may not view less insurance and more out-of-pocket expenses as desirable

Organized labor, which could potentially lose much of the relative advantage in terms of health benefits that union workers enjoy and have negotiated for over long periods of time

Employers for whom new procedures, coupled with administrative costs for maintaining multiple health insurance options, could be more burdensome than existing procedures

Individual providers who may feel that competitive models will work to their detriment (especially physicians in solo, fee-for-service smaller practices)

Health care delivery as it exists today has been described as organized, controlled, and managed by the most highly-trained health professionals, primarily physicians, presumably for the common—and their own—good. Physicians tend to dominate the entire health care system, including all nonphysician providers. If the direction in health policy is toward greater reliance on market forces to control costs, it is critical for policy makers to recognize and attempt to reduce the effective control of health care delivery by physicians.

The domination of nonphysician providers by physicians is expressed in a variety of ways, such as through

denial of admitting privileges in hospitals and other facilities, thereby restraining totally a provider's practice

denial of reimbursement without physician supervision or sign-off, even when the provider is operating within the legitimate scope of practice for services otherwise covered by a particular carrier

restrictive licensure laws, often promulgated by physicians

retaliation against physicians who cooperate with nonphysician providers, such as through denial of privileges

Medicine's dominance has often helped to stifle true competition in the health care market by impeding the growth and availability of alternative providers. For competition among providers to develop, alternative, nonphysician providers including nurses must be allowed to engage in more independent practice than is currently permitted. The attitude on the part of physicians that they legitimately should control all aspects of health care runs counter to the desire for competitive reform.

For consumers to gain responsibility for health care and make prudent and cost-effective choices, a shift away from physician control is needed. Consumers or their agents (employers or insurers acting on their behalf) could force the health care delivery industry to become more cost conscious. Consumers must be permitted a free choice of credentialed providers responsive to their particular health needs. For example, if a pregnant woman prefers a nurse midwife to a physician to assist with her delivery, that choice should not be denied, as it is so often today, when the midwife is denied hospital admitting privileges or is not reimbursed by the insurance company involved. The fact that the midwife's services cost half as much as the physician's services should be of interest to any real advocate of price competition in health care. Avoiding organized provider domination is one key to success for a pro-competitive model. Anti-competitive practices have served to limit consumer choice, impede the delivery of alternative forms of care, and greatly contribute to escalating health care costs. Whatever pro-competitive concepts might be adopted, they need to assure that all providers can compete freely in the marketplace.

Implications for Nursing

The public and political debate on the merits of competition in the health care industry has made little or no mention regarding the role of nursing. In many ways, the proposals focus on major changes in the tax code and little else. Such changes in the manner in which health care is delivered and reimbursed, however, do offer a unique opportunity for nursing to improve its professional standing in the health system and equate it more nearly with that of medicine.

The nursing profession must have a hand in shaping competitive concepts in order to ensure fair representation in this emerging health care arena. The following ingredients would be essential to a competitive system that would be equitable to both consumers and nonphysician providers, including nurses.

Nondiscrimination

Insurance companies can discriminate against less costly, alternative care. In order to guarantee consumer choice, a provision similar to State Insurance Equality Laws should be included in all competitive health care concepts. This would require reimbursement for nursing services if the same services provided by a physician would be reimbursed. If a plan covers a particular service, consumers must have the freedom to choose which provider they want. In addition, a pro-competitive approach should preempt any state or local law or regulation that impedes this reform of the health care system, including restrictive state licensure laws.

The varying types of services provided by nurses should be included in the minimum benefit package that must be provided by all certified health plans. The decision as to which services are included in these health plans will have tremendous impact on provider access to the market. For example, qualifying plans could mandate that prenatal and pregnancy benefits would be covered, and the parents would choose who would deliver those services. In such a situation, the cost effectiveness of nursing services would be clearly reflected in the price of the plan and would be obvious to both insurers and consumers. Cost savings would undoubtedly result.

Antitrust

Rigorous antitrust enforcement would be needed to adequately police a deregulated market. Words like competition and deregulation are often used to cloak the removal of selective regulations that particular groups do not like. Competitive health care proposals may be judged "acceptable" if they eliminate the regulatory burden that prevents one group from pursuing its vested self-interest, but this attitude changes radically when competition would actually pose a potential loss of status or income. Yet, in order for competition to succeed, protective laws which shield groups, particularly providers, from competitive forces must also be removed. Currently, anticompetitive practices by physicians against nonphysician providers are numerous and in need of remedy. This situation could be exacerbated even more in a competitive health care system. As a result, appropriate regulations must be in place and enforced in order to ensure that all competitors *can* compete freely. If antitrust laws are not applied, it is hard to imagine how providers, let alone consumers, could be protected from the adverse consequences of economic boycotts or barriers to access of particular services or markets. Given the authority it needs, the Federal Trade Commission would be the appropriate agency to fulfill this role.

Identification of Nursing Costs

Currently, few institutions identify nursing costs accurately or in a way that could be used for reimbursement purposes. Nursing service costs are put into the general category of "routine inpatient operating costs," which also includes the costs of such activities as room and board, housekeeping, laundry, and maintenance services. Separate identification of nursing costs would be appropriate under a pro-competitive health care delivery system so that consumers can better evaluate the value of nursing care and also to provide a more accurate financial picture for reimbursement purposes.

Information

Consumers lack sophistication regarding health costs and alternatives. Competitive models assume that informed choices will be made by consumers and their agents regarding choice of plans, choice of providers, and so forth. If consumers are to help restrain costs, they must have access to plentiful and accurate information about choices in health care. Consumers have learned to engage in careful shopping in other markets, and they could be highly motivated to learn about similar choices in health care.

References

American Nurses' Association. (1988). *Report on the demand for nursing services and the supply of nurses.* Kansas City, MO: Author.

Division of National Cost Estimates. (1987). National health expenditures, 1986-2000. *Health Care Financing Review, 8* (4) 1–36.

McKibbin, R.C., Brimmer, P.F., Clinton, J.F., et al. (1985). *DRGs and nursing care.* (HCFA Grant No. 15-C-98421-7). Kansas City, MO: American Nurses' Association.

Smits, H.L., Fetter, R.B. & McMahon, L.F. Jr. (1984). Variation in resource use within diagnosis-related groups: the severity issue. *Health Care Financing Review, 5* (Annual Supplement) 71–78.

Thompson, J. (1984). The measurement of nursing intensity. *Health Care Financing Review, 5* (Annual Supplement) 47–55.

Wessell, D. (1988, September 12). Rising Medicare costs. *The Wall Street Journal, 69* 38.

Chapter 12

Conclusion: Nursing, Economics, and the Health Care System

Some Questions in Conclusion

Other economic considerations for nursing?

Economic influences are pervasive in nursing and in the health care delivery system. The preceding chapters have illustrated some aspects of these economic influences. They were not intended to be comprehensive examinations of the relationships between economics and nursing or, more generally, between economics and health care. For example, other economic aspects related to nursing that can be examined include:

An analysis of the specific contributions and economic value that nursing care provides as an input to health

Empirical studies of the economic contributions of nursing care to health

Economic models to illustrate and measure the factors that influence the demand for nursing services

The impact of third-party payments by government and private insurers on the demand for nursing services

The impact of regulation on nursing services

The role of federal support for nursing education

The current shortage of nurses and how it results from or is leading to changes in the demand for nurses, the supply of nurses, compensation, work patterns, and the use of temporary agency nurse personnel.

While some of these topics were mentioned, they were not fully discussed. The purpose of this book is to demonstrate how the tools of economics can be applied to the study of nursing care and nurses themselves. Economic principles, as has been shown, can help to delineate, clarify, and illustrate various aspects of nursing, thus making meaningful analysis of nursing and its role in the health care delivery system possible.

What health services should be supported?

Economics in many ways is the study of scarcity: How best to manage with limited resources. Thus, economics can contribute to the understanding of nursing and the health care system through the analysis of problems in nursing that relate to scarcity. The current nursing shortage is an obvious example. More subtle is the decision, or the multitude of decisions, that leads to society's choice about how much of its limited resources will be spent on nursing care. The tendency of the United States has been to emphasize more costly, physician-oriented *curative* interventions and services while allotting much less for *caring* services and health promotion activities.

Should decisions about the allocation of resources within the total health system be changed? Perhaps so, perhaps not. This may be more a value judgment than an economic decision. What is important is to recognize the capability of economic science to contribute to the understanding of nursing and health care concerns by clarifying and illustrating issues and choices.

Who decides?

In terms of scarcity and economics, another fundamental issue is who decides? Shall the resources devoted to nursing and health care be determined by consumers or by government? In other words, should the allocation of resources to nursing and health care be determined by freely made decisions in the marketplace or by regulation? Some argue that the free market process, where supply and demand are expressed by producers and consumers through the price mechanism, is an inappropriate basis for health care decisions and resource allocation. Consumers cannot fully and independently evaluate their health status or needs. If so, some other decision-making process must be used; this would typically be a governmentally-regulated process.

Most developed economies in the world rely heavily on national systems of health care, such as the United Kingdom's National Health Service, where government decides basic questions such as how much the nation spends for health care and how much nurses and other health care workers are paid. In such settings, nurses and physicians are government employees. National health systems also regulate what services are available and to whom. For example, in the British system those over age 55 with end-stage renal disease are not eligible for either dialysis or transplant. They can purchase private treatment if they have sufficient personal funds or private insurance.

In contrast, Canada has developed an extensive system of national health insurance that covers all residents of all ages for all ailments. Health facilities and physicians operate much as they would in a private economy but with some government regulation and control. Canada has avoided a national system where government openly manages and controls health care facilities and personnel.

The U.S. health system is subject to less government decision making than the British system, though regulation of health care is widespread and major government programs such as Medicare and Medicaid exert strong economic influences on all aspects of health care delivery. Our health system is an evolving one, experimenting with new approaches (i.e., the prospective payment system for Medicare) to the economic problems and issues arising from the fundamental economic reality of scarcity.

An unresolved, basic economic issue for our health care system is the question of equity. Who, or which groups in the population, should receive nursing and health services, both in terms of the amounts of services received and the payment arrangements for them. Currently, a mixture of programs (Medicare, Medicaid, Blue Cross and Blue Shield, commercial insurance carriers, etc.) provide varying levels of entitlement and payment for health services. At the same time over 35 million Americans, including millions of children, lack coverage for health care. Some more comprehensive mechanisms for redistributing the financial capability to access nursing and other health care services appears warranted.

The market system and the market for nursing care have been examined to reveal how supply, demand, and prices help to allocate resources and promote efficiency in the delivery of nursing care. Economic principles that underlie determination of nurses' salaries and benefits have been considered. The economic components of health expenditures and the sources of funding for health services have been examined, as have the economic effects of federal fiscal polices for health care.

There are many ways in which the science of economics can be applied to nursing-related issues to provide better understanding. This understanding should facilitate recognition of the costs and benefits of different choices, treatments, approaches, and protocols in nursing and health care. Thus, economics can contribute to nursing's understanding of itself and of its role in the health care delivery system.

Nursing's Goals

In the first chapter of this book, three continuing goals of nursing's leadership relative to the profession of nursing are mentioned. The first goal is to foster actions that promote the professionalization of nursing. This is viewed as an evolving process in which major accomplishments occur over time. The development of doctoral programs in nursing to prepare professional nurses to conduct the research that defines the knowledge base of the discipline of nursing is an important example of this activity. The continuing process of adding new knowledge enables a profession to refine and expand the nature of its service to clients and the technology that make its services effective.

The second continuing goal of nursing is to control the preparation of all categories of nursing personnel constituting the work force of nursing. Discontinuation of LPN programs and diploma programs, which lie outside the mainstream of general education and block further education and upward mobility of graduates of these programs, is an example of activities associated with this goal. This goal recognizes that from professions evolve other categories of personnel who carry out activities delegated from the professional group. If the delegated work becomes quite distinct and specialized, an independent profession may evolve. For example, the fields of dietetics and medical social work evolved, in part, from nursing but are now independent. Nursing evolved, in part, from medicine. This fact becomes apparent when one examines the practice of medicine in countries where professional nursing has not developed. In those settings, physicians continue to do much of what is professional nursing in the United States. The creation of ancillary groups is part of the process of professionalization, and these evolve from distinctions between that which is core and that which is ancillary to the profession. Where the delegation involves tasks rather than broad service functions, the profession controls the scope of practice. Tasks and activities, for which the knowledge base is well-established and the results or effects are quite predictable, are delegated to persons with less preparation than the professional worker. This provides an economic savings to clients while utilizing employment of persons who cannot obtain, or do not wish to obtain, the broader knowledge base of the professional. The use of paraprofessionals, responsible for delegated activities, enables the profession to increase its own educational standards as the knowledge base expands without denying its professional services to a broad spectrum of the public.

The third goal is closely related. Nursing leadership wishes to influence the supply, demand, utilization, and evaluation of nursing care relative to the market for that care. The profession's leadership collaborates with officials from the federal and state governments and trade associations to determine nursing's human resource needs including the facilities and faculties for preparing nurses. Nursing service administrators have a major responsibility in the appropriate utilization of nursing personnel by level of preparation and use legal and professional standards derived from registration and certification. Administrators also are responsible for providing evaluation of nursing care though quality assurance programs in service institutions using criteria derived from professional practice standards. It is nursing administrators who are directly responsible for the efficiency and effectiveness of programs of nursing care.

Each of these major goals and the activities related to their achievement are interdependent upon economics, political science, and health policy. Economics most often defines the problem, political science identifies the parties to the change, and health policy provides the mechanism for locking in the change.

Role of the Professional Organization

It is important for professional nurses to develop an understanding of the economic principles that affect the market for nursing care and to understand the effects of federal and state governments' fiscal policies upon health service payments and, thus, upon the demand for nursing care services. Beyond that, nurses must be able to influence decisions of choice that are made by elected and appointed officials relative to the use of scarce resources.

Government officials listen to presentations and are influenced by representatives of organized groups in our society. The clearest messages are heard from groups that have a broad inclusive membership, that serve as advocates for the public welfare and not solely for their group's or members' welfare, and can be counted on for accurate valid information. Officials want information about the likely effects of proposed policies or regulatory changes.

The professional voice of nursing is heard through the American Nurses' Association. The ANA is registered with the federal government as a lobbying organization. Political action taken by the elected officials of the ANA is based upon positions taken by the association's House of Delegates. A broadly-based membership is required to produce sufficient revenues to maintain the Washington office of the ANA and to employ the specialized staff (nurses and non-nurses) to prepare background papers from which elected representatives develop association positions. Additionally, a broadly-based membership promotes wider opportunities for review and careful consideration of various policies and positions.

Membership in a clinical specialty society provides a nurse with important collegial relationships, but these specialty groups are usually not involved in the governmental arena and do not attempt to influence economic and political policies. Nurses who maintain membership in the ANA simultaneously with membership in a specialty society have the broadest opportunities to influence and be part of the development of nursing policies. There is a place for multiple and diverse voices as nursing develops its positions. Once a given position has been developed through an open and democratic process within the membership organization, it then becomes essential for nurses to speak with unity and clarity if the profession is to be successful. Specialty nursing societies can provide expert testimony but to be effective their position must be congruent with the profession's general policy position on a given topic or in a particular area.

Nursing will only achieve the status of a fully mature profession when members learn to develop and promote diverse positions within the professional association, but, once policy positions are taken, speak with unity outside the association. For everyone, there is a time to lead and a time to follow. The effectiveness of nurses as members of an essential profession depends both on understanding of economic factors that relate to nursing and on how to best use this understanding to advance the goals of the profession, of individual nurses, and of nursing's client constituency.

Index

Page numbers followed by *f* refer to figures. Page numbers followed by *t* refer to tables.

Page numbers followed by *f* refer to figures. Page numbers followed by *t* refer to tables.

Page numbers followed by *f* refer to figures. Page numbers followed by *t* refer to tables.

Page numbers followed by *f* refer to figures. Page numbers followed by *t* refer to tables.

Page numbers followed by *f* refer to figures. Page numbers followed by *t* refer to tables.

Page numbers followed by *f* refer to figures. Page numbers followed by *t* refer to tables.

Page numbers followed by *f* refer to figures. Page numbers followed by *t* refer to tables.

Page numbers followed by *f* refer to figures. Page numbers followed by *t* refer to tables.